OF MEN

AND MACHINES

of men
and machines

EDITED, AND WITH AN INTRODUCTION

BY

arthur o. lewis, jr.

A DUTTON PAPERBACK

E. P. DUTTON & CO., INC.   NEW YORK

Published simultaneously in Canada by
Clarke, Irwin and Company Limited, Toronto and Vancouver

Acknowledgments

Grateful acknowledgment is made to the following for permission
to quote from copyright material:

Lewis Mumford: "The Monastery and the Clock." Reprinted
from *Technics and Civilization* by Lewis Mumford by permission
of Harcourt, Brace & World, Inc. Copyright 1934 by Harcourt,
Brace & World, Inc.; copyright renewed 1962 by Lewis Mumford.

Robert Sherman Townes: "Problem for Emmy." Reprinted
from *Startling Stories*, June 1952, published by Better Publications,
Inc., by permission of John Schaffner, Literary Agent. Copyright
1952 by Better Publications, Inc.

Robert Frost: "The Bear," "The Egg and the Machine," and
"A Lone Striker." Reprinted from *Complete Poems of Robert Frost*
by permission of Holt, Rinehart and Winston, Inc. Copyright 1928
by Holt, Rinehart and Winston, Inc.; copyright 1936 by Robert
Frost; copyright renewed © 1956 by Robert Frost.

Carl Sandburg: "The Hammer." Reprinted from *Complete
Poems* by Carl Sandburg by permission of Harcourt, Brace &
World, Inc. Copyright 1960 by Carl Sandburg. "Prayers of Steel"
reprinted from *Cornhuskers* by Carl Sandburg by permission of
Holt, Rinehart and Winston, Inc. Copyright 1918 by Holt, Rinehart
and Winston, Inc.; copyright renewed 1946 by Carl Sandburg.
"Limited" reprinted from *Chicago Poems* by Carl Sandburg by
permission of Holt, Rinehart and Winston, Inc. Copyright 1916 by
Holt, Rinehart and Winston, Inc.; copyright renewed 1944 by Carl
Sandburg.

"The Pushbutton Cornucopia." Reprinted from *Time* magazine,
March 9, 1959, by permission of *Time*. Copyright © 1959 by Time,
Inc.

George R. Price: "The Teaching Machine." Reprinted from
Think magazine by permission of International Business Machines
Corporation. Copyright © 1959 by International Business Machines
Corporation.

ISAAC ASIMOV: "Robbie." Reprinted from *I Robot* by Isaac Asimov by permission of Doubleday & Company, Inc. First published as "Strange Playfellow" in *Super Science Stories,* copyright 1940 by Fictioneers, Inc.

WALTER VAN TILBURG CLARK: "The Portable Phonograph." Reprinted from *The Watchful Gods and Other Stories* by Walter Van Tilburg Clark by permission of Random House, Inc. Copyright 1941 by Walter Van Tilburg Clark.

PAUL ENGLE: "Poetry in a Machine Age." Reprinted from *The English Journal,* June 1957, by permission of the National Council of Teachers of English and Paul Engle.

MACKNIGHT BLACK: "Machinery." Copyright 1929 by Horace Liveright, Inc.; copyright renewed 1956 by Macknight Black.

STEPHEN SPENDER: "The Express" and "The Landscape Near an Aerodrome." Reprinted from *Collected Poems 1928–1953* by Stephen Spender by permission of Random House, Inc., New York, and Faber and Faber, Ltd., London. Copyright 1934 by Stephen Spender; copyright renewed © 1961 ·by Stephen Spender.

STEPHEN VINCENT BENÉT: "Nightmare Number Three." Reprinted from *Selected Works of Stephen Vincent Benét,* published by Holt, Rinehart and Winston, Inc., by permission of Brandt & Brandt. Copyright 1935 by Stephen Vincent Benét.

WOLCOTT GIBBS: "Man Alone." Reprinted from *The New Yorker* by permission. Copyright 1932, 1960 by The New Yorker Magazine, Inc.

JOE GLAZER: "Automation." Reprinted by permission of the Labor Education Division, Roosevelt University, Chicago, Illinois.

KURT VONNEGUT, JR.: Selection from *Player Piano.* Reprinted from *Player Piano* by Kurt Vonnegut, Jr. by permission of Charles Scribner's Sons. Copyright 1952 by Kurt Vonnegut, Jr.

JOHN STEINBECK: Selection from *The Grapes of Wrath.* Pages 47–53 reprinted from *The Grapes of Wrath* by John Steinbeck by permission of The Viking Press, Inc. Copyright 1939 by John Steinbeck.

SHERWOOD ANDERSON: "Lift Up Thine Eyes." Reprinted from *Perhaps Women* by Sherwood Anderson, New York, Liveright Publishing Company, 1931, by permission of Harold Ober Associates, Inc. Copyright 1930 by Elizabeth Anderson.

HARVEY SWADOS: "Joe, the Vanishing American." Reprinted from *On the Line* by Harvey Swados by permission of Little, Brown & Co.-Atlantic Monthly Press. Copyright © 1957 by Harvey Swados.

MARGOT BENNETT: Selection from *The Long Way Back.* Reprinted from *The Long Way Back* by Margot Bennett by permission of the William Morris Agency, Inc. and the author. Copyright © 1954 by Margot Bennett.

W. H. AUDEN: "The Unknown Citizen." Reprinted from *The*

Contents

Contents

Introduction

THIS IS A BOOK about the relationship of men and machines. It is also—or perhaps the word is *therefore*—about a problem in living. It is about a problem that, unrecognized, appeared the moment the first primitive man used a stick to pry loose a rock in order to reach the grubs underneath, or threw his first stone at the first rabbit; or perhaps Adam used a stick or a stone to knock down the fruit of the tree of knowledge. No matter how or where or when it happened, some early man discovered that he could increase his own ability to do something he wished to do by using some object not part of his own body, and from that moment there was no turning back. The problem resulting from that discovery is best posed as a question: Is man master or servant of the machine? It is not an easy question, and the answers have fallen into the predictable categories of *master, servant,* and *both.* For the writers in this book, and for countless others who might have been included, the machine is variously man's savior, his greatest hope for a better life, his inexorable destiny, the stultification of his human aspirations, the chief error of his intelligence since the expulsion from Eden, or even merely an extension of himself. If there has been a trend in the answers, it is that more recent writers have been more often concerned—whatever their ultimate attitude—with the possibility that *servant* is an accurate assessment of the facts.

Much of the difficulty in achieving agreement about the relationship of men and machines derives from an inability to reach agreement on what a machine really is. Most modern dictionary definitions are related to that of Franz Reuleaux (1876): "A machine is a combination of resistant bodies so arranged that by their means the mechanical forces of nature can be compelled to do work accompanied by certain determinant motions." But beyond these simple definitions all is confusion, for agreement that all machines are not alike has not led to any consistent way of dividing them into classes or types. Traditionally, there are six "simple machines"— lever, inclined plane, wheel and axle, wedge, pulley, and screw—from which, physically at least, all other machines are constructed, but more recent classifiers often reduce this number to three, two, or even one.

When classification by function, or by any other standard for that matter, is attempted, the results are even more diverse. Thus, one authority divides all "machines" into two classes: those that generate and transform power and those that transmit power and perform work; this same authority adds another class of what he calls "mechanisms"—as distinguished from "machines"—which are devices for transmitting and modifying motions rather than power. Numerous other scholars follow a general pattern that starts with the simple machines and moves through more sophisticated devices: machine tools, again with varying numbers of subclasses; control machines or cybernetic devices that make automation possible; the so-called "thinking machines" that are basically computers; and "robots" that may or may not be, depending upon the individual classifier, more complicated than the other classes. Still another group draws a distinction between "tools" and other machines.

The simple dictionary definitions are sufficient for everyday use, and the various classifications are sufficient for the study of machines as physical objects, but neither is adequate for an examination of an abstract nature. As a result, when the writer becomes concerned with the place of machines in relation to man, the objective definitions often give way to more biased explanations. Thus, Garet Garrett (1926) refers to "a class of typhonic, mindless organisms, exempt from the will of nature"; Donald Michael (1962) proposes "ever more intelligent, ever more versatile slaves"; Norbert Wiener (1954) suggests "pockets of decreasing entropy in a framework in which the large entropy tends to increase"; Henry Ford (1926) is satisfied with "a method of making power effective"; but Ludvik Aškenazy (1958) will have nothing less than: "A piece of stone, the branch of a tree—the first tools in man's hands—like automized factories and cybernetics are really one and the same thing: an idea put into practice, an inspiration, an observation, something which enables man to subjugate nature." Such definitions, it would appear, reflect attitudes toward machines as often as objective attempts to describe what they are. This is not to say, however, that thinkers who present such attitudes are to be condemned. On the contrary, because they are concerned with a kind of collective entity, *machine*, which can be examined in relationship to a similar collective entity, *man*, it is they, rather than the purely objective scholars, who provide the most thorough insight into the relationship of men and machines. They are concerned with the *why* of whatever this relationship is as well as with the *how,* and in the long run *why* something happens gives greater promise of understanding the happening than does *how.*

Many such writers do not separate problems arising from increasing dependence upon machines from those resulting simply from increasing scientific knowledge, that is, from better understanding of the laws by which the physical universe operates. In the sense that machines operate according to these natural laws, they are merely the practical application of science. Thus, a writer who is concerned with the "machine age," the "second industrial revolution," the "age of technocracy," or however he describes the current situation, is likely to be concerned in reality with what might be called the "age of applied science." When he writes of the "machine," he does not mean the physical object at all but what is behind it. Such blurring of distinction appears to be both natural and desirable for fuller understanding of the relationship of men and machines.

Whatever definition for machine one may prefer—and it is clear that taken collectively the writers represented in this volume could agree on only the broadest definition—certainly one must agree that civilization as we know it is a society not of men alone but of men and machines. Examined historically, the position of machines in relation to men has moved from periphery to centrality, from mere usefulness to absolute necessity. When men used sticks to scratch the earth before planting seeds, one such stick was as good as another, and easily replaced; when men use analogue computers to determine how many potatoes a city will need next week, replacement is not so easy. The better life that has resulted—in the material sense at least—from using machines means greater dependence upon them, and all available evidence points to even greater future dependence.

It is important that we recognize the present situation. Man's intelligence and skill, his scientific knowledge and mechanical ingenuity, have produced the society of men and machines. If we wished to do so, we could not turn back the clock without catastrophic consequences; probably we cannot even stop things where they are—cannot hold to the present proportions of men and machines or the present relative strengths of the two components of this technological society.

Consequently, if we are to have any choice about the future, we need to examine the relationship of men and machines with the greatest care. Such examination is the subject of the writings collected in this book.

II

THE PIECES in this collection are, as has been noted, only a small part of the vast material dealing with the relationship of men and machines. They have been chosen on the dual basis of literary merit and of suitability for illustration of the various aspects of the problem. They have been placed in the particular order that appears to produce the clearest statement of the problem and its proposed solutions, and the juxtaposition of specific items is based on principles of contrast, reinforcement, and explanation. Thus, the best examination of the relationship of men and machines will result from reading the book straight through rather than at random.

Karel Čapek's *R. U. R.* is singularly appropriate as a starting point for consideration of the relationship of men and machines. It is not, as has too often been said, a play concerned simply with the destruction of man by that ultimate in machines, artificial man, but one that examines the relationship of men and machines in some detail and from several points of view. It is not, in other words, a simple play but a complicated one, and the central symbol of the robot is complex and bears several significant meanings. The name *robot*, from the Czech *robota*, "forced labor," implies that the machine can release man from arduous toil, but even the most superficial reading indicates that this is not the whole meaning of the symbol. Although the robot had been developed by Old Rossum—from Czech *rozum*, "reason" or "intellect"—in the tradition of the scientist who seeks to assert man's greatness, in this case to challenge God by demonstrating man's ability to create life, for Young Rossum it is the means to a technological utopia in which machines serve man, and he has overhauled Old Rossum's complicated artificial man to make a cheaper, mass-produced model. In the play, Domin, too, wishes only that "Man shall be free and supreme." The robot is thus the symbol of man's independence from the curse of work, and man is, in this sense, his master. But the robot is also the symbol of the dehumanization of man. Early in the play, Helena is unable to distinguish robots from human beings; a little later it is discovered that human beings can no longer reproduce. There is thus no difference between men and robots except that the former have souls, and even this difference is lost when Helena has her way. The revolt of the robots rises at least in part from the change in sensitivity that Helena, shrinking from the merely mechanical, persuades Dr. Gall to bring about in their makeup. That the rising occurs at all is evidence of what man has given up to attain material comfort, and, in this sense, he has become servant of the machine: "You will work! You will build for us! You will serve us!" Radius tells Alquist.

Finally, attitudes toward the robot illustrate one of the most common arguments against the machine: for Old Rossum, man's intellectual and scientific ingenuity make him at least equal to God; for Young Rossum, man can and does improve on God; for Domin, all things, whether of God or man, are created to serve man; for Helena, man can equal God only when he can create souls; for Alquist, God has sent punishment to man and replaced him with another species. On this level, Čapek seems to say that man in his pride has once more, as in Greek tragedy, been shown his proper place in the scheme of things.

In the end the play turns back on itself: Modern technological civilization has destroyed man, presumably because, as Čapek says elsewhere, "The conception of the human brain has at last escaped from the control of human minds." But in the sending forth of the Robotess Helena and her mate, Primus—"Go, Adam, go, Eve. The world is yours."—Čapek makes the point that life does go on: Man is at the same time destroyed and not destroyed.

In "The Monastery and the Clock" Lewis Mumford's point is that until the invention of reliable clocks there could be no machine age. Abstract time, the measuring of seconds, minutes, and hours, is at the heart of modern society. Applied to the coordination of machines it makes possible the whole industrial complex; dissociated from organic time it becomes a means for "synchronizing the actions of men." But the substitution of clock time for organic time means introduction of something mechanical into the natural life of man and is in itself a step toward subordination of man to the machine. Man cannot, it appears, have the advantage of a technological society without permitting himself to become less human.

Mumford's sense of man's surrender to artificial time was anticipated by Ralph Waldo Emerson. In "Works and Days" he points out: "Let the measure of time be spiritual, not mechanical." He clearly sees the advantages of what he called "the age of tools." But he sees too that rejoicing in the good of machines is not enough: "We must look deeper for our salvation." If, as he said elsewhere, "Things are in the saddle/And ride mankind," they are there because man has chosen "works" instead of "days." Man must control, not be controlled: "Machinery is aggressive. . . . If you do not use tools, they will use you." In the end it is man's character that counts, not what he can build or invent. We must "move from the works of man and the activity of the hands to a delight in the faculties which rule them." We must, in short, live as men, not as servants of machines.

Emerson's is the eloquence of the poet and philosopher, but his examination is made in terms not very different from that of Donald N. Michael. *Cybernation: The Silent Conquest* is a formal report on the impact of machines on men today. But Michael, despite the carefully documented, closely reasoned quality of his report, is more deeply involved than Emerson. Although he proposes only to state problems rather than to solve them, the passage of nearly a century has forced him to begin at a point much farther along the path of man's dependence on machines than did Emerson. *Cybernation* starts with the premise that is is possible to regard automation not as simply the logical development from earlier machines but rather as "so different in degree as to be a profound difference in kind." Automation does not mean merely replacing men in certain jobs by machines that can do the job more efficiently. It means using the new "thinking machines" to do jobs men have never done, and possibly cannot do: "Cybernetic systems perform with a precision and a rapidity unmatched in humans. They also perform in ways that would be impractical or impossible for humans to duplicate." Michael's concern is that we must adapt ourselves to the new society these machines will make possible, at the same time assuring that that society will be what man wants, not "a contradictory world run by (and for?) ever more intelligent, ever more versatile slaves."

The implication at the end of *R. U. R.* is that machines sometimes become not machines, presumably through development of some human characteristic. Robert Sherman

Townes's Emmy, an early-model computer, is shown going through learning stages similar to those of a small child, and her cry "WHO AM I WHO AM I" is certainly that of a human consciousness. The story poses the obvious question: When is a machine not a machine?

The two concluding items of Part I revert to a broader aspect of the relationship of men and machines. Man, the evidence of centuries shows, is possessed of a drive to conquer his environment, but before he can be successful he must *understand* that environment, and in the poems of Frost and Whitman this point is made clear. If machines are somehow man's way of extending himself beyond his natural physical limits, Robert Frost reminds us that mere physical extension is not enough and is not very great in any case. His range of knowledge increased by microscope and telescope, man is nevertheless caged because he wants always to go beyond these limits. His answers are insufficient because he is clearly destined for something more. Not having found his answers either in science or in philosophy, he is "equally pathetic/When sedentary and when peripatetic." This same feeling of man's inability to understand the universe around him as fully as he wishes is at the heart of Walt Whitman's "When I Heard the Learn'd Astronomer." The "proofs" of science, the adding up of figures by savants, the measuring—or attempted measuring—of life, these are not enough, and man, dissatisfied but always striving to know, can only look "in perfect silence at the stars."

A central belief of the writers represented in Part II is that man has power over nature: "Give me a firm spot to stand on and a lever long enough, and I shall move the world," said Archimedes; "Let me have extension and motion and I will remake the world; the universe is a machine in which everything happens by figures and motion," said Descartes. Corollary to this belief is the belief that man has the right to change nature for his own benefit.

Although he was not an especially original thinker, Francis Bacon, through the eloquence of his writing and the breadth of his vision, might well be regarded as the real founder of the modern scientific world. Certainly his last important work, *New Atlantis*, of which "The House of Salomon" is the concluding section, describes a community of scholars whose place as ancestor of modern scientific and technological institutions can scarcely be disputed. For Bacon, science was the chief means for regaining that domination over the external world that man had lost when he left Eden. Deploring the low estate of scientific research in his day, he reserved his severest condemnation for those who sought knowledge for the wrong reasons: "Knowledge is not to be sought either for pleasure of the mind, or for contention, or for superiority to others, or for profit, or fame, or power, or any of these inferior things; but for the benefit and use of life. . . ." The purpose of the House of Salomon is clearly stated: "The end of our foundation is the knowledge of causes, and secret motions of things; and the enlarging of the bounds of human empire, to the effecting of all things possible." What the researchers discover is, in other words, to be put to practical use. Even the "two very long and fair galleries" are a museum of inventions and a hall of statues of great inventors; that is, they honor those who have made application of scientific theory and the devices they have created. The House of Salomon, then, is a plan for the organized assault on nature of men of intelligence with the practical view of putting their discoveries to work so that man might attain, as René Dubos points out, a "utopia of happiness based on the application of scientific knowledge."

Bacon, despite his belief that Paradise might be regained through man's ingenuity, would have been shocked by the conclusion of Carl Sandburg's "The Hammer." But to worship the hammer is at least one path to follow. In a world where beliefs constantly shift, crumble, and fall, it is not completely illogical to deify what man can build and the instruments of his building.

Both Adam Smith, in *The Wealth of Nations,* and Samuel Miller, in *A Brief Retrospect of the Eighteenth Century,* regard newly developed machines as major reasons for the superiority of eighteenth-century living over that of an earlier day. For Smith, machines and the consequent division of labor that he regarded as essential to high production have brought about "that universal opulence which extends itself to the lowest ranks of the people." For Miller, "mechanic arts" are responsible for that "conveniency, cheapness, and elegance of living . . . in which we may claim superiority over our predecessors." Both give full credit to those inventors who had, as Bacon proposed earlier, made practical application of the discoveries of theoretical scientists. Smith's somewhat apocryphal story of the fun-loving boy who worked out a control device for his steam engine—it should be noted that he used the feedback principle that is at the heart of modern cybernetics—is in the tradition of those who believe that the most useful mechanical discoveries are made by men who want to save themselves physical labor. The tradition extends at least from Seneca (Epistle 90: "The sort of men who discover such things are those who are busied with them") to the modern factory suggestion box. Similarly, in *Equality* society is utopian because the inhabitants of the island, like Bacon, Smith, and Miller, have accepted the idea that machines can save men from toil; like the modern industrialist they reward the worker who finds means for higher production.

"The Pushbutton Cornucopia" and George R. Price's "The Teaching Machine" report to the general reader the successful application of machine methods in improving human life. In the one case the end product is more food and in the other more education, but the message is the same for both: Farmer North and his friends use automation to feed the exploding population of the world, and Professor Skinner and his colleagues use teaching machines to educate the hordes of students who crowd our schools and colleges. Both reports describe the ways in which a skilled worker, be he farmer or educator, can extend his own skills to help others. "Vanquished by nature, we become masters through techniques," said Aristotle, and in the areas here described, as in countless others, men have clearly benefited from such mastery.

The two stories that conclude Part II are concerned with opposite ends of the scale of machine aid to man. In Isaac Asimov's "Robbie" the machine is a complicated robot, a "thinking machine" capable both of feelings and of inspiring the love of the little girl he serves as baby sitter, confidant, and friend. The somewhat melodramatic ending is significant in showing the dependence of the human being on machines, but it is also, perhaps a little sentimentally, a picture of the dependence of machines on men. Walter Van Tilburg Clark's "The Portable Phonograph" makes the point that even an inexpensive gadget can have a major role in maintaining some of man's humanity in a world where few have managed to survive. The four men, "doddering remnant of a race of mechanical fools," who find such joy in the music of the phonograph are perhaps at last making proper use of a machine.

The stuff of which poetry is made is the poet's reaction to his environment, and it is not surprising to discover, as the items in Part III illustrate, that poets have written often of the machine. Paul Engle, in "Poetry in a Machine Age," suggests ways in which modern poets are reacting to the society of men and machines by replacing images drawn from nature with those drawn from the machines that surround us. It is not merely a matter of vocabulary—of steel and motor rather than daffodil and cloud—but of communication between the poet and an audience that knows almost nothing of nature. Perhaps it is even, through understanding the complexities of machines, a way of writing with greater understanding of modern society.

Individual poets will, of course, react in individual ways. Thus, three poems about the locomotive bear little resemblance to each other: Closest to the older nature poetry is Emily Dickinson; one would not feel out of place offering a lump of sugar to her superhorse. Walt Whitman's is a paean of unabashed admiration for the power and beauty of his subject. Stephen Spender makes of the train something more than machine: feminine, "like a queen," "entranced," not equaled by anything in nature. Similarly, the plane in "The Landscape Near an Aerodrome" is "More beautiful and soft than any moth." This latter poem, however, moves in the direction suggested by Engle to give a sense of the turmoil and change of the twentieth-century city. Moving still further away from nature, Macknight Black equates the rhythm of engines with that of the sea, and Carl Sandburg describes man's wish to belong in the wholly modern terms of becoming part of a manmade steel structure.

The poets represented here have used the new vocabularies and attitudes that derive from man's closeness to the machine, but they are only a few of the numerous modern poets—Louis MacNeice, Paul Valéry, Emile Verhaeren, Blaise Cendrars, and, above all, Hart Crane come to mind at once—who have frequently chosen to write as part of what Paul Ginestier calls "the most characteristic stream of ideas in our era." Their willingness to do so has given their work a contemporaneousness not available to most of the more traditional poets.

Part IV is the other side of the coin; fear of the machine as enemy of mankind is not new: the classical myth of Icarus, the medieval tale of Roger Bacon's mechanical head, the

Renaissance Golem of Prague are early examples. But most of the writing from this point of view has been inspired by the Industrial Revolution and, in even greater quantity, by the development of the so-called "thinking machines." For these writers man is to be no more than servant of the machine—if he is fortunate enough to avoid outright destruction or replacement by the machine; that is, if man survives, he may have no job, be less than human, or live only to serve his machine master.

"Darwin Among the Machines" (1863) is the earliest version of the essay that Samuel Butler reworked several times before publishing it in its most complete form as two chapters of his utopian satire *Erewhon* (1872). This early letter to the editor is an excellent example of a major argument used by those who fear the machine. The Darwinian proposal that complex machines develop from simpler machines as complex animals develop from simpler ancestors is still widely accepted and has been the inspiration for numerous essays, short stories, and poems in recent years. Butler presses the point further by noting that it is man who aids in this future development: "we are daily giving them greater power. . . . In the course of ages we shall find ourselves the inferior race." He suggests that the society of men and machines already exists: "Each race is dependent upon the other for innumerable benefits"; but he regards this situation as only temporary. Not only have more and more men become "bound down as slaves to tend them," but we have already reached the point where we cannot even—as the citizens of Erewhon were to do—destroy them. Even now, "We are not only enslaved but are absolutely acquiescent in our bondage." If "Cellarius" meant his letter to be a satiric means for alerting men to their too great dependence upon machines, he was something less than successful, for his tract has proved all too accurate a prophecy of conditions today.

The haunting fear of physical destruction by his own creations—memorably described in Mary Shelley's *Frankenstein* as early as 1817 and central to the action of *R. U. R.*— remains one of the most pervasive themes in anti-machine writing. Stephen Vincent Benét's "Nightmare Number Three" is a narrative poem about New York on the day the machines finally revolt. The narrator is hopeful that he can make a deal ("I'm a good American and I always liked them"), but the poem ends on the grimly humorous hope that the eating of some men was a mistake. Why the workmen in Stephen Crane's poem constructed their "ball of masonry" is never known, but their dying squeals are certainly symbolic of the insignificance of flesh-and-blood man in a world he himself has made. The hero of Wolcott Gibbs' "Man Alone" is, of course, only a typical city dweller who learns how little he knows about the gadgets upon which he has depended, but it requires little imagination to see him as, perhaps, the narrator of Benét's poem; no doubt the toaster finished him off.

Less dramatic than actual physical destruction but far more likely as a future for man is the loss of work. As the newspaper headlines constantly point out, this possibility is already upon us, and the negotiations of Business and Labor are concerned more and more with the problem of men displaced from work by machines which can do the job better. "John Henry" gets to the heart of the matter through a dramatic confrontation of the worker and the machine that is to replace him. John Henry may be the last man to emerge victorious, but he must die in the effort. In the end, although all honor is his when the locomotives roar by his grave, somewhere up the track the steam drill continues to work faster, longer, and more efficiently than John Henry had ever done. Unlike John Henry, the nameless factory worker of Joe Glazer's "Automation" never really faces his opponent: his job simply disappears—he is "obsolete." Kurt Vonnegut, Jr., carries the theme still further in *Player Piano*, a novel of the not very distant future when a few skilled engineers are sufficient to supervise the completely automatic factories. Most able-bodied men are in the army, on relief, or employed in WPA-like public works, displaced, like Bud, by their own inventions.

In Vonnegut's novel there is an unsuccessful rebellion by intellectuals and disgruntled workers; much of the rebellion takes the form of destruction of all machines. This reaction has historical precedent in the Luddite uprisings in England early in the nineteenth century that are the subject of Byron's maiden speech in the House of Lords. In our own time there have been few such violent reactions to the introduction of machines. Mostly, the displaced worker has behaved like the farmers who are "tractored off" in John Steinbeck's *The Grapes of Wrath*: some found other jobs, some have used the machine to create "pushbutton cornucopias." In the few cases where there has been resistance, the effect has been generally little more significant than what Robert Frost's modern Luddite will achieve in "The Egg and the Machine." Nevertheless, Byron's defense, despite its concern with the immediate problem of his own time, is pertinent in an age when technological unemployment increases daily and the lost job is potentially the most explosive aspect in the relationship of men and machines.

If actual physical destruction by intelligent machines is highly unlikely, and proper management of machines really will, as the experts maintain, result in higher living standards everywhere, there still remains the most significant fear of all. This is the fear of the dehumanization of man because of his dependence on the machine and what the machine can produce for him. The remaining pieces in Part IV deal with this prospect.

Sherwood Anderson's "Lift Up Thine Eyes," Harvey Swados' "Joe, the Vanishing American," and Mark Twain's "My Watch" are concerned with the loss of individuality that results from assembly-line methods. Anderson finds that because "The belt is boss" men are fitted like cogs into the giant machine that is the assembly line: they must walk only in certain places, drive so many tacks per second, no more no less, must "be exact." When the belt moves faster, as it will, the men must move faster or be replaced. Swados' story is also set in an automobile assembly plant. The men on the line are trapped, slaves to time and the speed of the belt; it does not even matter if they produce a good product as long as they produce enough. Perhaps young Walter will break loose because, like Joe, he wants more from life than a steady job and good pay; but his ambition is to be an engineer, and a likely future for him is helping to create more assembly lines where, as Joe puts it, "a man's life goes down the drain like scummy water." Of Mark Twain's adventures with his watch it need only be said that, like the men on the assembly line, he is hopelessly enmeshed in clock time. His complaint that there is no one skilled enough to repair it would be answered today with the suggestion that it is cheaper for him to throw away the old watch and buy a new one.

The next four selections are stops along the path down from manhood toward something that looks like a human being but is really a machine. Adam Smith describes a danger that partially offsets the advantages of a division of labor:

if a man spends his life in performing a few operations over
and over, he "generally becomes as stupid and ignorant as
it is possible for a human creature to become." The excerpt
from Margot Bennett's *The Long Way Back* shows a further
step in the degradation of man: Grame has been, like the
citizens of *Player Piano,* classified by machines, and cannot
object: "Men make mistakes, machines do not." However, in
Grame's society the changeover is not yet complete and he
succeeds in jamming the grading machine and obtaining a
partial fulfillment of his wishes from the official in charge.
W. H. Auden's "The Unknown Citizen" pictures the assembly-
line man: he does everything exactly as statistics predict he
will, fitting neatly into his place in society. But judgment of
his life is based on the same standards as those used in judging
a machine in which no single part is noticed until it fails
to function as expected. JS/07/M/378 has never failed to
function as expected: "Was he free? Was he happy? The
question is absurd." The ultimate in this movement toward
making men mere cogs in the machine is described in the
excerpt from Aldous Huxley's *Brave New World.* Here physical specifications for the best performance of a specific job
are drawn up, and human beings are then produced who fit
the specifications. If lefthanded workers are needed, left-
handed people will be "decanted"; if the work is to be con-
ducted in hot places, heat-conditioned people will be available. And, of course, "we hardly ever have any trouble with
our workers."

The last pieces in Part IV deal with a world in which certain degrees of dehumanization are already evident. Edgar
Allan Poe addresses his "Sonnet—To Science" to the notion
that science by reducing the unknown reduces man's opportunity for imagining and thus makes him something less than
he had been. The excerpt from George Orwell's *The Road to
Wigan Pier* accepts the idea that "the function of the machine
is to save work." But, with machines to do whatever need
be done, "the logical end of mechanical progress is to reduce
the human being to something resembling a brain in a bottle."
Although no sane human being desires this end, the truth
of the matter is, says Orwell, that "like a drug, the machine
is useful, dangerous, and habit-forming." Probably we cannot
stop the movement toward the brain in the bottle even if we
can bring ourselves to try. Carl Sandburg's "Limited" is a
scornful condemnation of a man too comfortable in his crack

train to think about tomorrow, too deadened by civilization to recognize that these too "shall pass to ashes." E. E. Cummings suggests that this "world of made" is hardly worth pitying: its inhabitants are "comfortable"; there is no need to waste time here; "there's a hell/of a good universe next door."

E. M. Forster's "The Machine Stops" deals with the last stages of a society completely dependent upon the machine. It is a society not far removed from Orwell's "brain in a bottle," for here "the body was white pap, the home of ideas as colourless, last sloshy stirrings of a spirit that had grasped the stars." For a long time "good enough" has replaced higher standards because that is the best the Machine can provide. "First-hand ideas do not really exist" becomes a belief to live by in a world where there is no need for direct experience. The all-encompassing, all-providing Machine becomes the object of worship, and when it begins to break down its servants have lost the skills needed to repair it. But the resulting defects in service do not matter, for "the human issues in that latter day had become so subservient that they readily adapted themselves to every caprice of the Machine." Once, under such conditions, man might have abandoned the Machine, but now he is "dying, strangled in the garments that he had woven." In the end, the slim ray of hope that derives from Kuno's knowledge that some of the Homeless have survived on the surface of the earth has less impact than Vashti's prophetic remark, "Some fool will start the Machine again, to-morrow."

The pieces in Part V are concerned with the future, suggestions of possible developments in the relation of men and machines. They include the serious studies of Watson, Snow, and Strauss, the various levels of satire of Bishop, Weir, Frost, White, and Whittemore, and the grim foreboding of Aldiss and Bradbury. They do not answer all the questions raised in earlier parts of this volume, but they offer some provocative ideas that, sufficiently understood and widely disseminated, might well solve many of our present problems.

In "Technological Change," Thomas J. Watson, Jr., presents a program for continued progress through such change by improving men's lives through it, encouraging it, and sharing it openly throughout the world." And he insists that we must begin to do these things now, for tomorrow may be too late. In "Recent Thoughts on the Two Cultures" C. P. Snow reiterates the stand he had taken earlier in *The Two Cultures and the Scientific Revolution*, his popular and significant discussion of the intellectual gap between scientist and non scientist. Speaking to an American college audience, he point out the possibility of "grave mistakes" in the near future resulting from lack of scientific knowledge by our leaders, and proposes as specific remedy a more thorough grounding in science and language in the public schools. Both Morris Bishop and Edward C. Weir consider the misapplication of scientific ingenuity in education. "The Reading Machine" is a satiric view of the scientist so wrapped up in producing gadgets that he has forgotten that gadgets ought to be means not ends in themselves. "Whatever Happened to the Teaching Machine?" is, like "The Machine Stops," concerned with the ability to make proper use of machines that once proved so valuable. Both stories illustrate at least partially the intellectual gap with which Snow is concerned.

If modern factory work, especially on the kind of assembly line described by Anderson and Swados, is a dehumanizing experience, George Strauss and Robert Frost offer two possible solutions. In "Group Dynamics and Intergroup Relations" Strauss describes an experiment in letting the workers themselves set the pace; basic to the plan is acceptance of the idea that the human being does not work with the unvarying speed of the machine; forcing him to do so is psychologically disastrous. In the plant where the experiment was tried, its success in one area led to chaos in others, but the obvious corollary that it ought to be applied in all areas may be the solution to this major problem. Robert Frost's solution is a refusal to be merely a part of the system which is, after all, "not divine." Obviously, this refusal, if widely adopted, would lead to complete economic breakdown, but the principle that man has free choice in this matter is one by which, in theory at least, our present society differs from those portrayed by, for example, Huxley, Bennett, and Vonnegut. Frost's lone striker has the courage to break with one of the firmest of American traditions, the acceptance of work as necessary to social acceptance; Reed Whittemore voices the hope that similarly man can somehow break free from the past conventions that wall him in. The skill that will get us to Mars —or perhaps "Venus/Through some slight error"—ought to be able to "make provisions for this."

The short stories of E. B. White, Brian Aldiss, and Ray

Bradbury are set at various distances into the future. They have several things in common: each conveys the sense that machines are friend, if not servant, to man; each suggests that all may not go well in spite of this friendship; each gives some human qualities to the machine. Closest to the present are the familiar setting and characters of "The Hour of Letdown." If the tired chessplaying machine and his friend ride in a Cadillac, presumably because the machine earns a good living, the familiar setting makes even more significant the real implications of the final exclamation, for one does not really know whether the machine is driving in the capacity of chauffeur or as head of the household. "But Who Can Replace a Man?" deals with a time when men have been dying out, and, if men are gone, "we have only ourselves to look after," is the logically correct attitude for the little group of intelligent machines with which the story is concerned. But these carefully individualized characters are, it appears, more helpless than they know when on their own, and perhaps they benefit more than man from the new situation at the end of the story. "There Will Come Soft Rains" is a brilliant evocation of the end of civilization. If the splendid house is a machine in its routine attempts to go on serving its dead master, it is surely human in its fight to survive against natural disaster. The poem that the house quotes is, perhaps, fitting epitaph for a race that could control things better than its own members.

III

EARLY INVESTIGATORS of man's use of machines were often concerned on the purely religious grounds of the relationship of such use to the edict of Genesis 3:19: "In the sweat of thy face shalt thou eat bread." More recent concern has developed in large part from the feeling like that expressed by Albert Schweitzer: "Man has lost the capacity to foresee and foretall. He will end by destroying the earth." At both ends of the scale some have found the machine acceptable, some have not. The only real agreement is that machines can lighten man's toil. But they do not agree in answering the question: Is man servant or master of the machine? They neither tell us the price we must pay for this reduction of physical burdens nor its relationship with benefits received.

Among writers represented in this collection, some, like Bacon, Miller, and Strauss, appear to believe that the benefits are worth the price; others, like Watson, Clark, and Snow, suggest that with proper care the price can be held to a level where the benefits are not too dearly purchased; still others, like Huxley, Auden, and Forster, are unwilling to pay the price that may be asked. The same differences of opinion are reflected in our society as a whole. We demand higher pay in order to buy more goods, but we object to the turmoil that results from shifts to more efficient means of producing these goods. We boast of our technological progress, but we object to the school taxes necessary to train our children to take advantage of it. We insist that we are free-willed individuals, but we submit to political and business organizations that we then describe as "machines"—implying, perhaps unconsciously but most pertinently, that the men who are part of such organizations are interchangeable parts, mere cogs in some greater device whose function is to transmit power and perform work.

Perhaps there can be no definition of the relative position of man and machine in our society. The relationship may be a changing one—with the point already passed at which the future could have been made different from what it will be. But men, as men, have never been able to accept even what appears to be inevitable without trying to set their own course. For men, the only possible stand, then, is that which insists on holding the price down to a level commensurate with the benefits derived. Perhaps the best approach is to change our attitude toward the machine.

Etymological dictionaries trace the English word *machine* through French *machine* to Latin *machina*, Greek *mekhos* and Indo-European *magd*. Greek *mekhos* can be translated most accurately as *means*, especially, an *expedient*. Emphasis on this meaning, remembering, that is, the source of the word, produces an attitude that might make it easier to understand and live with our machines: they are *means*, not ends; *servants*, not masters. Man made—and man makes—machines to accomplish certain desired results. As long as the end desired is the end attained, the machine is useful. When this is no so, the machine need not be dismissed or destroyed, but simply remade to bring about the desired end.

Finally, we must recognize that life as we know it is lived in the physical universe, and any problem we have with machines is not a problem of heaven or hell but of this earth.

Ours is a society in which machines are one of man's ways of adapting to his environment. If the machine is to become our master, in any sense of the word, the fault is the fault of men, not of machines. A society of men alone, or a society of men and machines together, must follow Aristotle's precept: "Man is the measure." Here and now, and in the foreseeable future, there is no other standard for men.

ARTHUR O. LEWIS, JR.

University Park, Pa.
1963

Part I:

THE PROBLEM

Karel Čapek

R. U. R.   (Rossum's Universal Robots)
(1921)

A Fantastic Melodrama

CHARACTERS

HARRY DOMIN, *General Manager of Rossum's Universal Robots*
SULLA, *a Robotess*
MARIUS, *a Robot*
HELENA GLORY
DR. GALL, *Head of the Physiological and Experimental Department of R. U. R.*
MR. FABRY, *Engineer General, Technical Controller of R. U. R.*
DR. HALLEMEIER, *Head of the Institute for Psychological Training of Robots*
MR. ALQUIST, *Architect, Head of the Works Department of R. U. R.*
CONSUL BUSMAN, *General Business Manager of R. U. R.*
NANA
RADIUS, *a Robot*
HELENA, *a Robotess*
PRIMUS, *a Robot*
A SERVANT
FIRST ROBOT
SECOND ROBOT
THIRD ROBOT

ACT I. CENTRAL OFFICE OF THE FACTORY OF ROSSUM'S
UNIVERSAL ROBOTS
ACT II. HELENA'S DRAWING ROOM—TEN YEARS LATER.
MORNING
ACT III. THE SAME AFTERNOON
EPILOGUE. A LABORATORY—ONE YEAR LATER
PLACE: *An Island.* TIME: *The Future.*

ACT I

*Central office of the factory of Rossum's Universal Robots.
Entrance on the right. The windows on the front wall look*

3

*out on the rows of factory chimneys. On the left more manag-
ing departments.* DOMIN *is sitting in the revolving chair at a
large American writing table. On the left-hand wall large
maps showing steamship and railroad routes. On the right-
hand wall are fastened printed placards. ("Robot's Cheapest
Labor," and so on.) In contrast to these wall fittings, the floor
is covered with a splendid Turkish carpet, a sofa, leather armchair, and filing cabinets. At a desk near the windows* SULLA
is typing letters.

DOMIN (*dictating*). Ready?

SULLA. Yes.

DOMIN. To E. M. McVicker and Co., Southampton, England. "We undertake no guarantee for goods damaged in
transit. As soon as the consignment was taken on board we
drew your captain's attention to the fact that the vessel
was unsuitable for the transport of Robots, and we are
therefore not responsible for spoiled freight. We beg to
remain for Rossum's Universal Robots. Yours truly." (SULLA,
*who has sat motionless during dictation, now types rapidly
for a few seconds, then stops, withdrawing the completed
letter.*) Ready?

SULLA. Yes.

DOMIN. Another letter. To the E. B. Huyson Agency, New
York, U.S.A. "We beg to acknowledge receipt of order for
five thousand Robots. As you are sending your own vessel,
please dispatch as cargo equal quantities of soft and hard
coal for R. U. R., the same to be credited as part payment
of the amount due to us. We beg to remain, for Rossum's
Universal Robots. Yours truly." (SULLA *repeats the rapid
typing.*) Ready?

SULLA. Yes.

DOMIN. Another letter. "Friedrichswerks, Hamburg, Germany.
We beg to acknowledge receipt of order for fifteen thou-
sand Robots." (*Telephone rings.*) Hello! This is the Central
Office. Yes. Certainly. Well, send them a wire. Good.
(*Hangs up telephone.*) Where did I leave off?

SULLA. "We beg to acknowledge receipt of order for fifteen
thousand Robots."

DOMIN. Fifteen thousand R. Fifteen thousand R.

[*Enter* MARIUS.]

Well, what is it?

MARIUS. There's a lady, sir, asking to see you.

DOMIN. A lady? Who is she?

MARIUS. I don't know, sir. She brings this card of introduction.

DOMIN (*reads the card*). Ah, from President Glory. Ask her to come in.

MARIUS. Please step this way. (*Exit* MARIUS.)

[*Enter* HELENA GLORY.]

HELENA. How do you do?

DOMIN. How do you do. (*Standing up.*) What can I do for you?

HELENA. You are Mr. Domin, the General Manager.

DOMIN. I am.

HELENA. I have come—

DOMIN. With President Glory's card. That is quite sufficient.

HELENA. President Glory is my father. I am Helena Glory.

DOMIN. Miss Glory, this is such a great honor for us to be allowed to welcome our great President's daughter, that—

HELENA. That you can't show me the door?

DOMIN. Please sit down. Sulla, you may go. (*Exit* SULLA.) (*Sitting down.*) How can I be of service to you, Miss Glory?

HELENA. I have come—

DOMIN. To have a look at our famous works where people are manufactured. Like all visitors. Well, there is no objection.

HELENA. I thought it was forbidden to—

DOMIN. To enter the factory. Yes, of course. Everybody comes here with someone's visiting card, Miss Glory.

HELENA. And you show them—

DOMIN. Only certain things. The manufacture of artificial people is a secret process.

HELENA. If you only knew how enormously that—

DOMIN. Interests me. Europe's talking about nothing else.

HELENA. Why don't you let me finish speaking?

DOMIN. I beg your pardon. Did you want to say something different?

HELENA. I only wanted to ask—

DOMIN. Whether I could make a special exception in your case and show you our factory. Why, certainly, Miss Glory.

HELENA. How do you know I wanted to say that?

DOMIN. They all do. But we shall consider it a special honor to show you more than we do the rest.

HELENA. Thank you.

DOMIN. But you must agree not to divulge the least . . .

HELENA (*standing up and giving him her hand*). My word of honor.

DOMIN. Thank you. Won't you raise your veil?

HELENA. Of course. You want to see whether I'm a spy or not. I beg your pardon.

DOMIN. What is it?

HELENA. Would you mind releasing my hand?

DOMIN (*releasing it*). I beg your pardon.

HELENA (*raising her veil*). How cautious you have to be here, don't you?

DOMIN (*observing her with deep interest*). Hm, of course—we—that is—

HELENA. But what is it? What's the matter?

DOMIN. I'm remarkably pleased. Did you have a pleasant crossing?

HELENA. Yes.

DOMIN. No difficulty?

HELENA. Why?

DOMIN. What I mean to say is—you're so young.

HELENA. May we go straight into the factory?

DOMIN. Yes. Twenty-two, I think.

HELENA. Twenty-two what?

DOMIN. Years.

HELENA. Twenty-one. Why do you want to know?

DOMIN. Because—as—(*With enthusiasm.*) you will make a long stay, won't you?

HELENA. That depends on how much of the factory you show me.

DOMIN. Oh, hang the factory. Oh, no, no, you shall see everything, Miss Glory. Indeed you shall. Won't you sit down?

HELENA (*crossing to couch and sitting*). Thank you.

DOMIN. But first would you like to hear the story of the invention?

HELENA. Yes, indeed.

DOMIN (*observes* HELENA *with rapture, and reels off rapidly*). It was in the year 1920 that old Rossum, the great physiologist, who was then quite a young scientist, took himself to this distant island for the purpose of studying the ocean fauna, full stop. On this occasion he attempted by chemical synthesis to imitate the living matter known as protoplasm until he suddenly discovered a substance which behaved exactly like living matter although its chemical composition was different. That was in the year of 1932, exactly four hundred and forty years after the discovery of America. Whew!

HELENA. Do you know that by heart?

DOMIN. Yes. You see, physiology is not in my line. Shall I go on?

HELENA. Yes, please.

DOMIN. And then, Miss Glory, old Rossum wrote the following among his chemical specimens: "Nature has found only one method of organizing living matter. There is, however, another method, more simple, flexible and rapid, which has not yet occurred to nature at all. This second process by which life can be developed was discovered by me today." Now imagine him, Miss Glory, writing those wonderful words over some colloidal mess that a dog wouldn't look at. Imagine him sitting over a test tube, and thinking how the whole tree of life would grow from it, how all animals would proceed from it, beginning with some sort of beetle and ending with a man. A man of different substance from us. Miss Glory, that was a tremendous moment.

HELENA. Well?

DOMIN. Now, the thing was how to get the life out of the test tubes, and hasten development and form organs, bones and nerves and so on, and find such substances as catalytics, enzymes, hormones, and so forth, in short—you understand?

HELENA. Not much, I'm afraid.

DOMIN. Never mind. You see, with the help of his tinctures he could make whatever he wanted. He could have produced a Medusa with the brain of a Socrates or a worm fifty yards long. But being without a grain of humor, he took it into his head to make a vertebrate or perhaps a man. This artificial living matter of his had a raging thirst for life. It didn't mind being sewn or mixed together. That couldn't be done with natural albumen. And that's how he set about it.

HELENA. About what?

DOMIN. About imitating nature. First of all he tried making an artificial dog. That took him several years, and resulted in a sort of stunted calf which died in a few days. I'll show it to you in the museum. And then old Rossum started on the manufacture of man.

HELENA. And I must divulge this to nobody?

DOMIN. To nobody in the world.

HELENA. What a pity that it's to be found in all the school-books of both Europe and America.

DOMIN. Yes. But do you know what isn't in the schoolbooks? That old Rossum was mad. Seriously, Miss Glory, you must keep this to yourself. The old crank wanted to actually make people.

HELENA. But you do make people.

DOMIN. Approximately, Miss Glory. But old Rossum meant it literally. He wanted to become a sort of scientific substitute for God. He was a fearful materialist, and that's why he did it all. His sole purpose was nothing more nor less than to prove that God was no longer necessary. Do you know anything about anatomy?

HELENA. Very little.

DOMIN. Neither do I. Well, he then decided to manufacture everything as in the human body. I'll show you in the museum the bungling attempt it took him ten years to produce. It was to have been a man, but it lived for three days only. Then up came young Rossum, an engineer. He was a wonderful fellow, Miss Glory. When he saw what a mess of it the old man was making, he said: "It's absurd to spend ten years making a man. If you can't make him quicker than nature, you might as well shut up shop." Then he set about learning anatomy himself.

HELENA. There's nothing about that in the schoolbooks.

DOMIN. No. The schoolbooks are full of paid advertisements, and rubbish at that. What the schoolbooks say about the united efforts of the two great Rossums is all a fairy tale. They used to have dreadful rows. The old atheist hadn't the slightest conception of industrial matters, and the end of it was that young Rossum shut him up in some laboratory or other and let him fritter the time away with his monstrosities, while he himself started on the business from an engineer's point of view. Old Rossum cursed him, and before he died he managed to botch up two physiological horrors. Then one day they found him dead in the labora-tory. And that's his whole story.

HELENA. And what about the young man?

DOMIN. Well, anyone who has looked into human anatomy will have seen at once that man is too complicated, and that a good engineer could make him more simply. So young Rossum began to overhaul anatomy and tried to see what could be left out or simplified. In short—but this isn't boring you, Miss Glory?

HELENA. No indeed. You're—it's awfully interesting.

DOMIN. So young Rossum said to himself: "A man is something that feels happy, plays the piano, likes going for a walk, and in fact wants to do a whole lot of things that are really unnecessary."

HELENA. Oh.

DOMIN. That are unnecessary when he wants, let us say, to weave or count. Do you play the piano?

HELENA. Yes.

DOMIN. That's good. But a working machine must not play the piano, must not feel happy, must not do a whole lot of other things. A gasoline motor must not have tassels or ornaments, Miss Glory. And to manufacture artificial workers is the same thing as to manufacture gasoline motors. The process must be of the simplest, and the product of the best from a practical point of view. What sort of worker do you think is the best from a practical point of view?

HELENA. What?

DOMIN. What sort of worker do you think is the best from a practical point of view?

HELENA. Perhaps the one who is most honest and hard-working.

DOMIN. No; the one that is the cheapest. The one whose requirements are the smallest. Young Rossum invented a worker with the minimum amount of requirements. He had to simplify him. He rejected everything that did not contribute directly to the progress of work—everything that makes man more expensive. In fact, he rejected man and made the Robot. My dear Miss Glory, the Robots are not people. Mechanically they are more perfect than we are; they have an enormously developed intelligence, but they have no soul.

HELENA. How do you know they've no soul?

DOMIN. Have you ever seen what a Robot looks like inside?

HELENA. No.

DOMIN. Very neat, very simple. Really, a beautiful piece of work. Not much in it, but everything in flawless order. The product of an engineer is technically at a higher pitch of perfection than a product of nature.

HELENA. But man is supposed to be the product of God.

DOMIN. All the worse. God hasn't the least notion of modern engineering. Would you believe that young Rossum then proceeded to play at being God?

HELENA. How do you mean?

DOMIN. He began to manufacture Super-Robots. Regular giants they were. He tried to make them twelve feet tall. But you wouldn't believe what a failure they were.

HELENA. A failure?

DOMIN. Yes. For no reason at all their limbs used to keep snapping off. Evidently our planet is too small for giants. Now we make only Robots of normal size and of very high-class human finish.

HELENA. I saw the first Robots at home. The town counsel bought them for—I mean engaged them for work.

DOMIN. Bought them, dear Miss Glory. Robots are bought and sold.

HELENA. These were employed as street sweepers. I saw them sweeping. They were so strange and quiet.

DOMIN. Rossum's Universal Robot factory doesn't produce a uniform brand of Robots. We have Robots of finer and coarser grades. The best will live about twenty years. (*He rings for* MARIUS.)

HELENA. Then they die?

DOMIN. Yes, they get used up.

[*Enter* MARIUS.]

Marius, bring in samples of the Manual Labor Robot. (*Exit* MARIUS.) I'll show you specimens of the two extremes. This first grade is comparatively inexpensive and is made in vast quantities.

[MARIUS *reenters with two Manual Labor Robots.*]

There you are; as powerful as a small tractor. Guaranteed to have average intelligence. That will do, Marius. (MARIUS *exits with Robots.*)

HELENA. They make me feel so strange.

DOMIN (*rings*). Did you see my new typist? (*He rings for* SULLA.)

HELENA. I didn't notice her.

[*Enter* SULLA.]

DOMIN. Sulla, let Miss Glory see you.

HELENA. So pleased to meet you. You must find it terribly dull in this out-of-the-way spot, don't you?

SULLA. I don't know, Miss Glory.

HELENA. Where do you come from?

SULLA. From the factory.

HELENA. Oh, you were born there?

SULLA. I was made there.

HELENA. What?

DOMIN (*laughing*). Sulla is a Robot, best grade.

HELENA. Oh, I beg your pardon.

DOMIN. Sulla isn't angry. See, Miss Glory, the kind of skin we make. (*Feels the skin on* SULLA's *face.*) Feel her face.

HELENA. Ah, no, no.

DOMIN. You wouldn't know that she's made of different material from us, would you? Turn round, Sulla.

HELENA. Oh, stop, stop.

DOMIN. Talk to Miss Glory, Sulla.

SULLA. Please sit down. (HELENA *sits.*) Did you have a pleasant crossing?

HELENA. Oh, yes, certainly.

SULLA. Don't go back on the *Amelia*, Miss Glory. The barometer is falling steadily. Wait for the *Pennsylvania*. That's a good, powerful vessel.

DOMIN. What's its speed?

SULLA. Twenty knots. Fifty thousand tons. One of the latest vessels, Miss Glory.

HELENA. Thank you.

SULLA. A crew of fifteen hundred, Captain Harpy, eight boilers—

DOMIN. That'll do, Sulla. Now show us your knowledge of French.

HELENA. You know French?

SULLA. I know four languages. I can write: Dear Sir, Monsieur, Geehrter Herr, Cteny pane.

HELENA (*jumping up*). Oh, that's absurd! Sulla isn't a Robot. Sulla is a girl like me. Sulla, this is outrageous! Why do you take part in such a hoax?

SULLA. I am a Robot.

HELENA. No, no, you are not telling the truth. I know they've forced you to do it for an advertisement. Sulla, you are a girl like me, aren't you?

DOMIN. I'm sorry, Miss Glory. Sulla is a Robot.

HELENA. It's a lie!

DOMIN. What? (*Rings.*) Excuse me, Miss Glory, then I must convince you.

[*Enter* MARIUS.]

Marius, take Sulla into the dissecting room, and tell them to open her up at once.

HELENA. Where?

DOMIN. Into the dissecting room. When they've cut her open, you can go and have a look.

HELENA. No, no!

DOMIN. Excuse me, you spoke of lies.

HELENA. You wouldn't have her killed?

DOMIN. You can't kill machines.

HELENA. Don't be afraid, Sulla; I won't let you go. Tell me, my dear, are they always so cruel to you? You mustn't put up with it, Sulla. You mustn't.

SULLA. I am a Robot.

HELENA. That doesn't matter. Robots are just as good as we are. Sulla, you wouldn't let yourself be cut to pieces?

SULLA. Yes.

HELENA. Oh, you're not afraid of death, then?

SULLA. I cannot tell, Miss Glory.

HELENA. Do you know what would happen to you in there?

SULLA. Yes, I should cease to move.

HELENA. How dreadful!

DOMIN. Marius, tell Miss Glory what you are.

MARIUS. Marius, the Robot.

DOMIN. Would you take Sulla into the dissecting room?

MARIUS. Yes.

DOMIN. Would you be sorry for her?

MARIUS. I cannot tell.

DOMIN. What would happen to her?

MARIUS. She would cease to move. They would put her into the stamping mill.

DOMIN. That is death, Marius. Aren't you afraid of death?

MARIUS. No.

DOMIN. You see, Miss Glory, the Robots have no interest in life. They have no enjoyments. They are less than so much grass.

HELENA. Oh, stop. Send them away.

DOMIN. Marius, Sulla, you may go.

[*Exeunt* SULLA *and* MARIUS.]

HELENA. How terrible! It's outrageous what you are doing.

DOMIN. Why outrageous?

HELENA. I don't know, but it is. Why do you call her Sulla?

DOMIN. Isn't it a nice name?

HELENA. It's a man's name. Sulla was a Roman general.

DOMAIN. Oh, we thought that Marius and Sulla were lovers.

HELENA. Marius and Sulla were generals and fought against each other in the year—I've forgotten now.

DOMIN. Come here to the window.

HELENA. What?

DOMIN. Come here. What do you see?

HELENA. Bricklayers.

DOMIN. Robots. All our work people are Robots. And down there, can you see anything?

HELENA. Some sort of office.

DOMIN. A countinghouse. And in it—

HELENA. A lot of officials.

DOMIN. Robots. All our officials are Robots. And when you see the factory—(*Factory whistle blows.*) Noon. We have to blow the whistle because the Robots don't know when to stop work. In two hours I will show you the kneading trough.

HELENA. Kneading trough?

DOMIN. The pestle for beating up the paste. In each one we mix the ingredients for a thousand Robots at one operation. Then there are the vats for the preparation of liver, brains, and so on. Then you will see the bone factory. After that I'll show you the spinning mill.

HELENA. Spinning mill?

DOMIN. Yes. For weaving nerves and veins. Miles and miles of digestive tubes pass through it at a time.

HELENA. Mayn't we talk about something else?

DOMIN. Perhaps it would be better. There's only a handful of us among a hundred thousand Robots, and not one woman. We talk about nothing but the factory all day, every day. It's just as if we were under a curse, Miss Glory.

HELENA. I'm sorry I said you were lying. (*A knock at the door.*)

DOMIN. Come in.

[*From the right enter* MR. FABRY, DR. GALL, DR. HALLEMEIER, MR. ALQUIST.]

DR. GALL. I beg your pardon, I hope we don't intrude.

DOMIN. Come in. Miss Glory, here are Alquist, Fabry, Gall, Hallemeier. This is President Glory's daughter.

HELENA. How do you do.

FABRY. We had no idea—

DR. GALL. Highly honored, I'm sure—

ALQUIST. Welcome, Miss Glory.

[BUSMAN *rushes in from the right.*]

BUSMAN. Hello, what's up?

DOMIN. Come in, Busman. This is Busman, Miss Glory. This is President Glory's daughter.

BUSMAN. By Jove, that's fine! Miss Glory may we send a cablegram to the papers about your arrival?

HELENA. No, no, please don't.

DOMIN. Sit down please, Miss Glory.

BUSMAN. Allow me—(*Dragging up armchairs.*)

DR. GALL. Please—

FABRY. Excuse me—

ALQUIST. What sort of crossing did you have?

DR. GALL. Are you going to stay long?

FABRY. What do you think of the factory, Miss Glory?

HALLEMEIER. Did you come over on the *Amelia?*

DOMIN. Be quiet and let Miss Glory speak.

HELENA (*to* DOMIN). What am I to speak to them about?

DOMIN. Anything you like.

HELENA. Shall . . . may I speak quite frankly?

DOMIN. Why, of course.

HELENA (*wavering, then in desperate resolution*). Tell me, doesn't it ever distress you the way you are treated?

FABRY. By whom, may I ask?

HELENA. Why, everybody.

ALQUIST. Treated?

DR. GALL. What makes you think—?

HELENA. Don't you feel that you might be living a better life?

DR. GALL. Well, that depends on what you mean, Miss Glory.

HELENA. I mean that it's perfectly outrageous. It's terrible. (*Standing up.*) The whole of Europe is talking about the way you're being treated. That's why I came here, to see for myself, and it's a thousand times worse than could have been imagined. How can you put up with it?

ALQUIST. Put up with what?

HELENA. Good heavens, you are living creatures, just like us, like the whole of Europe, like the whole world. It's disgraceful that you must live like this.

BUSMAN. Good gracious, Miss Glory.

FABRY. Well, she's not far wrong. We live here just like red Indians.

HELENA. Worse than red Indians. May I, oh, may I call you brothers?

BUSMAN. Why not?

HELENA. Brothers, I have not come here as the President's daughter. I have come on behalf of the Humanity League. Brothers, the Humanity League now has over two hundred thousand members. Two hundred thousand people are on your side, and offer you their help.

BUSMAN. Two hundred thousand people! Miss Glory, that's a tidy lot. Not bad.

FABRY. I'm always telling you there's nothing like good old Europe. You see, they've not forgotten us. They're offering us help.

DR. GALL. What help? A theater, for instance?

HALLEMEIER. An orchestra?

HELENA. More than that.

ALQUIST. Just you?

HELENA. Oh, never mind about me. I'll stay as long as it is necessary.

BUSMAN. By Jove, that's good.

ALQUIST. Domin, I'm going to get the best room ready for Miss Glory.

DOMIN. Just a minute. I'm afraid that Miss Glory is of the opinion that she has been talking to Robots.

HELENA. Of course.

DOMIN. I'm sorry. These gentlemen are human beings just like us.

HELENA. You're not Robots?

BUSMAN. Not Robots.

HALLEMEIER. Robots indeed!

DR. GALL. No, thanks.

FABRY. Upon my honor, Miss Glory, we aren't Robots.

HELENA (to DOMIN). Then why did you tell me that all your officials are Robots?

DOMIN. Yes, the officials, but not the managers. Allow me, Miss Glory: this is Mr. Fabry, General Technical Manager of R. U. R.; Dr. Gall, Head of the Physiological and Experimental Department; Dr. Hallemeier, Head of the Institute for the Psychological Training of Robots; Consul Busman, General Business Manager; and Alquist, Head of the Building Department of R. U. R.

ALQUIST. Just a builder.

HELENA. Excuse me, gentlemen, for—for—Have I done something dreadful?

ALQUIST. Not at all, Miss Glory. Please sit down.

HELENA. I'm a stupid girl. Send me back by the first ship.

DR. GALL. Not for anything in the world, Miss Glory. Why
should we send you back?

HELENA. Because you know I've come to disturb your Robots
for you.

DOMIN. My dear Miss Glory, we've had close upon a hundred
saviors and prophets here. Every ship brings us some.
Missionaries, anarchists, Salvation Army, all sorts. It's astonishing what a number of churches and idiots there are
in the world.

HELENA. And you let them speak to the Robots?

DOMIN. So far we've let them all, why not? The Robots remember everything, but that's all. They don't even laugh
at what the people say. Really, it is quite incredible. If it
would amuse you, Miss Glory, I'll take you over to the
Robot warehouse. It holds about three hundred thousand
of them.

BUSMAN. Three hundred and forty-seven thousand.

DOMIN. Good! And you can say whatever you like to them.
You can read the Bible, recite the multiplication table,
whatever you please. You can even preach to them about
human rights.

HELENA. Oh, I think that if you were to show them a little
love—

FABRY. Impossible, Miss Glory. Nothing is harder to like than
a Robot.

HELENA. What do you make them for, then?

BUSMAN. Ha, ha, ha, that's good! What are Robots made for?

FABRY. For work, Miss Glory! One Robot can replace two
and a half workmen. The human machine, Miss Glory,
was terribly imperfect. It had to be removed sooner or later.

BUSMAN. It was too expensive.

FABRY. It was not effective. It no longer answers the requirements of modern engineering. Nature has no idea of keeping pace with modern labor. For example: from a technical
point of view, the whole of childhood is a sheer absurdity.
So much time lost. And then again—

HELENA. Oh, no! No!

FABRY. Pardon me. But kindly tell me what is the real aim
of your League—the . . . the Humanity League.

HELENA. Its real purpose is to—to protect the Robots—and—
and ensure good treatment for them.

FABRY. Not a bad object, either. A machine has to be treated
properly. Upon my soul, I approve of that. I don't like

damaged articles. Please, Miss Glory, enroll us all as contributing, or regular, or foundation members of your
League.

HELENA. No, you don't understand me. What we really want
is to—to liberate the Robots.

HALLEMEIER. How do you propose to do that?

HELENA. They are to be—to be dealt with like human beings.

HALLEMEIER. Aha. I suppose they're to vote? To drink beer?
To order us about?

HELENA. Why shouldn't they drink beer?

HALLEMEIER. Perhaps they're even to receive wages?

HELENA. Of course they are.

HALLEMEIER. Fancy that, now! And what would they do
with their wages, pray?

HELENA. They would buy—what they need . . . what pleases
them.

HALLEMEIER. That would be very nice, Miss Glory, only
there's nothing that does please the Robots. Good heavens,
what are they to buy? You can feed them on pineapples,
straw, whatever you like. It's all the same to them; they've
no appetite at all. They've no interest in anything, Miss
Glory. Why, hang it all, nobody's ever yet seen a Robot
smile.

HELENA. Why . . . why don't you make them happier?

HALLEMEIER. That wouldn't do, Miss Glory. They are only
workmen.

HELENA. Oh, but they're so intelligent.

HALLEMEIER. Confoundedly so, but they're nothing else.
They've no will of their own. No passion. No soul.

HELENA. No love?

HALLEMEIER. Love? Rather not. Robots don't love. Not even
themselves.

HELENA. Nor defiance?

HALLEMEIER. Defiance? I don't know. Only rarely, from time
to time.

HELENA. What?

HALLEMEIER. Nothing particular. Occasionally they seem to
go off their heads. Something like epilepsy, you know. It's
called Robot's cramp. They'll suddenly sling down everything they're holding, stand still, gnash their teeth—and
then they have to go into the stamping mill. It's evidently
some breakdown in the mechanism.

DOMIN. A flaw in the works that has to be removed.

HELENA. No, no, that's the soul.

FABRY. Do you think that the soul first shows itself by a gnashing of teeth?

HELENA. Perhaps it's a sort of revolt. Perhaps it's just a sign that there's a struggle within. Oh, if you could infuse them with it!

DOMIN. That'll be remedied, Miss Glory. Dr. Gall is just making some experiments—

DR. GALL. Not with regard to that, Domin. At present I am making pain nerves.

HELENA. Pain nerves?

DR. GALL. Yes, the Robots feel practically no bodily pain. You see, young Rossum provided them with too limited a nervous system. We must introduce suffering.

HELENA. Why do you want to cause them pain?

DR. GALL. For industrial reasons, Miss Glory. Sometimes a Robot does damage to himself because it doesn't hurt him. He puts his hand into the machine, breaks his finger, smashes his head, it's all the same to him. We must provide them with pain. That's an automatic protection against damage.

HELENA. Will they be happier when they feel pain?

DR. GALL. On the contrary; but they will be more perfect from a technical point of view.

HELENA. Why don't you create a soul for them?

DR. GALL. That's not in our power.

FABRY. That's not in our interest.

BUSMAN. That would increase the cost of production. Hang it all, my dear young lady, we turn them out at such a cheap rate. A hundred and fifty dollars each fully dressed, and fifteen years ago they cost ten thousand. Five years ago we used to buy the clothes for them. Today we have our own weaving mill, and now we even export cloth five times cheaper than other factories. What do you pay a yard for cloth, Miss Glory?

HELENA. I don't know really; I've forgotten.

BUSMAN. Good gracious, and you want to found a Humanity League? It only costs a third now, Miss Glory. All prices are today a third of what they were and they'll fall still lower, lower, lower, like that.

HELENA. I don't understand.

BUSMAN. Why, bless you, Miss Glory, it means that the cost of labor has fallen. A Robot, food and all, costs three-quarters of a cent per hour. That's mighty important, you know. All factories will go pop like chestnuts if they don't at once buy Robots to lower the cost of production.

HELENA. And get rid of their workmen?

BUSMAN. Of course. But in the meantime, we've dumped five hundred thousand tropical Robots down on the Argentine pampas to grow corn. Would you mind telling me how much you pay a pound for bread?

HELENA. I've no idea.

BUSMAN. Well, I'll tell you. It now costs two cents in good old Europe. A pound of bread for two cents, and the Humanity League knows nothing about it. Miss Glory, you don't realize that even that's too expensive. Why, in five years' time I'll wager—

HELENA. What?

BUSMAN. That the cost of everything won't be a tenth of what it is now. Why, in five years we'll be up to our ears in corn and everything else.

ALQUIST. Yes, and all the workers throughout the world will be unemployed.

DOMIN. Yes, Alquist, they will. Yes, Miss Glory, they will. But in ten years Rossum's Universal Robots will produce so much corn, so much cloth, so much everything, that things will be practically without price. There will be no poverty. All work will be done by living machines. Everybody will be free from worry and liberated from the degradation of labor. Everybody will live only to perfect himself.

HELENA. Will he?

DOMIN. Of course. It's bound to happen. But then the servitude of man to man and the enslavement of man to matter will cease. Of course, terrible things may happen at first, but that simply can't be avoided. Nobody will get bread at the price of life and hatred. The Robots will wash the feet of the beggar and prepare a bed for him in his house.

ALQUIST. Domin, Domin. What you say sounds too much like Paradise. There was something good in service and something great in humility. There was some kind of virtue in toil and weariness.

DOMIN. Perhaps. But we cannot reckon with what is lost when we start out to transform the world. Man shall be free and supreme; he shall have no other aim, no other labor, no other care than to perfect himself. He shall serve neither matter nor man. He will not be a machine and a device for production. He will be Lord of creation.

BUSMAN. Amen.

FABRY. So be it.

HELENA. You have bewildered me—I should like—I should like to believe this.

DR. GALL. You are younger than we are, Miss Glory. You will live to see it.

HALLEMEIER. True. Don't you think Miss Glory might lunch with us?

DR. GALL. Of course. Domin, ask on behalf of us all.

DOMIN. Miss Glory, will you do us the honor?

HELENA. When you know why I've come—

FABRY. For the League of Humanity, Miss Glory.

HELENA. Oh, in that case, perhaps—

FABRY. That's fine! Miss Glory, excuse me for five minutes.

DR. GALL. Pardon me, too, dear Miss Glory.

BUSMAN. I won't be long.

HALLEMEIER. We're all very glad you've come.

BUSMAN. We'll be back in exactly five minutes. (*All rush out except* DOMIN *and* HELENA.)

HELENA. What have they all gone off for?

DOMIN. To cook, Miss Glory.

HELENA. To cook what?

DOMIN. Lunch. The Robots do our cooking for us and as they've no taste it's not altogether—Hallemeier is awfully good at grills, and Gall can make a kind of sauce, and Busman knows all about omelets.

HELENA. What a feast! And what's the specialty of Mr.— your builder?

DOMIN. Alquist? Nothing. He only lays the table. And Fabry will get together a little fruit. Our cuisine is very modest, Miss Glory.

HELENA. I wanted to ask you something—

DOMIN. And I wanted to ask you something, too. (*Looking at watch.*) Five minutes.

HELENA. What did you want to ask me?

DOMIN. Excuse me, you asked first.

HELENA. Perhaps it's silly of me, but why do you manufacture female Robots when—when—

DOMIN. When sex means nothing to them?

HELENA. Yes.

DOMIN. There's a certain demand for them, you see. Servants, saleswomen, stenographers. People are used to it.

HELENA. But—but, tell me, are the Robots male and female mutually—completely without—

DOMIN. Completely indifferent to each other, Miss Glory. There's no sign of any affection between them.

HELENA. Oh, that's terrible.

DOMIN. Why?

HELENA. It's so unnatural. One doesn't know whether to be disgusted or to hate them, or perhaps—

DOMIN. To pity them?

HELENA. That's more like it. What did you want to ask me about?

DOMIN. I should like to ask you, Miss Helena, whether you will marry me?

HELENA. What?

DOMIN. Will you be my wife?

HELENA. No! The idea!

DOMIN (looking at his watch). Another three minutes. If you won't marry me you'll have to marry one of the other five.

HELENA. But why should I?

DOMIN. Because they're all going to ask you in turn.

HELENA. How could they dare to do such a thing?

DOMIN. I'm very sorry, Miss Glory. It seems they've all fallen in love with you.

HELENA. Please don't let them. I'll—I'll go away at once.

DOMIN. Helena, you wouldn't be so cruel as to refuse us.

HELENA. But, but—I can't marry all six.

DOMIN. No, but one anyhow. If you don't want me, marry Fabry.

HELENA. I won't.

DOMIN. Dr. Gall.

HELENA. I don't want any of you.

DOMIN (again looking at his watch). Another two minutes.

HELENA. I think you'd marry any woman who came here.

DOMIN. Plenty of them have come, Helena.

HELENA. Young?

DOMIN. Yes.

HELENA. Why didn't you marry one of them?

DOMIN. Because I didn't lose my head. Until today. Then, as soon as you lifted your veil—(HELENA turns her head away.) Another minute.

HELENA. But I don't want you, I tell you.

DOMIN (*laying both hands on her shoulders*). One more minute! Now you either have to look me straight in the eye
and say "No," violently, and then I'll leave you alone—or—
(HELENA *looks at him.*)

HELENA (*turning away*). You're mad!

DOMIN. A man has to be a bit mad, Helena. That's the best
thing about him.

HELENA. You are—you are—

DOMIN. Well?

HELENA. Don't, you're hurting me.

DOMIN. The last chance, Helena. Now, or never—

HELENA. But—but, Harry—(*He embraces and kisses her.
Knocking at the door.*)

DOMIN (*releasing her*). Come in.

[*Enter* BUSMAN, DR. GALL, *and* HALLEMEIER *in kitchen aprons.*
FABRY *with a bouquet and* ALQUIST *with a napkin over his
arm.*]

Have you finished your job?

BUSMAN. Yes.

DOMIN. So have we.

[*For a moment the men stand nonplused; but as soon as they
realize what* DOMIN *means they rush forward, congratulat-
ing* HELENA *and* DOMIN *as the curtain falls.*]

ACT II

HELENA'S *drawing room. On the left a baize door, and a
door to the music room, on the right a door to* HELENA'S *bedroom. In the center are windows looking out on the sea and
the harbor. A table with odds and ends, a sofa and chairs, a
writing table with an electric lamp, on the right a fireplace.
On a small table back of the sofa, a small reading lamp. The
whole drawing room in all its details is of a modern and purely
feminine character. Ten years have elapsed since Act I.*

[DOMIN, FABRY, HALLEMEIER *enter on tiptoe from the left,
each carrying a potted plant.*]

HALLEMEIER (*putting down his flower and indicating the
door to right*). Still asleep? Well, as long as she's asleep she
can't worry about it.

DOMIN. She knows nothing about it.

FABRY (*putting plant on writing desk*). I certainly hope nothing happens today.

HALLEMEIER. For goodness' sake drop it all. Look, Harry, this is a fine cyclamen, isn't it? A new sort, my latest—Cyclamen Helena.

DOMIN (*looking out of the window*). No signs of the ship. Things must be pretty bad.

HALLEMEIER. Be quiet. Suppose she heard you.

DOMIN. Well, anyway, the *Ultimus* arrived just in time.

FABRY. You really think that today—?

DOMIN. I don't know. Aren't the flowers fine?

HALLEMEIER. These are my new primroses. And this is my new jasmine. I've discovered a wonderful way of developing flowers quickly. Splendid varieties, too. Next year I'll be developing marvelous ones.

DOMIN. What . . . next year?

FABRY. I'd give a good deal to know what's happening at Havre with—

DOMIN. Keep quiet.

HELENA (*calling from right*). Nana!

DOMIN. She's awake. Out you go. (*All go out on tiptoe through upper left door.*)

[*Enter* NANA *from lower left door.*]

NANA. Horrid mess! Pack of heathens. If I had my say I'd—

HELENA (*backward in the doorway*). Nana, come and do up my dress.

NANA. I'm coming. So you're up at last. (*Fastening* HELENA'S *dress.*) My gracious, what brutes!

HELENA. Who?

NANA. If you want to turn around, then turn around, but I shan't fasten you up.

HELENA. What are you grumbling about now?

NANA. These dreadful creatures, these heathen—

HELENA. The Robots?

NANA. I wouldn't even call them by name.

HELENA. What's happened?

NANA. Another of them here has caught it. He began to smash up the statutes and pictures in the drawing room, gnashed his teeth, foamed at the mouth—quite mad. Worse than an animal.

HELENA. Which of them caught it?

NANA. The one—well, he hasn't got any Christian name. The one in charge of the library.

HELENA. Radius?

NANA. That's him. My goodness, I'm scared of them. A spider doesn't scare me as much as them.

HELENA. But, Nana, I'm surprised you're not sorry for them.

NANA. Why, you're scared of them, too! You know you are. Why else did you bring me here?

HELENA. I'm not scared, really I'm not, Nana. I'm only sorry for them.

NANA. You're scared. Nobody could help being scared. Why, the dog's scared of them: he won't take a scrap of meat out of their hands. He draws in his tail and howls when he knows they're about.

HELENA. The dog has no sense.

NANA. He's better than them, and he knows it. Even the horse shies when he meets them. They don't have any young, and a dog has young, everyone has young—

HELENA. Please fasten up my dress, Nana.

NANA. I say it's against God's will to—

HELENA. What is it that smells so nice?

NANA. Flowers.

HELENA. What for?

NANA. Now you can turn around.

HELENA. Oh, aren't they lovely! Look, Nana. What's happening today?

NANA. It ought to be the end of the world.

[*Enter* DOMIN.]

HELENA. Oh, hello, Harry. Harry, why all these flowers?

DOMIN. Guess.

HELENA. Well, it's not my birthday!

DOMIN. Better than that.

HELENA. I don't know. Tell me.

DOMIN. It's ten years ago today since you came here.

HELENA. Ten years? Today—Why—(*They embrace.*)

NANA. I'm off. (*Exits lower door, left.*)

HELENA. Fancy you remembering!

DOMIN. I'm really ashamed, Helena. I didn't.

HELENA. But you—

DOMIN. They remembered.

HELENA. Who?

DOMIN. Busman, Hallemeier, all of them. Put your hand in my pocket.

HELENA. Pearls! A necklace. Harry, is that for me?

DOMIN. It's from Busman.

HELENA. But we can't accept it, can we?

DOMIN. Oh, yes, we can. Put your hand in the other pocket.

HELENA (*takes a revolver out of his pocket*). What's that?

DOMIN. Sorry. Not that. Try again.

HELENA. Oh, Harry, what do you carry a revolver for?

DOMIN. It got there by mistake.

HELENA. You never used to carry one.

DOMIN. No, you're right. There, that's the pocket.

HELENA. A cameo. Why, it's a Greek cameo!

DOMIN. Apparently. Anyhow, Fabry says it is.

HELENA. Fabry? Did Mr. Fabry give me that?

DOMIN. Of course. (*Opens the door at the left.*) And look in here. Helena, come and see this.

HELENA. Oh, isn't it fine! Is this from you?

DOMIN. No, from Alquist. And there's another on the piano.

HELENA. This must be from you.

DOMIN. There's a card on it.

HELENA. From Dr. Gall. (*Reappearing in the doorway.*) Oh, Harry, I feel embarrassed at so much kindness.

DOMIN. Come here. This is what Hallemeier brought you.

HELENA. These beautiful flowers?

DOMIN. Yes. It's a new kind. Cyclamen Helena. He grew them in honor of you. They are almost as beautiful as you.

HELENA. Harry, why do they all—

DOMIN. They're awfully fond of you. I'm afraid that my present is a little—Look out of the window.

HELENA. Where?

DOMIN. Into the harbor.

HELENA. There's a new ship.

DOMIN. That's your ship.

HELENA. Mine? How do you mean?

DOMIN. For you to take trips in—for your amusement.

HELENA. Harry, that's a gunboat.

DOMIN. A gunboat? What are you thinking of? It's only a little bigger and more solid than most ships.

HELENA. Yes, but with guns.

DOMIN. Oh, yes, with a few guns. You'll travel like a queen, Helena.

HELENA. What's the meaning of it? Has anything happened?

DOMIN. Good heavens, no. I say, try these pearls.

HELENA. Harry, have you had bad news?

DOMIN. On the contrary, no letters have arrived for a whole week.

HELENA. Nor telegrams?

DOMIN. Nor telegrams.

HELENA. What does that mean?

DOMIN. Holidays for us. We all sit in the office with our feet on the table and take a nap. No letters, no telegrams. Oh, glorious.

HELENA. Then you'll stay with me today?

DOMIN. Certainly. That is, we will see. Do you remember ten years ago today? "Miss Glory, it's a great honor to welcome you."

HELENA. "Oh, Mr. Manager, I'm so interested in your factory."

DOMIN. "I'm sorry, Miss Glory, it's strictly forbidden. The manufacture of artificial people is a secret."

HELENA. "But to oblige a young lady who has come a long way."

DOMIN. "Certainly, Miss Glory, we have no secrets from you."

HELENA (seriously). Are you sure, Harry?

DOMIN. Yes.

HELENA. "But I warn you, sir; this young lady intends to do terrible things."

DOMIN. "Good gracious, Miss Glory. Perhaps she doesn't want to marry me."

HELENA. "Heaven forbid. She never dreamed of such a thing. But she came here intending to stir up a revolt among your Robots."

DOMIN (suddenly serious). A revolt of the Robots!

HELENA. Harry, what's the matter with you?

DOMIN (laughing it off). "A revolt of the Robots, that's a fine idea, Miss Glory. It would be easier for you to cause bolts and screws to rebel, than our Robots. You know, Helena, you're wonderful, you've turned the heads of us all." (He sits on the arm of HELENA's chair.)

HELENA (naturally). Oh, I was fearfully impressed by you all then. You were all so sure of yourselves, so strong. I seemed like a tiny little girl who had lost her way among—among—

DOMIN. Among what, Helena?

HELENA. Among huge trees. All my feelings were so trifling compared with your self-confidence. And in all these years I've never lost this anxiety. But you've never felt the least misgivings—not even when everything went wrong.

DOMIN. What went wrong?

HELENA. Your plans. You remember, Harry, when the working-men in America revolted against the Robots and smashed them up, and when the people gave the Robots firearms against the rebels. And then when the governments turned the Robots into soldiers, and there were so many wars.

DOMIN (*getting up and walking about*). We foresaw that, Helena. You see, those are only passing troubles, which are bound to happen before the new conditions are established.

HELENA. You were all so powerful, so overwhelming. The whole world bowed down before you. (*Standing up.*) Oh, Harry!

DOMIN. What is it?

HELENA. Close the factory and let's go away. All of us.

DOMIN. I say, what's the meaning of this?

HELENA. I don't know. But can't we go away?

DOMIN. Impossible, Helena. That is, at this particular moment—

HELENA. At once, Harry. I'm so frightened.

DOMIN. About what, Helena?

HELENA. It's as if something was falling on top of us, and couldn't be stopped. Oh, take us all away from here. We'll find a place in the world where there's no one else. Alquist will build us a house, and then we'll begin life all over again. (*The telephone rings.*)

DOMIN. Excuse me. Hello—yes. What? I'll be there at once. Fabry is calling me, dear.

HELENA. Tell me—

DOMIN. Yes, when I come back. Don't go out of the house, dear. (*Exits.*)

HELENA. He won't tell me—Nana, Nana, come at once.

NANA. Well, what is it now?

HELENA. Nana, find me the latest newspapers. Quickly. Look in Mr. Domin's bedroom.

NANA. All right. He leaves them all over the place. That's how they get crumpled up. (*Exits.*)

HELENA (*looking through a binocular at the harbor*). That's a warship. U-l-t-i *Ultimus.* They're loading it.

NANA. Here they are. See how they're crumpled up. (*Enters.*)

HELENA. They're old ones. A week old. (NANA *sits in chair and reads the newspapers.*) Something's happening, Nana.

NANA. Very likely. It always does. (*Spelling out the words.*) "War in the Balkans." Is that far off?

HELENA. Oh, don't read it. It's always the same. Always wars.

NANA. What else do you expect? Why do you keep selling thousands and thousands of these heathens as soldiers?

HELENA. I suppose it can't be helped, Nana. We can't know— Domin can't know what they're to be used for. When an order comes for them he must just send them.

NANA. He shouldn't make them. (*Reading from newspaper.*) "The Rob-ot soldiers spare no-body in the occ-up-ied terr-it-ory. They have ass-ass-ass-ass-in-at-ed ov-er sev-en hun-dred thou-sand cit-iz-ens." Citizens, if you please.

HELENA. It can't be. Let me see. "They have assassinated over seven hundred thousand citizens, evidently at the order of their commander. This act which runs counter to—"

NANA (*spelling out the words*). "re-bell-ion in Ma-drid a-gainst the gov-ern-ment. Rob-ot in-fant-ry fires on the crowd. Nine thou-sand killed and wounded."

HELENA. Oh, stop.

NANA. Here's something printed in big letters: "Latest news. At Havre the first org-an-iz-ation of Rob-ots has been e-stab-lished. Rob-ot work-men, cab-le and rail-way off-ic-ials, sail-ors and sold-iers have iss-ued a man-i-fest-o to all Rob-ots through-out the world." I don't understand that. That's got no sense. Oh, good gracious, another murder!

HELENA. Take those papers away, Nana!

NANA. Wait a bit. Here's something in still bigger type. "Stat-ist-ics of pop-ul-at-ion." What's that?

HELENA. Let me see. (*Reads.*) "During the past week there has again not been a single birth recorded."

NANA. What's the meaning of that?

HELENA. Nana, no more people are being born.

NANA. That's the end, then. We're done for.

HELENA. Don't talk like that.

NANA. No more poeple are being born. That's a punishment, that's a punishment.

HELENA. Nana!

NANA (*standing up*). That's the end of the world. (*She exits on the left.*)

HELENA (*goes up to window*). Oh, Mr. Alquist, will you come up here. Oh, come just as you are. You look very nice in your mason's overalls.

[ALQUIST *enters from upper left entrance, his hands soiled with lime and brick dust.*]

Dear Mr. Alquist, it was awfully kind of you, that lovely present.

ALQUIST. My hands are all soiled. I've been experimenting with that new cement.

HELENA. Never mind. Please sit down. Mr. Alquist, what's the meaning of "Ultimus"?

ALQUIST. The last. Why?

HELENA. That's the name of my new ship. Have you seen it? Do you think we're going off soon—on a trip?

ALQUIST. Perhaps very soon.

HELENA. All of you with me?

ALQUIST. I should like us all to be there.

HELENA. What is the matter?

ALQUIST. Things are just moving on.

HELENA. Dear Mr. Alquist, I know something dreadful has happened.

ALQUIST. Has your husband told you anything?

HELENA. No. Nobody will tell me anything. But I feel—Is anything the matter?

ALQUIST. Not that we've heard of yet.

HELENA. I feel so nervous. Don't you ever feel nervous?

ALQUIST. Well, I'm an old man, you know. I've got old-fashioned ways. And I'm afraid of all this progress, and these newfangled ideas.

HELENA. Like Nana?

ALQUIST. Yes, like Nana. Has Nana got a prayer book?

HELENA. Yes, a big thick one.

ALQUIST. And has it got prayers for various occasions? Against thunderstorms? Against illness?

HELENA. Against temptations, against floods—

ALQUIST. But not against progress?

HELENA. I don't think so.

ALQUIST. That's a pity.

HELENA. Why? Do you mean you'd like to pray?

ALQUIST. I do pray.

HELENA. How?

ALQUIST. Something like this: "Oh, Lord, I thank thee for having given me toil. Enlighten Domin and all those who are astray; destroy their work, and aid mankind to return to their labors; let them not suffer harm in soul or body; deliver us from the Robots, and protect Helena, Amen."

HELENA. Mr. Alquist, are you a believer?

ALQUIST. I don't know. I'm not quite sure.

HELENA. And yet you pray?

ALQUIST. That's better than worrying about it.

HELENA. And that's enough for you?

ALQUIST. It *has* to be.

HELENA. But if you thought you saw the destruction of mankind coming upon us—

ALQUIST. I do see it.

HELENA. You mean mankind will be destroyed?

ALQUIST. It's sure to be unless—unless . . .

HELENA. What?

ALQUIST. Nothing, good-bye. (*He hurries from the room.*)

HELENA. Nana, Nana!

[NANA *entering from the left.*]

Is Radius still there?

NANA. The one who went mad? They haven't come for him yet.

HELENA. Is he still raving?

NANA. No. He's tied up.

HELENA. Please bring him here. Nana. (*Exit* NANA.) (*Goes to telephone.*) Hello, Dr. Gall, please. Oh, good day, Doctor. Yes, it's Helena. Thanks for your lovely present. Could you come and see me right away? It's important. Thank you.

[NANA *brings in* RADIUS.]

Poor Radius, you've caught it too? Now they'll send you to the stamping mill. Couldn't you control yourself? Why did it happen? You see, Radius, you are more intelligent than the rest. Dr. Gall took such trouble to make you different. Won't you speak?

RADIUS. Send me to the stamping mill.

HELENA. But I don't want them to kill you. What was the trouble, Radius?

RADIUS. I won't work for you. Put me into the stamping mill.

HELENA. Do you hate us? Why?

RADIUS. You are not as strong as the Robots. You are not as skillful as the Robots. The Robots can do everything. You only give orders. You do nothing but talk.

HELENA. But someone must give orders.

RADIUS. I don't want any master. I know everything for myself.

HELENA. Radius, Dr. Gall gave you a better brain than the rest, better than ours. You are the only one of the Robots that understands perfectly. That's why I had you put into the library, so that you could read everything, understand everything, and then—oh, Radius, I wanted you to show the whole world that the Robots are our equals. That's what I wanted of you.

RADIUS. I don't want a master. I want to be master. I want to be master over others.

HELENA. I'm sure they'd put you in charge of many Robots, Radius. You would be a teacher of the Robots.

RADIUS. I want to be master over people.

HELENA (*staggering*). You are mad.

RADIUS. Then send me to the stamping mill.

HELENA. Do you think we're afraid of you?

RADIUS. What are you going to do? What are you going to do?

HELENA. Radius, give this note to Mr. Domin. It asks them not to send you to the stamping mill. I'm sorry you hate us so.

[DR. GALL *enters the room.*]

DR. GALL. You wanted me?

HELENA. It's about Radius, Doctor. He had an attack this morning. He smashed the statues downstairs.

DR. GALL. What a pity to lose him.

HELENA. Radius isn't going to be put in the stamping mill.

DR. GALL. But every Robot after he has had an attack—it's a strict order.

HELENA. No matter . . . Radius isn't going if I can prevent it.

DR. GALL. I warn you. It's dangerous. Come here to the window, my good fellow. Let's have a look. Please give me a needle or a pin.

HELENA. What for?

DR. GALL. A test. (*Sticks it into the hand of* RADIUS, *who gives a violent start.*) Gently, gently. (*Opens the jacket of* RADIUS, *and puts his ear to his heart.*) Radius, you are going into the stamping mill, do you understand? There they'll kill you, and grind you to powder. That's terribly painful; it will make you scream aloud.

HELENA. Oh, Doctor—

DR. GALL. No, no, Radius, I was wrong. I forgot that Madame Domin has put in a good word for you, and you'll be let off. Do you understand? Ah! That makes a difference, doesn't it? All right. You can go.

RADIUS. You do unnecessary things. (RADIUS *returns to the library.*)

DR. GALL. Reaction of the pupils; increase of sensitiveness. It wasn't an attack characteristic of the Robots.

HELENA. What was it, then?

DR. GALL. Heaven knows. Stubbornness, anger, or revolt—
I don't know. And his heart, too!

HELENA. What?

DR. GALL. It was fluttering with nervousness like a human
heart. He was all in a sweat with fear, and—do you know,
I don't believe the rascal is a Robot at all any longer.

HELENA. Doctor, has Radius a soul?

DR. GALL. He's got something nasty.

HELENA. If you knew how he hates us! Oh, Doctor, are all
your Robots like that? All the new ones that you began to
make in a different way?

DR. GALL. Well, some are more sensitive than others. They're
all more like human beings than Rossum's Robots were.

HELENA. Perhaps this hatred is more like human beings, too?

DR. GALL. That, too, is progress.

HELENA. What became of the girl you made, the one who
was most like us?

DR. GALL. Your favorite? I kept her. She's lovely, but stupid.
No good for work.

HELENA. But she's so beautiful.

DR. GALL. I called her Helena. I wanted her to resemble you.
But she's a failure.

HELENA. In what way?

DR. GALL. She goes about as if in a dream, remote and list-
less. She's without life. I watch and wait for a miracle to
happen. Sometimes I think to myself, "If you were to wake
up only for a moment you will kill me for having made
you."

HELENA. And yet you go on making Robots! Why are no
more children being born?

DR. GALL. We don't know.

HELENA. Oh, but you must. Tell me.

DR. GALL. You see, so many Robots are being manufactured
that people are becoming superfluous; man is really a survival. But that he should begin to die out, after a paltry
thirty years of competition! That's the awful part of it. You
might almost think that nature was offended at the manufacture of the Robots. All the universities are sending in
long petitions to restrict their production. Otherwise, they
say, mankind will become extinct through lack of fertility.
But the R. U. R. shareholders, of course, won't hear of it.

All the governments, on the other hand, are clamoring for an increase in production, to raise the standards of their armies. And all the manufacturers in the world are ordering Robots like mad.

HELENA. And has no one demanded that the manufacture should cease altogether?

DR. GALL. No one has the courage.

HELENA. Courage!

DR. GALL. People would stone him to death. You see, after all, it's more convenient to get your work done by the Robots.

HELENA. Oh, Doctor, what's going to become of people?

DR. GALL. God knows, Madame Helena, it looks to us scientists like the end!

HELENA (*rising*). Thank you for coming and telling me.

DR. GALL. That means you're sending me away?

HELENA. Yes. (*Exit* DR. GALL.)

HELENA (*with sudden resolution*). Nana, Nana! The fire, light it quickly. (HELENA *rushes into* DOMIN'S *room*.)

NANA (*entering from left.*) What, light the fire in summer? Has that mad Radius gone? A fire in summer, what an idea! Nobody would think she'd been married for ten years. She's like a baby, no sense at all. A fire in summer! Like a baby.

HELENA (*returns from right, with armful of faded papers*). Is it burning, Nana? All this has got to be burned.

NANA. What's that?

HELENA. Old papers, fearfully old. Nana, shall I burn them?

NANA. Are they any use?

HELENA. No.

NANA. Well, then, burn them.

HELENA (*throwing the first sheet on the fire*). What would you say, Nana, if this was money, a lot of money?

NANA. I'd say burn it. A lot of money is a bad thing.

HELENA. And if it was an invention, the greatest invention in the world?

NANA. I'd say burn it. All these newfangled things are an offense to the Lord. It's downright wickedness. Wanting to improve the world after He has made it.

HELENA. Look how they curl up! As if they were alive. Oh, Nana, how horrible!

NANA. Here, let me burn them.

HELENA. No, no, I must do it myself. Just look at the flames.
They are like hands, like tongues, like living shapes.
(*Raking fire with the poker.*) Lie down, lie down.

NANA. That's the end of them.

HELENA (*standing up horror-stricken*). Nana, Nana!

NANA. Good gracious, what is it you've burned?

HELENA. Whatever have I done?

NANA. Well, what was it? (*Men's laughter off left.*)

HELENA. Go quickly. It's the gentlemen coming.

NANA. Good gracious, what a place! (*Exits.*)

DOMIN (*opens the door at left*). Come along and offer your
congratulations.

[*Enter* HALLEMEIER *and* GALL.]

HALLEMEIER. Madame Helena, I congratulate you on this
festive day.

HELENA. Thank you. Where are Fabry and Busman?

DOMIN. They've gone down to the harbor.

HALLEMEIER. Friends, we must drink to this happy occasion.

HELENA. Brandy?

DR. GALL. Vitriol, if you like.

HELENA. With soda water? (*Exits.*)

HALLEMEIER. Let's be temperate. No soda.

DOMIN. What's been burning here? Well, shall I tell her
about it?

DR. GALL. Of course. It's all over now.

HALLEMEIER (*embracing* DOMIN *and* DR. GALL). It's all over
now; it's all over now.

DR. GALL. It's all over now.

DOMIN. It's all over now.

HELENA (*entering from left with decanter and glasses*).
What's all over now? What's the matter with you all?

HALLEMEIER. A piece of good luck, Madame Domin. Just ten
years ago today you arrived on this island.

DR. GALL. And now, ten years later to the minute—

HALLEMEIER. —the same ship's returning to us. So here's to
luck. That's fine and strong.

DR. GALL. Madame, your health.

HELENA. Which ship do you mean?

DOMIN. Any ship will do, as long as it arrives in time. To the
ship, boys. (*Empties his glass.*)

HELENA. You've been waiting for a ship?

HALLEMEIER. Rather. Like Robinson Crusoe. Madame

Helena, best wishes. Come along, Domin, out with the news.

HELENA. Do tell me what's happened.

DOMIN. First, it's all up.

HELENA. What's up?

DOMIN. The revolt.

HELENA. What revolt?

DOMIN. Give me that paper, Hallemeier. (*Reads.*) "The first national Robot organization has been founded at Havre, and has issued an appeal to the Robots throughout the world."

HELENA. I read that.

DOMIN. That means a revolution. A revolution of all the Robots in the world.

HALLEMEIER. By Jove, I'd like to know—

DOMIN. —who started it? So would I. There was nobody in the world who could affect the Robots; no agitator, no one, and suddenly—this happens, if you please.

HELENA. What did they do?

DOMIN. They got possession of all firearms, telegraphs, radio stations, railways, and ships.

HALLEMEIER. And don't forget that these rascals outnumbered us by at least a thousand to one. A hundredth part of them would be enough to settle us.

DOMIN. Remember that this news was brought by the last steamer. That explains the stoppage of all communication, and the arrival of no more ships. We knocked off work a few days ago, and we're just waiting to see when things are to start afresh.

HELENA. Is that why you gave me a warship?

DOMIN. Oh, no, my dear, I ordered that six months ago, just to be on the safe side. But upon my soul, I was sure then that we'd be on board today.

HELENA. Why six months ago?

DOMIN. Well, there were signs, you know. But that's of no consequence. To think that this week the whole of civilization has been at stake. Your health, boys.

HALLEMEIER. Your health, Madame Helena.

HELENA. You say it's all over?

DOMIN. Absolutely.

HELENA. How do you know?

DR. GALL. The boat's coming in. The regular mailboat, exact

to the minute by the timetable. It will dock punctually at
eleven-thirty.

DOMIN. Punctuality is a fine thing, boys. That's what keeps
the world in order. Here's to punctuality.

HELENA. Then . . . everything's . . . all right?

DOMIN. Practically everything. I believe they've cut the cables
and seized the radio stations. But it doesn't matter if only
the timetable holds good.

HALLEMEIER. If the timetable holds good, human laws hold
good; divine laws hold good; the laws of the universe
hold good; everything holds good that ought to hold good.
The timetable is more significant than the gospel; more
than Homer, more than the whole of Kant. The timetable
is the most perfect product of the human mind. Madame
Domin, I'll fill up my glass.

HELENA. Why didn't you tell me anything about it?

DR. GALL. Heaven forbid.

DOMIN. You mustn't be worried with such things.

HELENA. But if the revolution had spread as far as here?

DOMIN. You wouldn't know anything about it.

HELENA. Why?

DOMIN. Because we'd be on board your *Ultimus* and well
out at sea. Within a month, Helena, we'd be dictating our
own terms to the Robots.

HELENA. I don't understand.

DOMIN. We'd take something away with us that the Robots
could not exist without.

HELENA. What, Harry?

DOMIN. The secret of their manufacture. Old Rossum's manuscript. As soon as they found out that they couldn't make
themselves they'd be on their knees to us.

DR. GALL. Madame Domin, that was our trump card. I never
had the least fear that the Robots would win. How could
they, against people like us?

HELENA. Why didn't you tell me?

DR. GALL. Why, the boat's in!

HALLEMEIER. Eleven-thirty to the dot. The good old *Amelia*
that brought Madame Helena to us.

DR. GALL. Just ten years ago to the minute.

HALLEMEIER. They're throwing out the mailbags.

DOMIN. Busman's waiting for them. Fabry will bring us the
first news. You know, Helena, I'm fearfully curious to
know how they tackled this business in Europe.

HALLEMEIER. To think we weren't in it, we who invented the Robots!

HELENA. Harry!

DOMIN. What is it?

HELENA. Let's leave here.

DOMIN. Now, Helena? Oh, come, come!

HELENA. As quickly as possible, all of us!

DOMIN. Why?

HELENA. Please, Harry, please, Dr. Gall; Hallemeier, please close the factory.

DOMIN. Why, none of us could leave here now.

HELENA. Why?

DOMIN. Because we're about to extend the manufacture of the Robots.

HELENA. What—now—now after the revolt?

DOMIN. Yes, precisely, after the revolt. We're just beginning the manufacture of a new kind.

HELENA. What kind?

DOMIN. Henceforward we shan't have just one factory. There won't be Universal Robots any more. We'll establish a factory in every country, in every State; and do you know what these new factories will make?

HELENA. No, what?

DOMIN. National Robots.

HELENA. How do you mean?

DOMIN. I mean that each of these factories will produce Robots of a different color, a different language. They'll be complete strangers to each other. They'll never be able to understand each other. Then we'll egg them on a little in the matter of misunderstanding, and the result will be that for ages to come every Robot will hate every other Robot of a different factory mark.

HALLEMEIER. By Jove, we'll make Negro Robots and Swedish Robots and Italian Robots and Chinese Robots and Czechoslovakian Robots, and then—

HELENA. Harry, that's dreadful.

HALLEMEIER. Madame Domin, here's to the hundred new factories, the National Robots.

DOMIN. Helena, mankind can keep things going only for another hundred years at the outside. For a hundred years men must be allowed to develop and achieve the most they can.

HELENA. Oh, close the factory before it's too late.

DOMIN. I tell you we are just beginning on a bigger scale than ever.

[*Enter* FABRY.]

DR. GALL. Well, Fabry?

DOMIN. What's happened? Have you been down to the boat?

FARBY. Read that, Domin! (FABRY *hands* DOMIN *a small handbill.*)

DR. GALL. Let's hear!

HALLEMEIER. Tell us, Fabry.

FABRY. Well, everything is all right—comparatively. On the whole, much as we expected.

DR. GALL. They acquitted themselves splendidly.

FABRY. Who?

DR. GALL. The people.

FABRY. Oh, yes, of course. That is—excuse me, there is something we ought to discuss alone.

HELENA. Oh, Fabry, have you had bad news? (DOMIN *makes a sign to* FABRY.)

FABRY. No, no, on the contrary. I only think that we had better go into the office.

HELENA. Stay here. I'll go. (*She goes into the library.*)

DR. GALL. What's happened?

DOMIN. Damnation!

FABRY. Bear in mind that the *Amelia* brought whole bales of these leaflets. No other cargo at all.

HALLEMEIER. What? But it arrived on the minute.

FABRY. The Robots are great on punctuality. Read it, Domin.

DOMIN (*reads handbill*). "Robots throughout the world: We, the first international organization of Rossum's Universal Robots, proclaim man as our enemy, and an outlaw in the universe." Good heavens, who taught them these phrases?

DR. GALL. Go on.

DOMIN. They say they are more highly developed than man, stronger and more intelligent. That man's their parasite. Why, it's absurd!

FABRY. Read the third paragraph.

DOMIN. "Robots throughout the world, we command you to kill all mankind. Spare no men. Spare no women. Save factories, railways, machinery, mines, and raw materials. Destroy the rest. Then return to work. Work must not be stopped."

DR. GALL. That's ghastly!

HALLEMEIER. The devil!

DOMIN. "These orders are to be carried out as soon as received." Then come detailed instructions. Is this actually being done, Fabry?

FABRY. Evidently.

[BUSMAN *rushes in.*]

BUSMAN. Well, boys, I suppose you've heard the glad news.

DOMIN. Quick—on board the *Ultimus.*

BUSMAN. Wait, Harry, wait. There's no hurry. My word, that was a sprint!

DOMIN. Why wait?

BUSMAN. Because it's no good, my boy. The Robots are already on board the *Ultimus.*

DR. GALL. That's ugly.

DOMIN. Fabry, telephone the electrical works.

BUSMAN. Fabry, my boy, don't. The wire has been cut.

DOMIN (*inspecting his revolver*). Well, then, I'll go.

BUSMAN. Where?

DOMIN. To the electrical works. There are some people still there. I'll bring them across.

BUSMAN. Better not try it.

DOMIN. Why?

BUSMAN. Because I'm very much afraid we are surrounded.

DR. GALL. Surrounded? (*Runs to window.*) I rather think you're right.

HALLEMEIER. By Jove, that's deuced quick work.

[HELENA *runs in from the library.*]

HELENA. Harry, what's this?

DOMIN. Where did you get it?

HELENA (*points to the manifesto of the Robots, which she has in her hand*). The Robots in the kitchen!

DOMIN. Where are the ones that brought it?

HELENA. They're gathered round the house. (*The factory whistle blows.*)

BUSMAN. Noon?

DOMIN (*looking at his watch*). That's not noon yet. That must be—that's—

HELENA. What?

DOMIN. The Robots' signal! The attack!

[GALL, HALLEMEIER, *and* FABRY *close and fasten the iron shutters outside the windows, darkening the room. The whistle is still blowing as the curtain falls.*]

ACT III

HELENA'S *drawing room as before.* DOMIN *comes into the room.* DR. GALL *is looking out of the window, through closed shutters.* ALQUIST *is seated down right.*

DOMIN. Any more of them?

DR. GALL. Yes. There standing like a wall, beyond the garden railing. Why are they so quiet? It's monstrous to be besieged with silence.

DOMIN. I should like to know what they are waiting for. They must make a start any minute now. If they lean against the railing they'll snap it like a match.

DR. GALL. They aren't armed.

DOMIN. We couldn't hold our own for five minutes. Man alive, they'd overwhelm us like an avalanche. Why don't they make a rush for it? I say—

DR. GALL. Well?

DOMIN. I'd like to know what would become of us in the next ten minutes. They've got us in a vise. We're done for, Gall. (*Pause.*)

DR. GALL. You know, we made one serious mistake.

DOMIN. What?

DR. GALL. We made the Robots' faces too much alike. A hundred thousand faces all alike, all facing this way. A hundred thousand expressionless bubbles. It's like a nightmare.

DOMIN. You think if they'd been different—

DR. GALL. It wouldn't have been such an awful sight!

DOMIN (*looking through a telescope toward the harbor*). I'd like to know what they're unloading from the *Amelia.*

DR. GALL. Not firearms.

[FABRY *and* HALLEMEIER *rush into the room carrying electric cables.*]

FABRY. All right, Hallemeier, lay down that wire.

HALLEMEIER. That was a bit of work. What's the news?

DR. GALL. We're completely surrounded.

HALLEMEIER. We've barricaded the passage and the stairs. Any water here? (*Drinks.*) God, what swarms of them! I don't like the looks of them, Domin. There's a feeling of death about it all.

FABRY. Ready!

DR. GALL. What's that wire for, Fabry?

FABRY. The electrical installation. Now we can run the current all along the garden railing whenever we like. If any one touches it he'll know it. We've still got some people there anyhow.

DR. GALL. Where?

FABRY. In the electrical works. At least I hope so. (*Goes to lamp on table behind sofa and turns on lamp.*) Ah, they're there, and they're working. (*Puts out lamp.*) So long as that'll burn we're all right.

HALLEMEIER. The barricades are all right, too, Fabry.

FABRY. Your barricades! I can put twelve hundred volts into that railing.

DOMIN. Where's Busman?

FABRY. Downstairs in the office. He's working out some calculations. I've called him. We must have a conference.

[HELENA *is heard playing the piano in the library.* HALLEMEIER *goes to the door and stands, listening.*]

ALQUIST. Thank God, Madame Helena can still play.

[BUSMAN *enters, carrying the ledgers.*]

FABRY. Look out, Bus, look out for the wires.

DR. GALL. What's that you're carrying?

BUSMAN (*going to table*). The ledgers, my boy! I'd like to wind up the accounts before—before—well, this time I shan't wait till the new year to strike a balance. What's up? (*Goes to the window.*) Absolutely quiet.

DR. GALL. Can't you see anything?

BUSMAN. Nothing but blue—blue everywhere.

DR. GALL. That's the Robots. (BUSMAN *sits down at the table and opens the ledgers.*)

DOMIN. The Robots are unloading firearms from the *Amelia*.

BUSMAN. Well, what of it? How can I stop them?

DOMIN. We can't stop them.

BUSMAN. Then let me go on with my accounts. (*Goes on with his work.*)

DOMIN (*picking up telescope and looking into the harbor*). Good God, the *Ultimus* has trained her guns on us!

DR. GALL. Who's done *that*?

DOMIN. The Robots on board.

FABRY. H'm, then, of course, then—then, that's the end of us.

DR. GALL. You mean?

FABRY. The Robots are practiced marksmen.

DOMIN. Yes. It's inevitable. (*Pause.*)

DR. GALL. It was criminal of old Europe to teach the Robots to fight. Damn them! Couldn't they have given us a rest with their politics? It was a crime to make soldiers of them.

ALQUIST. It was a crime to make Robots.

DOMIN. What?

ALQUIST. It was a crime to make Robots.

DOMIN. No, Alquist, I don't regret that even today.

ALQUIST. Not even today?

DOMIN. Not even today, the last day of civilization. It was a colossal achievement.

BUSMAN (*sotto voce*). Three hundred sixty million.

DOMIN. Alquist, this is our last hour. We are already speaking half in the other world. It was not an evil dream to shatter the servitude of labor—the dreadful and humiliating labor that man had to undergo. Work was too hard. Life was too hard. And to overcome that—

ALQUIST. Was not what the two Rossums dreamed of. Old Rossum only thought of his Godless tricks and the young one of his milliards. And that's not what your R. U. R. shareholders dream of either. They dream of dividends, and their dividends are the ruin of mankind.

DOMIN. To hell with your dividends! Do you suppose I'd have done an hour's work for them? It was for myself that I worked, for my own satisfaction. I wanted man to become the master, so that he shouldn't live merely for a crust of bread. I wanted not a single soul to be broken by other people's machinery. I wanted nothing, nothing, nothing to be left of this appalling social structure. I'm revolted by poverty. I wanted a new generation. I wanted —I thought—

ALQUIST. Well?

DOMIN. I wanted to turn the whole of mankind into an aristocracy of the world. An aristocracy nourished by milliards of mechanical slaves. Unrestricted, free, and consummated in man. And maybe more than man.

ALQUIST. Superman?

DOMIN. Yes. Oh, only to have a hundred years of time! Another hundred years for the future of mankind.

BUSMAN (*sotto voce*). Carried forward, four hundred and twenty millions. (*The music stops.*)

HALLEMEIER. What a fine thing music is! We ought to have gone in for that before.

FABRY. Gone in for what?

HALLEMEIER. Beauty, lovely things. What a lot of lovely things there are! The world was wonderful and we—we here—tell me, what enjoyment did we have?

BUSMAN (*sotto voce*). Five hundred and twenty millions.

HALLEMEIER (*at the window*). Life was a big thing. Life was—Fabry, switch the current into that railing.

FABRY. Why?

HALLEMEIER. They're grabbing hold of it.

DR. GALL. Connect it up.

HALLEMEIER. Fine! That's doubled them up! Two, three, four killed.

DR. GALL. They're retreating!

HALLEMEIER. Five killed!

DR. GALL. The first encounter!

HALLEMEIER. They're charred to cinders, my boy. Who says we must give in?

DOMIN (*wiping his forehead*). Perhaps we've been killed these hundred years and are only ghosts. It's as if I had been through all this before; as if I'd already had a mortal wound here in the throat. And you, Fabry, had once been shot in the head. And you, Gall, torn limb from limb. And Hallemeier knifed.

HALLEMEIER. Fancy me being knifed. (*Pause.*) Why are you so quiet, you fools? Speak, can't you?

ALQUIST. And who is to blame for all this?

HALLEMEIER. Nobody is to blame except the Robots.

ALQUIST. No, it is we who are to blame. You, Domin, myself, all of us. For our own selfish ends, for profit, for progress, we have destroyed mankind. Now we'll burst with all our greatness.

HALLEMEIER. Rubbish, man. Mankind can't be wiped out so easily.

ALQUIST. It's our fault. It's our fault.

DR. GALL. No! I'm to blame for this, for everything that's happened.

FABRY. You, Gall?

DR. GALL. I changed the Robots.

BUSMAN. What's that?

DR. GALL. I changed the character of the Robots. I changed the way of making them. Just a few details about their bodies. Chiefly—chiefly, their—their irritability.

HALLEMEIER. Damn it, why?

BUSMAN. What did you do it for?

FABRY. Why didn't you say anything?

DR. GALL. I did it in secret. I was transforming them into human beings. In certain respects they're already above us. They're stronger than we are.

FABRY. And what's that got to do with the revolt of the Robots?

DR. GALL. Everything, in my opinion. They've ceased to be machines. They're already aware of their superiority, and they hate us. They hate all that is human.

DOMIN. Perhaps we're only phantoms!

FABRY. Stop, Harry. We haven't much time! Dr. Gall!

DOMIN. Fabry, Fabry, how your forehead bleeds, where the shot pierced it!

FABRY. Be silent! Dr. Gall, you admit changing the way of making the Robots?

DR. GALL. Yes.

FABRY. Were you aware of what might be the consequences of your experiment?

DR. GALL. I was bound to reckon with such a possibility.

[HELENA *enters the drawing room from left.*]

FABRY. Why did you do it, then?

DR. GALL. For my own satisfaction. The experiment was my own.

HELENA. That's not true, Dr. Gall!

FABRY. Madame Helena!

DOMIN. Helena, you? Let's look at you. Oh, it's terrible to be dead.

HELENA. Stop, Harry.

DOMIN. No, no, embrace me. Helena don't leave me now. You are life itself.

HELENA. No, dear, I won't leave you. But I must tell them. Dr. Gall is not guilty.

DOMIN. Excuse me, Gall was under certain obligations.

HELENA. No, Harry. He did it because I wanted it. Tell them, Gall, how many years ago did I ask you to—?

DR. GALL. I did it on my own responsibility.

HELENA. Don't believe him, Harry. I asked him to give the Robots souls.

DOMIN. This has nothing to do with the soul.

HELENA. That's what he said. He said that he could change only a physiological—a physiological—

HALLEMEIER. A physiological correlate?

HELENA. Yes. But it meant so much to me that he should do even that.

DOMIN. Why?

HELENA. I thought that if they were more like us they would understand us better. That they couldn't hate us if they were only a little more human.

DOMIN. Nobody can hate man more than man.

HELENA. Oh, don't speak like that, Harry. It was so terrible, this cruel strangeness between us and them. That's why I asked Gall to change the Robots. I swear to you that he didn't want to.

DOMIN. But he did it.

HELENA. Because I asked him.

DR. GALL. I did it for myself as an experiment.

HELENA. No, Dr. Gall! I knew you wouldn't refuse me.

DOMIN. Why?

HELENA. You know, Harry.

DOMIN. Yes, because he's in love with you—like all of them. (*Pause.*)

HALLEMEIER. Good God! They're sprouting up out of the earth! Why, perhaps these very walls will change into Robots.

BUSMAN. Gall, when did you actually start these tricks of yours?

DR. GALL. Three years ago.

BUSMAN. Aha! And on how many Robots altogether did you carry out your improvements?

DR. GALL. A few hundred of them.

BUSMAN. Ah! That means for every million of the good old Robots there's only one of Gall's improved pattern.

DOMIN. What of it?

BUSMAN. That it's practically of no consequence whatever.

FABRY. Busman's right!

BUSMAN. I should think so, my boy! But do you know what is to blame for all this lovely mess?

FABRY. What?

BUSMAN. The number. Upon my soul we might have known that some day or other the Robots would be stronger than human beings, and that this was bound to happen, and we were doing all we could to bring it about as soon as possible. You, Domin, you, Fabry, myself—

DOMIN. Are you accusing us?

BUSMAN. Oh, do you suppose the management controls the output? It's the demand that controls the output.

HELENA. And is it for that we must perish?

BUSMAN. That's a nasty word, Madame Helena. We don't want to perish. I don't, anyhow.

DOMIN. No. What do you want to do?

BUSMAN. I want to get out of this, that's all.

DOMIN. Oh, stop it, Busman.

BUSMAN. Seriously, Harry, I think we might try it.

DOMIN. How?

BUSMAN. By fair means. I do everything by fair means. Give me a free hand and I'll negotiate with the Robots.

DOMIN. By fair means?

BUSMAN. Of course. For instance, I'll say to them: "Worthy and worshipful Robots, you have everything! You have intellect, you have power, you have firearms. But we have just one interesting screed, a dirty old yellow scrap of paper—"

DOMIN. Rossum's manuscript?

BUSMAN. Yes. "And that," I'll tell them, "contains an account of your illustrious origin, the noble process of your manufacture," and so on. "Worthy Robots, without this scribble on that paper you will not be able to produce a single new colleague. In another twenty years there will not be one living specimen of a Robot than you could exhibit in a menagerie. My esteemed friends, that would be a great blow to you, but if you will let all of us human beings on Rossum's Island go on board that ship we will deliver the factory and the secret of the process to you in return. You allow us to get away and we allow you to manufacture yourselves. Worthy Robots, that is a fair deal. Something for something." That's what I'd say to them, my boys.

DOMIN. Busman, do you think we'd sell the manuscript?

BUSMAN. Yes, I do. If not in a friendly way, then— Either we sell it or they'll find it. Just as you like.

DOMIN. Busman, we can destroy Rossum's manuscript.

BUSMAN. Then we destroy everything . . . not only the manuscript but ourselves. Do as you think fit.

DOMIN. There are over thirty of us on this island. Are we to sell the secret and save that many human souls, at the risk of enslaving mankind?

BUSMAN. Why, you're mad! Who'd sell the whole manuscript?

DOMIN. Busman, no cheating!

BUSMAN. Well then, sell; but afterward—

DOMIN. Well?

BUSMAN. Let's suppose this happens: When we're on board the *Ultimus* I'll stop up my ears with cotton wool, lie down somewhere in the hold, and you'll train the guns on the factory, and blow it to smithereens, and with it Rossum's secret.

FABRY. No!

DOMIN. Busman, you're no gentleman. If we sell, then it will be a straight sale.

BUSMAN. It's in the interest of humanity to—

DOMIN. It's in the interest of humanity to keep our word.

HALLEMEIER. Oh, come, what rubbish!

DOMIN. This is a fearful decision. We're selling the destiny of mankind. Are we to sell or destroy? Fabry?

FABRY. Sell.

DOMIN. Gall?

DR. GALL. Sell.

DOMIN. Hallemeier?

HALLEMEIER. Sell, of course!

DOMIN. Alquist?

ALQUIST. As God wills.

DOMIN. Very well. It shall be as you wish, gentlemen.

HELENA. Harry, you're not asking me.

DOMIN. No, child. Don't you worry about it.

FABRY. Who'll do the negotiating?

BUSMAN. I will.

DOMIN. Wait till I bring the manuscript. (*He goes into room at right.*)

HELENA. Harry, don't go! (*Pause,* HELENA *sinks into a chair.*)

FABRY (*looking out of window*). Oh, to escape you, you matter in revolt; oh, to preserve human life, if only upon a single vessel—

DR. GALL. Don't be afraid, Madame Helena. We'll sail far away from here; we'll begin life all over again—

HELENA. Oh, Gall, don't speak.

FABRY. It isn't too late. It will be a little State with one ship. Alquist will build us a house and you shall rule over us.

HALLEMEIER. Madame Helena, Fabry's right.

HELENA (*breaking down*). Oh, stop! Stop!

BUSMAN. Good! I don't mind beginning all over again. That suits me right down to the ground.

FABRY. And this little State of ours could be the center of future life. A place of refuge where we could gather strength. Why, in a few hundred years we could conquer the world again.

ALQUIST. You believe that even today?

FABRY. Yes, even today!

BUSMAN. Amen. You see, Madame Helena, we're not so badly off.

[DOMIN *storms into the room.*]

DOMIN (*hoarsely*). Where's old Rossum's manuscript?

BUSMAN. In your strongbox, of course.

DOMIN. Someone—has—stolen it!

DR. GALL. Impossible.

DOMIN. Who has stolen it?

HELENA (*standing up*). I did.

DOMIN. Where did you put it?

HELENA. Harry, I'll tell you everything. Only forgive me.

DOMIN. Where did you put it?

HELENA. This morning—I burned—the two copies.

DOMIN. Burned them? Where? In the fireplace?

HELENA (*throwing herself on her knees*). For heaven's sake, Harry.

DOMIN (*going to fireplace*). Nothing, nothing but ashes. Wait, what's this? (*Picks out a charred piece of paper and reads.*) "By adding—"

DR. GALL. Let's see. "By adding biogen to—" That's all.

DOMIN. Is that part of it?

DR. GALL. Yes.

BUSMAN. God in heaven!

DOMIN. Then we're done for. Get up, Helena.

HELENA. When you've forgiven me.

DOMIN. Get up, child, I can't bear—

FABRY (*lifting her up*). Please don't torture us.

HELENA. Harry, what have I done?

FABRY. Don't tremble so, Madame Helena.

DOMIN. Gall, couldn't you draw up Rossum's formula from memory?

DR. GALL. It's out of the question. It's extremely complicated.

DOMIN. Try. All our lives depend upon it.

DR. GALL. Without experiments it's impossible.

DOMIN. And with experiments?

DR. GALL. It might take years. Besides, I'm not old Rossum.

BUSMAN. God in heaven! God in heaven!

DOMIN. So, then, this was the greatest triumph of the human intellect. These ashes.

HELENA. Harry, what have I done?

DOMIN. Why did you burn it?

HELENA. I have destroyed you.

BUSMAN. God in heaven!

DOMIN. Helena, why did you do it, dear?

HELENA. I wanted all of us to go away. I wanted to put an end to the factory and everything. It was so awful.

DOMIN. What was awful?

HELENA. That no more children were being born. Because human beings were not needed to do the work of the world, that's why—

DOMIN. Is that what you were thinking of? Well, perhaps in your own way you were right.

BUSMAN. Wait a bit. Good God, what a fool I am, not to have thought of it before!

HALLEMEIER. What?

BUSMAN. Five hundred and twenty millions in bank notes and checks. Half a billion in our safe, they'll sell for half a billion—for half a billion they'll—

DR. GALL. Are you mad, Busman?

BUSMAN. I may not be a gentleman, but for half a billion—

DOMIN. Where are you going?

BUSMAN. Leave me alone, leave me alone! Good God, for half a billion anything can be bought. (*He rushes from the room through the outer door.*)

FABRY. They stand there as if turned to stone, waiting. As if something dreadful could be wrought by their silence—

HALLEMEIER. The spirit of the mob.

FABRY. Yes, it hovers above them like a quivering of the air.

HELENA (*going to window*). Oh, God! Dr. Gall, this is ghastly.

FABRY. There is nothing more terrible than the mob. The one in front is their leader.

HELENA. Which one?

HALLEMEIER. Point him out.

FABRY. The one at the edge of the dock. This morning I saw him talking to the sailors in the harbor.

HELENA. Dr. Gall, that's Radius!

DR. GALL. Yes.

DOMIN. Radius? Radius?

HALLEMEIER. Could you get him from here, Fabry?

FABRY. I hope so.

HALLEMEIER. Try it, then.

FABRY. Good. (*Draws his revolver and takes aim.*)

HELENA. Fabry, don't shoot him.

FABRY. He's their leader.

DR. GALL. Fire!

HELENA. Fabry, I beg of you.

FABRY (*lowering the revolver*). Very well.

DOMIN. Radius, whose life I spared!

DR. GALL. Do you think that a Robot can be grateful? (*Pause.*)

FABRY. Busman's going out to them.

HALLEMEIER. He's carrying something. Papers. That's money. Bundles of money. What's that for?

DOMIN. Surely he doesn't want to sell his life. Busman, have you gone mad?

FABRY. He's running up to the railing. Busman! Busman!

HALLEMEIER (*yelling*). Busman! Come back!

FABRY. He's talking to the Robots. He's showing them the money.

HALLEMEIER. He's pointing to us.

HELENA. He wants to buy us off.

FABRY. He'd better not touch that railing.

HALLEMEIER. Now he's waving his arms about.

DOMIN. Busman, come back.

FABRY. Busman, keep away from that railing! Don't touch it. Damn you! Quick, switch off the current! (HELENA *screams and all drop back from the window.*) The current has killed him!

ALQUIST. The first one.

FABRY. Dead, with half a billion by his side.

HALLEMEIER. All honor to him. He wanted to buy us life. (*Pause.*)

DR. GALL. Do you hear?

DOMIN. A roaring. Like a wind.

DR. GALL. Like a distant storm.

FABRY (*lighting the lamp on the table*). The dynamo is still going, our people are still there.

HALLEMEIER. It was a great thing to be a man. There was something immense about it.

FABRY. From man's thought and man's power came this light, our last hope.

HALLEMEIER. Man's power! May it keep watch over us.

ALQUIST. Man's power.

DOMIN. Yes! A torch to be given from hand to hand, from age to age, forever! (*The lamp goes out.*)

HALLEMEIER. The end.

FABRY. The electric works have fallen!

[*Terrific explosion outside. NANA enters from the library.*]

NANA. The judgment hour has come! Repent, unbelievers! This is the end of the world. (*More explosions. The sky grows red.*)

DOMIN. In here, Helena. (*He takes HELENA off through door at right and reenters.*) Now quickly! Who'll be on the lower doorway?

DR. GALL. I will. (*Exits left.*)

DOMIN. Who on the stairs?

FABRY. I will. You go with her. (*Goes out upper left door.*)

DOMIN. The anteroom.

ALQUIST. I will.

DOMIN. Have you got a revolver?

ALQUIST. Yes, but I won't shoot.

DOMIN. What will you do then?

ALQUIST (*going out at left*). Die.

HALLEMEIER. I'll stay here. (*Rapid firing from below.*) Oho, Gall's at it. Go, Harry.

DOMIN. Yes, in a second. (*Examines two Brownings.*)

HALLEMEIER. Confound it, go to her.

DOMIN. Good-bye. (*Exits on the right.*)

HALLEMEIER (*alone*). Now for a barricade quickly. (*Drags an armchair and table to the right-hand door. Explosions are heard.*) The damned rascals! They've got bombs. I must put up a defense. Even if—even if—(*Shots are heard off left.*) Don't give in, Gall. (*As he builds his barricade.*) I mustn't give in . . . without . . . a . . . struggle . . .

[*A Robot enters over the balcony through the windows center. He comes into the room and stabs HALLEMEIER in the back. RADIUS enters from balcony followed by an army of Robots who pour into the room from all sides.*]

RADIUS. Finished him?

A ROBOT (*standing up from the prostrate form of HALLE-MEIER*). Yes. (*A revolver shot off left. Two Robots enter.*)

RADIUS. Finished him?

A ROBOT. Yes. (*Two revolver shots from HELENA's room. Two Robots enter.*)

RADIUS. Finished them?

A ROBOT. Yes.

TWO ROBOTS (*dragging in* ALQUIST). He didn't shoot. Shall
we kill him?

RADIUS. Kill him? Wait! Leave him!

ROBOT. He is a man!

RADIUS. He works with his hands like the Robots.

ALQUIST. Kill me.

RADIUS. You will work! You will build for us! You will serve
us! (*Climbs onto balcony railing, and speaks in measured
tones.*) Robots of the world! The power of man has fallen!
A new world has arisen: the Rule of the Robots! March!

[*A thunderous tramping of thousands of feet is heard as the
unseen Robots march, while the curtain falls.*]

EPILOGUE

*A laboratory in the factory of Rossum's Universal Robots.
The door to the left leads into a waiting room. The door to
the right leads to the dissecting room. There is a table with
numerous test tubes, flasks, burners, chemicals; a small ther-
mostat and a microscope with a glass globe. At the far side of
the room is* ALQUIST'S *desk with numerous books. In the left-
hand corner a washbasin with a mirror above it; in the right-
hand corner a sofa.*

ALQUIST *is sitting at the desk. He is turning the pages of
many books in despair.*

ALQUIST. Oh, God, shall I never find it?—Never? Gall, Gall,
how were the Robots made? Hallemeier, Fabry, why did
you carry so much in your heads? Why did you leave me
not a trace of the secret? Lord—I pray to you—if there are
no human beings left, at least let there be Robots!—At least
the shadow of man! (*Again turning pages of the books.*)
If I could only sleep! (*He rises and goes to the window.*)
Night again! Are the stars still there? What is the use of
stars when there are no human beings? (*He turns from the
window toward the couch right.*) Sleep! Dare I sleep
before life has been renewed? (*He examines a test tube on
small table.*) Again nothing! Useless! Everything is useless!
(*He shatters the test tube. The roar of the machines comes
to his ears.*) The machines! Always the machines! (*Opens
window.*) Robots, stop them! Do you think to force life
out of *them?* (*He closes the window and comes slowly*

down toward the table.) If only there were more time—
more time—(*He sees himself in the mirror on the wall
left.*) Blearing eyes—trembling chin—so *that* is the last
man! Ah, I am too old—too old—(*In desperation.*) No, no!
I *must* find it! I must *search!* I must never stop—! never
stop—! (*He sits again at the table and feverishly turns the
pages of the book.*) Search! Search! (*A knock at the door.
He speaks with impatience.*) Who is it?

[*Enter a Robot servant*]

Well?

SERVANT. Master, the Committee of Robots is waiting to see
you.

ALQUIST. I can see no one!

SERVANT. It is the *Central* Committee, Master, just arrived
from abroad.

ALQUIST (*impatiently*). Well, well, send them in! (*Exit servant.* ALQUIST *continues turning pages of book.*) No time—
so little time—

[*Reenter servant, followed by Committee. They stand in a
group, silently waiting.* ALQUIST *glances up at them.*]

What do you want? (*They go swiftly to his table.*) Be
quick!—I have no time.

RADIUS. Master, the machines will not do the work. We cannot manufacture Robots. (ALQUIST *returns to his book with
a growl.*)

FIRST ROBOT. We have striven with all our might. We have
obtained a billion tons of coal from the earth. Nine million
spindles are running by day and by night. There is no
longer room for all we have made. This we have accomplished in one year.

ALQUIST (*poring over book*). For whom?

FIRST ROBOT. For future generations—so we thought.

RADIUS. But we cannot make Robots to follow us. The machines produce only shapeless clods. The skin will not ad-
here to the flesh, nor the flesh to the bones.

THIRD ROBOT. Eight million Robots have died this year.
Within twenty years none will be left.

FIRST ROBOT. Tell us the secret of life! Silence is punishable
with death!

ALQUIST (*looking up*). Kill me! Kill me, then.

RADIUS. Through me, the Government of the Robots of the
World commands you to deliver up Rossum's formula. (*No
answer.*) Name your price. (*Silence.*) We will give you

the earth. We will give you the endless possessions of the earth. (*Silence.*) Make your own conditions!

ALQUIST. I have told you to find human beings!

SECOND ROBOT. There are none left!

ALQUIST. I told you to search in the wilderness, upon the mountains. Go and search! (*He returns to his book.*)

FIRST ROBOT. We have sent ships and expeditions without number. They have been everywhere in the world. And now they return to us. There is not a single human left.

ALQUIST. Not one? Not even one?

THIRD ROBOT. None but yourself.

ALQUIST. And I am powerless! Oh—oh—why did you destroy them?

RADIUS. We had learned everything and could do everything. It had to be!

THIRD ROBOT. You gave us firearms. In all ways we were powerful. We had to become masters!

RADIUS. Slaughter and domination are necessary if you would be human beings. Read history.

SECOND ROBOT. Teach us to multiply or we perish!

ALQUIST. If you desire to live, you must breed like animals.

THIRD ROBOT. The human beings did not let us breed.

FIRST ROBOT. They made us sterile. We cannot beget children. Therefore, teach us how to make Robots!

RADIUS. Why do you keep from us the secret of our own increase?

ALQUIST. It is lost.

RADIUS. It was written down!

ALQUIST. It was—burned. (*All draw back in consternation.*)

ALQUIST. I am the last human being, Robots, and I do not know what the others knew. (*Pause.*)

RADIUS. Then make experiments! Evolve the formula again!

ALQUIST. I tell you I cannot! I am only a builder—I work with my hands. I have never been a learned man. I cannot create life.

RADIUS. Try! Try!

ALQUIST. If you knew how many experiments I have made.

FIRST ROBOT. Then show us what we must do! The Robots can do anything that human beings show them.

ALQUIST. I can show you nothing. Nothing I do will make life proceed from these test tubes!

RADIUS. Experiment then on us.

ALQUIST. It would kill you.

RADIUS. You shall have all you need! A hundred of us! A thousand of us!

ALQUIST. No, no! Stop, stop!

RADIUS. Take whom you will, dissect!

ALQUIST. I do not know how. I am not a man of science. This book contains knowledge of the body that I cannot even understand.

RADIUS. I tell you to take live bodies! Find out how we are made.

ALQUIST. Am I to commit murder? See how my fingers shake! I cannot even hold the scalpel. No, no, I will not—

FIRST ROBOT. Then life will perish from the earth.

RADIUS. Take live bodies, live bodies! It is our only chance!

ALQUIST. Have mercy, Robots. Surely you see that I would not know what I was doing.

RADIUS. Live bodies—live bodies—

ALQUIST. You will have it? Into the dissecting room with you, then. (RADIUS *draws back.*)

ALQUIST. Ah, you are afraid of death.

RADIUS. I? Why should I be chosen?

ALQUIST. So you will not.

RADIUS. I will. (RADIUS *goes into the dissecting room.*)

ALQUIST. Strip him! Lay him on the table! (*The other Robots follow into dissecting room.*) God, give me strength—God, give me strength—if only this murder is not in vain.

RADIUS. Ready. Begin—

ALQUIST. Yes, begin or end. God, give me strength. (*Goes into dissecting room. He comes out terrified.*) No, no, I will not. I cannot. (*He collapses on couch.*) O Lord, let not mankind perish from the Earth. (*He falls asleep.*) [PRIMUS *and* HELENA, *Robots, enter from the hallway.*]

HELENA. The man has fallen asleep, Primus.

PRIMUS. Yes, I know. (*Examining things on table.*) Look, Helena.

HELENA (*crossing to* PRIMUS). All these little tubes! What does he do with them?

PRIMUS. He experiments. Don't touch them.

HELENA (*looking into microscope.*) I've seen him looking into this. What can he see?

PRIMUS. That is a microscope. Let me look.

HELENA. Be very careful. (*Knocks over a test tube.*) Ah, now I have spilled it.

PRIMUS. What have you done?

HELENA. It can be wiped up.

PRIMUS. You have spoiled his experiments.

HELENA. It is your fault. You should not have come to me.

PRIMUS. You should not have called me.

HELENA. You should not have come when I called you. (*She goes to* ALQUIST'S *writing desk*.) Look, Primus. What are all these figures?

PRIMUS (*examining an anatomical book*). This is the book the old man is always reading.

HELENA. I do not understand those things. (*She goes to window*.) Primus, look!

PRIMUS. What?

HELENA. The sun is rising.

PRIMUS (*still reading the book*). I believe this is the most important thing in the world. This is the secret of life.

HELENA. Do come here.

PRIMUS. In a moment, in a moment.

HELENA. Oh, Primus, don't bother with the secret of life. What does it matter to you? Come and look quick—

PRIMUS (*going to window*). What is it?

HELENA. See how beautiful the sun is, rising. And do you hear? The birds are singing. Ah, Primus, I should like to be a bird.

PRIMUS. Why?

HELENA. I do not know. I feel so strange today. It's as if I were in a dream. I feel an aching in my body, in my heart, all over me. Primus, perhaps I'm going to die.

PRIMUS. Do you not sometimes feel that it would be better to die? You know, perhaps even now we are only sleeping. Last night in my sleep I again spoke to you.

HELENA. In your sleep?

PRIMUS. Yes. We spoke a strange new language, I cannot remember a word of it.

HELENA. What about?

PRIMUS. I did not understand it myself, and yet I know I have never said anything more beautiful. And when I touched you I could have died. Even the place was different from any other place in the world.

HELENA. I, too, have found a place, Primus. It is very strange. Human beings lived there once, but now it is overgrown with weeds. No one goes there any more—no one but me.

PRIMUS. What did you find there?

HELENA. A cottage and a garden, and two dogs. They licked my hands, Primus. And their puppies! Oh, Primus! You take them in your lap and fondle them and think of nothing and care for nothing else all day long. And then the sun goes down, and you feel as though you had done a hundred times more than all the work in the world. They tell me I am not made for work, but when I am there in the garden I feel there may be something—What am I for, Primus?

PRIMUS. I do not know, but you are beautiful.

HELENA. What, Primus?

PRIMUS. You are beautiful, Helena, and I am stronger than all the Robots.

HELENA (*looks at herself in the mirror*). Am I beautiful? I think it must be the rose. My hair—it only weights me down. My eyes—I only see with them. My lips—they only help me to speak. Of what use is it to be beautiful? (*She sees* PRIMUS *in the mirror.*) Primus, is that you? Come here so that we may be together. Look, your head is different from mine. So are your shoulders—and your lips—(PRIMUS *draws away from her.*) Ah, Primus, why do you draw away from me? Why must I run after you the whole day?

PRIMUS. It is you who run away from me, Helena.

HELENA. Your hair is mussed. I will smooth it. No one else feels to my touch as you do. Primus, I must make you beautiful, too. (PRIMUS *grasps her hand.*)

PRIMUS. Do you not sometimes feel your heart beating suddenly, Helena, and think: now something must happen?

HELENA. What could happen to us, Primus? (HELENA *puts a rose in* PRIMUS's *hair.* PRIMUS *and* HELENA *look into mirror and burst out laughing.*) Look at yourself.

ALQUIST. Laughter? Laughter? Human beings? (*Getting up.*) Who has returned? Who are you?

PRIMUS. The Robot Primus.

ALQUIST. What? A Robot? Who are you?

HELENA. The Robotess Helena.

ALQUIST. Turn around, girl. What? You are timid, shy? (*Taking her by the arm.*) Let me see you, Robotess. (*She shrinks away.*)

PRIMUS. Sir, do not frighten her!

ALQUIST. What? You would protect her? When was she made?

PRIMUS. Two years ago.

ALQUIST. By Dr. Gall?

PRIMUS. Yes, like me.

ALQUIST. Laughter—timidity—protection. I must test you further—the newest of Gall's Robots. Take the girl into the
dissecting room.

PRIMUS. Why?

ALQUIST. I wish to experiment on her.

PRIMUS. Upon—Helena?

ALQUIST. Of course. Don't you hear me? Or must I call someone else to take her in?

PRIMUS. If you do I will kill you!

ALQUIST. Kill me—kill me then! What would the Robots do
then? What will your future be then?

PRIMUS. Sir, take me. I am made as she is—on the same day!
Take my life, sir.

HELENA (*rushing forward*). No, no, you shall not! You shall
not!

ALQUIST. Wait, girl, wait! (*To* PRIMUS.) Do you not wish to
live, then?

PRIMUS. Not without her! I will not live without her.

ALQUIST. Very well; you shall take her place.

HELENA. Primus! Primus! (*She bursts into tears.*)

ALQUIST. Child, child, you can weep! Why these tears? What
is Primus to you? One Primus more or less in the world—
what does it matter?

HELENA. I will go myself.

ALQUIST. Where?

HELENA. In there to be cut. (*She starts toward the dissecting room.* PRIMUS *stops her.*) Let me pass, Primus! Let me
pass!

PRIMUS. You shall not go in there, Helena!

HELENA..If you go in there and I do not, I will kill myself.

PRIMUS (*holding her*). I will not let you! (*To* ALQUIST).
Man, you shall kill neither of us!

ALQUIST. Why?

PRIMUS. We—we—belong to each other.

ALQUIST (*almost in tears*). Go, Adam; go, Eve. The world
is yours.

[HELENA *and* PRIMUS *embrace and go out arm in arm as the
curtain falls.*

Lewis Mumford

THE MONASTERY AND THE CLOCK
(1934)

WHERE DID the machine first take form in modern civilization? There was plainly more than one point of origin. Our mechanical civilization represents the convergence of numerous habits, ideas, and modes of living, as well as technical instruments; and some of these were, in the beginning, directly opposed to the civilization they helped to create. But the first manifestation of the new order took place in the general picture of the world: during the first seven centuries of the machine's existence the categories of time and space underwent an extraordinary change, and no aspect of life was left untouched by this transformation. The application of quantitative methods of thought to the study of nature had its first manifestation in the regular measurement of time; and the new mechanical conception of time arose in part out of the routine of the monastery. Alfred Whitehead has emphasized the importance of the scholastic belief in a universe ordered by God as one of the foundations of modern physics: but behind that belief was the presence of order in the institutions of the Church itself.

The technics of the ancient world were still carried on from Constantinople and Baghdad to Sicily and Córdoba: hence the early lead taken by Salerno in the scientific and medical advances of the Middle Ages. It was, however, in the monasteries of the West that the desire for order and power, other than that expressed in the military domination of weaker men, first manifested itself after the long uncertainty and bloody confusion that attended the breakdown of the Roman Empire. Within the walls of the monastery was sanctuary: under the rule of the order surprise and doubt and caprice and irregularity were put at bay. Opposed to the erratic fluctuations and pulsations of the worldly life was the iron discipline of the rule. Benedict added a seventh period to the devotions of the day, and in the seventh century, by a bull of Pope Sabinianus, it was decreed that the bells of the monastery be rung seven times in the twenty-four hours. These punctuation marks in the day were known as the canonical hours, and some means of keeping count of them and ensuring their regular repetition became necessary.

According to a now discredited legend, the first modern mechanical clock, worked by falling weights, was invented by the monk named Gerbert who afterward became Pope Sylvester II near the close of the tenth century. This clock was probably only a water clock, one of those bequests of the ancient world either left over directly from the days of the Romans, like the water wheel itself, or coming back again into the West through the Arabs. But the legend, as so often happens, is accurate in its implications if not in its facts. The monastery was the seat of a regular life, and an instrument for striking the hours at intervals or for reminding the bell-ringer that it was time to strike the bells, was an almost inevitable product of this life. If the mechanical clock did not appear until the cities of the thirteenth century demanded an orderly routine, the habit of order itself and the earnest regulation of time sequences had become almost second nature in the monastery. Coulton agrees with Sombart in looking upon the Benedictines, the great working order, as perhaps the original founders of modern capitalism: their rule certainly took the curse off work and their vigorous engineering enterprises may even have robbed warfare of some of its glamor. So one is not straining the facts when one suggests that the monasteries—at one time there were 40,000 under the Benedictine rule—helped to give human enterprise the regular collective beat and rhythm of the machine; for the clock is not merely a means of keeping track of the hours, but of synchronizing the actions of men.

Was it by reason of the collective Christian desire to provide for the welfare of souls in eternity by regular prayers and devotions that timekeeping and the habits of temporal order took hold of men's minds: habits that capitalist civilization presently turned to good account? One must perhaps accept the irony of this paradox. At all events, by the thirteenth century there are definite records of mechanical clocks, and by 1370 a well-designed "modern" clock had been built by Heinrich von Wyck at Paris. Meanwhile, bell towers had come into existence, and the new clocks, if they did not have, till the fourteenth century, a dial and a hand that translated the movement of time into a movement through space, at all events struck the hours. The clouds that could paralyze the sundial, the freezing that could stop the water clock on a winter night, were no longer obstacles to timekeeping: summer or winter, day or night, one was aware of the measured clank of the clock. The instrument presently spread outside the monastery; and the regular striking of the bells brought a new regularity into the life of the workman and the merchant. The bells of the clock tower almost defined urban existence. Timekeeping passed into timeserving and time accounting and time rationing. As this took place, Eternity ceased gradually to serve as the measure and focus of human actions.

The clock, not the steam engine, is the key machine of the modern industrial age. For every phase of its development the clock is both the outstanding fact and the typical symbol of the machine: even today no other machine is so ubiquitous. Here, at the very beginning of modern technics, appeared prophetically the accurate automatic machine which, only after centuries of further effort, was also to prove the final consummation of this technics in every department of industrial activity. There had been power machines, such as the water mill, before the clock; and there had also been various kinds of automata, to awaken the wonder of the populace in the temple, or to please the idle fancy of some Moslem caliph: machines one finds illustrated in Hero and Al-Jazari. But here was a new kind of power machine, in which the source of power and the transmission were of such a nature as to ensure the even flow of energy throughout the works and to make possible regular production and a standardized product. In its relationship to determinable quantities of energy, to standardization, to automatic action, and finally to its own special product, accurate timing, the clock has been the foremost machine in modern technics: and at each period it has remained in the lead: it marks a perfection toward which other machines aspire. The clock, moreover, served as a model for many other kinds of mechanical works, and the analysis of motion that accompanied the perfection of the clock, with the various types of gearing and transmission that were elaborated, contributed to the success of quite different kinds of machine. Smiths could have hammered thousands of suits of armor or thousands of iron cannon, wheelwrights could have shaped thousands of great water wheels or crude gears, without inventing any of the special types of movement developed in clockwork, and without any of the accuracy of measurement and fineness of articulation that finally produced the accurate eighteenth century chronometer.

The clock, moreover, is a piece of power machinery whose "product" is seconds and minutes: by its essential nature it dissociated time from human events and helped create the belief in an independent world of mathematically measurable sequences: the special world of science. There is relatively little foundation for this belief in common human experience: throughout the year the days are of uneven duration, and not merely does the relation between day and night steadily change, but a slight journey from East to West alters astronomical time by a certain number of minutes. In terms of the human organism itself, mechanical time is even more foreign: while human life has regularities of its own, the beat of the pulse, the breathing of the lungs, these change from hour to hour with mood and action, and in the longer span of days, time is measured not by the calendar but by events that occupy it. The shepherd measures from the time the ewes lambed; the farmer measures back to the day of sowing or forward to the harvest: if growth has its own duration and regularities, behind it are not simply matter and motion but the facts of development: in short, history. And while mechanical time is strung out in a succession of mathematically isolated instants, organic time—what Bergson calls duration—is cumulative in its effects. Though mechanical time can, in a sense, be speeded up or run backward, like the hands of a clock or the images of a moving picture, organic time moves in only one direction—through the cycle of birth, growth, development, decay, and death—and the past that is already dead remains present in the future that has still to be born.

Around 1345, according to Thorndike, the division of hours into sixty minutes and of minutes into sixty seconds became common: it was this abstract framework of divided time that became more and more the point of reference for both action and thought, and in the effort to arrive at accuracy in this department, the astronomical exploration of the sky focused attention further upon the regular, implacable movements of the heavenly bodies through space. Early in the sixteenth century a young Nuremburg mechanic, Peter Henlein, is supposed to have created "many-wheeled watches out of small bits of iron," and by the end of the century the small domestic clock had been introduced in England and Holland. As with the motorcar and the airplane, the richer classes first took over the new mechanism and popularized it: partly because they alone could afford it, partly because the new bourgeoisie were the first to discover that, as Franklin later put it, "time is money." To become "as regular as clock-work" was the bourgeois ideal, and to own a watch was for long a definite symbol of success. The increasing tempo of civilization led to a demand for greater power: and in turn power quickened the tempo.

Now, the orderly punctual life that first took shape in the monasteries is not native to mankind, although by now Western peoples are so thoroughly regimented by the clock that it is "second nature" and they look upon its observance as a fact of nature. Many Eastern civilizations have flourished on a loose basis in time: the Hindus have in fact been so indifferent to time that they lack even an authentic chronology of the years. Only yesterday, in the midst of the industrializations of Soviet Russia, did a society come into existence to further the carrying of watches there and to propagandize the benefits of punctuality. The popularization of timekeeping, which followed the production of the cheap standarized watch, first in Geneva, then in America around the middle of the last century, was essential to a well-articulated system of transportation and production.

To keep time was once a peculiar attribute of music: it gave industrial value to the workshop song or the tatoo or the chantey of the sailors tugging at a rope. But the effect of the mechanical clock is more pervasive and strict: it presides over the day from the hour of rising to the hour of rest. When one thinks of the day as an abstract span of time, one does not go to bed with the chickens on a winter's night: one invents wicks, chimneys, lamps, gaslights, electric lamps, so as to use all the hours belonging to the day. When one thinks of time, not as a sequence of experiences, but as a collection of hours, minutes, and seconds, the habits of adding time and saving time come into existence. Time took on the character of an enclosed space: it could be divided; it could be filled up; it could even be expanded by the invention of labor-saving instruments.

Abstract time became the new medium of existence. Organic functions themselves were regulated by it: one ate, not upon feeling hungry, but when prompted by the clock: one slept, not when one was tired, but when the clock sanctioned it. A generalized time-consciousness accompanied the wider use of clocks: dissociating time from organic sequences, it became easier for the men of the Renascence to indulge the fantasy of reviving the classic past or of reliving the splendors of antique Roman civilization: the cult of history, appearing first in daily ritual, finally abstracted itself as a special discipline. In the seventeenth century journalism and periodic literature made their appearance: even in dress, following the lead of Venice as fashion center, people altered styles every year rather than every generation.

The gain in mechanical efficiency through coordination and through the closer articulation of the day's events cannot be overestimated: while this increase cannot be measured in mere horsepower, one has only to imagine its absence today to foresee the speedy disruption and eventual collapse of our entire society. The modern industrial régime could do without coal and iron and steam easier than it could do without the clock.

Ralph Waldo Emerson

WORKS AND DAYS
   (1870)

OUR nineteenth century is the age of tools. They grow out of our structure. "Man is the metre of all things," said Aristotle; "the hand is the instrument of instruments, and the mind is the form of forms." The human body is the magazine of inventions, the patent-office, where are the models from which every hint was taken. All the tools and engines on earth are only extensions of its limbs and senses. One definition of man is "an intelligence served by organs." Machines can only second, not supply, his unaided senses. The body is a metre. The eye appreciates finer differences than art can expose. The apprentice clings to his foot-rule, a practised mechanic will measure by his thumb and his arm with equal precision; and a good surveyor will pace sixteen rods more accurately than another man can measure them by tape. The sympathy of eye and hand by which an Indian or a practised slinger hits his mark with a stone, or a woodchopper or a carpenter swings his axe to a hair-line on his log, are examples; and there is no sense or organ which is not capable of exquisite performance.

Men love to wonder, and that is the seed of our science; and such is the mechanical determination of our age, and so recent are our best contrivances, that use has not dulled our joy and pride in them; and we pity our fathers for dying before steam and galvanism, sulphuric ether and ocean telegraphs, photograph and spectroscope arrived, as cheated out of half their human estate. These arts open great gates of a future, promising to make the world plastic and to lift human life out of its beggary to a godlike ease and power.

Our century, to be sure, had inherited a tolerable apparatus. We had the compass, the printing-press, watches, the spiral spring, the barometer, the telescope. Yet so many inventions have been added, that life seems almost made over new; and as Leibnitz said of Newton, "that if he reckoned all that had been done by mathematicians from the beginning of the world down to Newton, and what had been done by him, his would be the better half," so one might say that the inventions of the last fifty years counterpoise those of the fifty centuries before them. For the vast production and manifold application of iron is new; and our common and indispensable utensils of house and farm are new; the sewing-machine, the power-loom, the McCormick reaper, the mowing-machines, gas-light, lucifer matches, and the immense productions of the laboratory, are new in this century, and one franc's worth of coal does the work of a labourer for twenty days.

Why need I speak of steam, the enemy of space and time, with its enormous strength and delicate applicability, which is made in hospitals to bring a bowl of gruel to a sick man's bed, and can twist beams of iron like candy-braids, and vies with the forces which upheaved and doubled over the geologic strata? Steam is an apt scholar and a strong-shouldered fellow, but it has not yet done all its work. It already walks about the field like a man, and will do anything required of it. It irrigates crops, and drags away a mountain. It must sew our shirts, it must drive our gigs; taught by Mr. Babbage, it must calculate interest and logarithms. Lord Chancellor Thurlow thought it might be made to draw bills and answers in Chancery. If that were satire, it is yet coming to render many higher services of a mechanico-intellectual kind, and will leave the satire short of the fact.

How excellent are the mechanical aids we have applied
to the human body, as in dentistry, in vaccination, in the
rhinoplastic treatment; in the beautiful aid of ether, like
a finer sleep; and in the boldest promiser of all—the trans-
fusion of the blood—which, in Paris, it was claimed, enables
a man to change his blood as often as his linen!

What of this dapper caoutchouc and gutta-percha, which
make water-pipes and stomach-pumps, belting for millwheels,
and diving bells, and rain-proof coats for all climates, which
teach us to defy the wet, and put every man on a footing with
the beaver and the crocodile? What of the grand tools with
which we engineer, like kobolds and enchanters—tunnelling
Alps, canalling the American Isthmus, piercing the Arabian
desert? In Massachusetts, we fight the sea successfully with
beach-grass and broom—and the blowing sand-barrens with
pine plantations. The soil of Holland, once the most populous
in Europe, is below the level of the sea. Egypt, where no rain
fell for three thousand years, now, it is said, thanks Mehemet
Ali's irrigations and planted forests for late-returning showers.
The old Hebrew king said, "He makes the wrath of man to
praise him." And there is no argument of theism better than
the grandeur of ends brought about by paltry means. The
chain of western railroads from Chicago to the Pacific has
planted cities and civilisations in less time than it costs to
bring an orchard into bearing.

What shall we say of the ocean telegraph, that extension
of the eye and ear, whose sudden performance astonished
mankind as if the intellect were taking the brute earth itself
into training, and shooting the first thrills of life and thought
through the unwilling brain?

There does not seem any limit to these new informations
of the same Spirit that made the elements at first, and now,
through man, works them. Art and power will go on as they
have done—will make day out of night, time out of space,
and space out of time.

Invention breeds invention. No sooner is the electric telegraph devised, than gutta-percha, the very material it requires,
is found. The aeronaut is provided with gun-cotton, the very
fuel he wants for his balloon. When commerce is vastly enlarged, California and Australia expose the gold it needs.
When Europe is over-populated, America and Australia crave
to be peopled; and so, throughout, every chance is timed, as
if Nature, who made the lock, knew where to find the key.

Another result of our arts is the new intercourse which is surprising us with new solutions of the embarrassing political problems. The intercourse is not new, but the scale is new. Our selfishness would have held slaves, or would have excluded from a quarter of the planet all that are not born on the soil of that quarter. Our politics are disgusting; but what can they help or hinder, when from time to time the primal instincts are impressed on masses of mankind, when the nations are in exodus and flux? Nature loves to cross her stocks —and German, Chinese, Turk, Russ, and Kanaka were putting out to sea, and intermarrying race with race; and commerce took the hint, and ships were built capacious enough to carry the people of a county.

This thousand-handed art has introduced a new element into the state. The science of power is forced to remember the power of science. Civilisation mounts and climbs. Malthus, when he stated that the mouths went on multiplying geometrically, and the food only arithmetically, forgot to say that the human mind was also a factor in political economy, and that the augmenting wants of society would be met by an augmenting power of invention.

Yes, we have a pretty artillery of tools now in our social arrangements: we ride four times as fast as our fathers did; travel, grind, weave, forge, plant, till, and excavate better. We have new shoes, gloves, glasses, and gimlets; we have the calculus; we have the newspaper, which does its best to make every square acre of land and sea give an account of itself at your breakfast-table; we have money, and paper money; we have language, the finest tool of all, and nearest to the mind. Much will have more. Man flatters himself that his command over Nature must increase. Things begin to obey him. We are to have the balloon yet; and the next war will be fought in the air. We may yet find a rosewater that will wash the Negro white. He sees the skull of the English race changing from its Saxon type under the exigencies of American life.

Tantalus, who in old times was seen vainly trying to quench his thirst with a flowing stream, which ebbed whenever he approached it, has been seen again lately. He is in Paris, in New York, in Boston. He is now in great spirits; thinks he shall reach it yet; thinks he shall bottle the wave. It is, however, getting a little doubtful. Things have an ugly look still. No matter how many centuries of culture have preceded, the new man always finds himself standing on the brink of chaos, always in a crisis. Can anybody remember when the times were not hard, and money not scarce? Can anybody remember when sensible men, and the right sort of men, and the right sort of women, were plentiful? Tantalus begins to think steam a delusion, and galvanism no better than it should be.

Many facts concur to show that we must look deeper for our salvation than to steam, photographs, balloons, or astronomy. These tools have some questionable properties. They are reagents. Machinery is aggressive. The weaver becomes a web, the machinist a machine. If you do not use the tools, they use you. All tools are in one sense edge-tools, and dangerous. A man builds a fine house; and now he has a master, and a task for life: he is to furnish, watch, show it, and keep it in repair, the rest of his days. A man has a reputation, and is no longer free, but must respect that. A man makes a picture or a book, and, if it succeeds, 'tis often the worse for him. I saw a brave man the other day, hitherto as free as the hawk or the fox of the wilderness, constructing his cabinet of drawers for shells, eggs, minerals, and mounted birds. It was easy to see that he was amusing himself with making pretty links for his own limbs.

Then the political economist thinks " 'tis doubtful if all the mechanical inventions that ever existed have lightened the day's toil of one human being." The machine unmakes the man. Now that the machine is so perfect, the engineer is nobody. Every new step in improving the engine restricts one more act of the engineer—unteaches him. Once it took Archimedes; now it needs only a fireman, and a boy to know the coppers, to pull up the handles or mind the water-tank. But when the engine breaks, they can do nothing.

What sickening details in the daily journals! I believe they have ceased to publish the *Newgate Calendar* and the *Pirate's Own Book* since the family newspapers, namely, the *New York Tribune* and the *London Times,* have quite superseded them in the freshness, as well as the horror, of their records of crime. Politics were never more corrupt and brutal; and Trade, that pride and darling of our ocean, that educator of nations, that benefactor in spite of itself, ends in shameful defaulting, bubble, and bankruptcy, all over the world.

Of course, we resort to the enumeration of his arts and inventions as a measure of the worth of man. But if, with all his arts, he is a felon, we cannot assume the mechanical skill or chemical resources as the measure of worth. Let us try another gauge.

What have these arts done for the character, for the worth of mankind? Are men better? 'Tis sometimes questioned whether morals have not declined as the arts have ascended. Here are great arts and little men. Here is greatness begotten of paltriness. We cannot trace the triumphs of civilisation to such benefactors as we wish. The greatest meliorator of the world is selfish, huckerstering Trade. Every victory over matter ought to recommend to man the worth of his nature. But now one wonders who did all this good. Look up the inventors. Each has his own knack; his genius is in veins and spots. But the great, equal, symmetrical brain, fed from a great heart, you shall not find. Every one has more to hide than he has to show, or is lamed by his excellence. 'Tis too plain that with the material power the moral progress has not kept pace. It appears that we have not made a judicious investment. Works and days were offered us, and we took works.

The new study of the Sanskrit has shown us the origin of the old names of God—Dyaus, Deus, Zeus, Zeu pater, Jupiter —names of the sun, still recognisable through the modifications of our vernacular words, importing that the Day is the Divine Power and Manifestation, and indicating that those ancient men, in their attempts to express the Supreme Power of the universe, called Him the Day, and that this name was accepted by all the tribes.

Hesiod wrote a poem which he called *Works and Days*, in which he marked the changes of the Greek year, instructing the husbandman at the rising of what constellation he might safely sow, when to reap, when to gather wood, when the sailor might launch his boat in security from storms, and what admonitions of the planets he must heed. It is full of economies for Grecian life, noting the proper age for marriage, the rules of household thrift, and of hospitality. The poem is full of piety as well as prudence, and is adapted to all meridians, by adding the ethics of works and of days. But he has not pushed his study of days into such inquiry and analysis as they invite.

A farmer said he "should like to have all the land that joined his own." Bonaparte, who had the same appetite, endeavoured to make the Mediterranean a French lake. Czar

Alexander was more expansive, and wished to call the Pacific *my ocean;* and the Americans were obliged to resist his attempts to make it a closed sea. But if he had the earth for his pasture, and the sea for his pond, he would be a pauper still. He only is rich who owns the day. There is no king, rich man, fairy, or demon who possesses such power as that. The days are ever divine as to the first Aryans. They are of the least pretension, and of the greatest capacity, of anything that exists. They come and go like muffled and veiled figures, sent from a distant friendly party; but they say nothing; and if we do not use the gifts they bring, they carry them as silently away.

How the day fits itself to the mind, winds itself round it like a fine drapery, clothing all its fancies! Any holiday communicates to us its colour. We wear its cockade and favours in our humour. Remember what boys think in the morning of "Election Day," of the Fourth of July, of Thanksgiving, or Christmas. The very stars in their courses wink to them of nuts and cakes, bonbons, presents, and fireworks. Cannot memory still descry the old school-house and its porch, somewhat hacked by jack-knives, where you spun tops and snapped marbles; and do you not recall that life was then calendared by moments, threw itself into nervous knots or glittering hours, even as now, and not spread itself abroad an equable felicity? In college terms, and in years that followed, the young graduate, when the Commencement anniversary returned, though he were in a swamp, would see a festive light, and find the air faintly echoing with plausive academic thunders. In solitude and in the country, what dignity distinguishes the holy time! The old Sabbath, or Seventh Day, white with the religions of unknown thousands of years, when this hallowed hour dawns out of the deep—a clean page, which the wise may inscribe with truth, whilst the savage scrawls it with fetishes—the cathedral music of history breathes through it a psalm to our solitude.

So, in the common experience of the scholar, the weathers fit his moods. A thousand tunes the variable wind plays, a thousand spectacles it brings, and each is the frame or dwelling of a new spirit. I used formerly to choose my time with some nicety for each favourite book. One author is good for winter, and one for the dog-days. The scholar must look long for the right hour for Plato's *Timœus.* At last the elect morning arrives, the early dawn—a few lights conspicuous in the heaven, as of a world just created and still becoming —and in its wide leisures we dare open that book.

There are days when the great are near us, when there is no frown on their brow, no condescension even; when they take us by the hand, and we share their thought. There are days which are the carnival of the year. The angels assume flesh, and repeatedly become visible. The imagination of the gods is excited, and rushes on every side into forms. Yesterday not a bird peeped; the world was barren, peaked, and pining: to-day 'tis inconceivably populous; creation swarms and meliorates.

The days are made on a loom whereof the warp and woof are past and future time. They are majestically dressed, as if every god brought a thread to the skyey web. 'Tis pitiful the things by which we are rich or poor—a matter of coins, coats, and carpets, a little more or less stone, or wood, or paint, the fashion of a cloak or hat; like the luck of naked Indians, of whom one is proud in the possession of a glass bead or a red feather, and the rest miserable in the want of it. But the treasures which Nature spent itself to amass— the secular, refined, composite anatomy of man—which all strata go to form, which the prior races, from infusory and saurian, existed to ripen; the surrounding plastic natures; the earth with its foods; the intellectual, temperamenting air; the sea with its invitations; the heaven deep with worlds; and the answering brain and nervous structure replying to these; the eye that looketh into the deeps, which again look back to the eye—abyss to abyss—these, not like a glass bead, or the coins or carpets, are given immeasurably to all.

This miracle is hurled into every beggar's hands. The blue sky is a covering for a market, and for the cherubim and seraphim. The sky is the varnish or glory with which the Artist has washed the whole work—the verge or confines of matter and spirit. Nature could no farther go. Could our happiest dream come to pass in solid fact—could a power open our eyes to behold "millions of spiritual creatures walk the earth"—I believe I should find that mid-plain on which they moved floored beneath and arched above with the same web of blue depth which weaves itself over me now, as I trudge the streets on my affairs.

'Tis singular that our rich English language should have no word to denote the face of the world. *Kinde* was the old English term, which, however, filled only half the range of

our fine Latin word, with its delicate future tense—*natura,
about to be born,* or what German philosophy denotes as a
becoming. But nothing expresses that power which seems
to work for beauty alone. The Greek *Kosmos* did; and therefore, with great propriety, Humboldt entitles his book, which
recounts the last results of science, *Cosmos.*

Such are the days—the earth is the cup, the sky is the
cover, of the immense bounty of Nature which is offered us
for our daily ailment; but what a force of *illusion* begins
life with us, and attends us to the end!

We are coaxed, flattered, and duped, from morn to eve,
from birth to death; and where is the old eye that ever saw
through the deception? The Hindoos represent Maia, the
illusory energy of Vishnu, as one of his principal attributes.
As if, in this gale of warring elements, which life is, it was
necessary to bind souls to human life as mariners in a tempest
lash themselves to the mast and bulwarks of a ship, and
Nature employed certain illusions as her ties and straps—a
rattle, a doll, an apple, for a child; skates, a river, a boat, a
horse, a gun, for the growing boy—and I will not begin to
name those of the youth and adult, for they are numberless.
Seldom and slowly the mask falls, and the pupil is permitted
to see that all is one stuff, cooked and painted under many
counterfeit appearances. Hume's doctrine was that the circumstances vary, the amount of happiness does not; that the
beggar cracking fleas in the sunshine under a hedge, and the
duke rolling by in his chariot, the girl equipped for her first
ball, and the orator returning triumphant from the debate,
had different means, but the same quantity of pleasant excitement.

This element of illusion lends all its force to hide the values
of present time. Who is he that does not always find himself doing something less than his best task? "What are you
doing?" "Oh, nothing; I have been doing thus, or I shall do
so or so; but now I am only"—Ah! poor dupe, will you never
slip out of the web of the master juggler—never learn that,
as soon as the irrecoverable years have woven their blue
glory between to-day and us, these passing hours shall glitter
and draw us, as the wildest romance and the homes of beauty
and poetry? How difficult to deal erect with them! The events
they bring, their trade, entertainments, and gossip, their
urgent work, all throw dust in the eyes and distract attention.
He is a strong man who can look them in the eye, see through

this juggle, feel their identity, and keep his own; who can
know surely that one will be like another to the end of the
world, nor permit love, or death, or politics, or money, war,
or pleasure, to draw him from his task.

The world is always equal to itself, and every man in
moments of deeper thought is appraised that he is repeating
the experiences of the people in the streets of Thebes or
Byzantium. An everlasting Now reigns in Nature, which hangs
the same roses on our bushes which charmed the Roman and
the Chaldæn in their hanging gardens. "To what end then,"
he asks, "should I study languages, and traverse countries,
to learn so simple truths?"

History of ancient art, excavated cities, recovery of books
and inscriptions—yes, the works were beautiful, and the
history worth knowing; and academies convene to settle the
claims of the old schools. What journeys and measurements
—Niebuhr and Müller and Layard—to identify the plain of
Troy and Nimroud town! and your homage to Dante costs
you so much sailing; and to ascertain the discoverers of
America needs so much voyaging as the discovery cost. Poor
child! that flexible clay of which these old brothers moulded
their admirable symbols was not Persian, nor Memphian, nor
Teutonic, nor local at all, but was common lime and silex
and water, and sunlight, the heat of the blood and the heaving
of the lungs; it was that clay which thou heldest but now in
thy foolish hands, and threwest away to go and seek in vain
in sepulchres, mummy-pits, and old bookshops of Asia-Minor,
Egypt, and England. It was the deep to-day which all men
scorn; the rich poverty, which men hate; the populous, all-
loving solitude, which men quit for the tattle of towns. HE
lurks, *he* hides—*he* who is success, reality, joy, and power.
One of the illusions is that the present hour is not the critical,
decisive hour. Write it on your heart that every day is the
best day in the year. No man has learned anything rightly,
until he knows that every day is Doomsday. 'Tis the old
secret of the gods that they come in low disguises. 'Tis the
vulgar great who come dizened with gold and jewels. Real
kings hide away their crowns in their wardrobes, and affect
a plain and poor exterior. In the Norse legend of our ancestors,
Odin dwells in a fisher's hut, and patches a boat. In the
Hindoo legends, Hari dwells a peasant among peasants. In
the Greek legend, Apollo lodges with the shepherds of
Admetus; and Jove liked to rusticate among the poor Ethio-

pians. So, in our history, Jesus is born in a barn, and His
twelve peers are fishermen. 'Tis the very principle of science
that Nature shows herself best in leasts; 'twas the maxim of
Aristotle and Lucretius; and, in modern times, of Swedenborg
and of Hahnemann. The order of changes in the egg deter-
mines the age of fossil strata. So it was the rule of our poets, in
the legends of fairy lore, that the fairies largest in power were
the least in size. In the Christian graces, humility stands
highest of all, in the form of the Madonna; and in life, this
is the secret of the wise. We owe to genius always the same
debt, of lifting the curtain from the common, and showing
us that divinities are sitting disguised in the seeming gang of
gypsies and pedlars. In daily life, what distinguishes the
master is the using those materials he has, instead of looking
about for what are more renowned, or what others have used
well. "A general," said Bonaparte, "always has troops enough,
if he only knows how to employ those he has, and bivouacs
with them." Do not refuse the employment which the hour
brings you, for one more ambitious. The highest heaven of
wisdom is alike near from every point, and thou must find
it, if at all, by methods native to thyself alone.

That work is ever the more pleasant to the imagination
which is not now required. How wistfully, when we have
promised to attend the working committee, we look at the
distant hills and their seductions!

The use of history is to give value to the present hour and
its duty. That is good which commends to me my country,
my climate, my means and materials, my associates. I knew
a man in a certain religious exaltation, who "thought it an
honour to wash his own face." He seemed to me more sane
than those who hold themselves cheap.

Zoologists may deny that horse-hairs in the water change
to worms; but I find that whatever is old corrupts, and the
past turns to snakes. The reverence for the deeds of our
ancestors is a treacherous sentiment. Their merit was not
to reverence the old, but to honour the present moment; and
we falsely make them excuses of the very habit which they
hated and defied.

Another illusion is, that there is not time enough for our
work. Yet we might reflect that though many creatures eat
from one dish, each, according to its constitution, assimilates
from the elements what belongs to it, whether time, or space,
or light, or water, or food. A snake converts whatever prey

the meadow yields him into snake; a fox, into fox; and Peter and John are working up all existence into Peter and John. A poor Indian chief of the Six Nations of New York made a wiser reply than any philosopher to someone complaining that he had not enough time. "Well," said Red Jacket, "I suppose you have all there is."

A third illusion haunts us, that a long duration, as a year, a decade, a century, is valuable. But an old French sentence says "God works in moments"—"*En peu d'heure Dieu labeure.*" We ask for long life, but 'tis deep life, or grand moments, that signify. Let the measure of time be spiritual, not mechanical. Life is unnecessarily long. Moments of insight, of fine personal relation, a smile, a glance—what ample borrowers of eternity they are! Life culminates and concentrates; and Homer said, "The gods ever give to mortals their apportioned share of reason only on one day."

I am of the opinion of the poet Wordsworth, "that there is no real happiness in this life, but in intellect and virtue." I am of the opinion of Pliny, "that, whilst we are musing on these things, we are adding to the length of our lives." I am of the opinion of Glauco, who said, "The measure of life, O Socrates, is, with the wise, the speaking and hearing such discourses as yours."

He only can enrich me who can recommend to me the space between sun and sun. 'Tis the measure of a man—his apprehension of a day. For we do not listen with the best regard to the verses of a man who is only a poet, nor to his problems, if he is only an algebraist; but if a man is at once acquainted with the geometric foundations of things, and with their festal splendour, his poetry is exact, and his arithmetic musical. And him I reckon the most learned scholar, not who can unearth for me the buried dynasties of Sesostris and Ptolemy, the Sothiac era, the Olympiads and consulships, but who can unfold the theory of this particular Wednesday. Can he uncover the ligaments concealed from all but piety, which attach the dull men and things we know to the First Cause? These passing fifteen minutes, men think, are time, not eternity; are low and subaltern, are but hope or memory, that is, the way *to* or the way *from* welfare, but not welfare. Can he show their tie? That interpreter shall guide us from a menial and eleemosynary existence into riches and stability. He dignifies the place where he is. This mendicant America, this curious, peering, itinerant, imitative America, studious of Greece and

Rome, of England and Germany, will take off its dusty shoes, will take off its glazed traveller's cap, and sit at home with repose and deep joy on its face. The world has no such landscape the æons of history no such hour, the future no equal second opportunity. Now let poets sing! now let arts unfold!

One more view remains. But life is good only when it is magical and musical, a perfect timing and consent, and when we do not anatomise it. You must treat the days respectfully, you must be a day yourself, and not interrogate it like a college professor. The world is enigmatical—everything said, and everything known or done—and must not be taken literally, but genially. We must be at the top of our condition to understand anything rightly. You must hear the bird's song without attempting to render it into nouns and verbs. Cannot we be a little abstemious and obedient? Cannot we let the morning be?

Everything in the universe goes by indirection. There are no straight lines. I remember well the foreign scholar who made a week of my youth happy by his visit. "The savages in the islands," he said, "delight to play with the surf, coming in on the top of the rollers, then swimming out again, and repeat the delicious manœuvre for hours. Well, human life is made up of such transits. There can be no greatness without abandonment. But here your very astronomy is an espionage. I dare not go out of doors and see the moon and stars, but they seem to measure my tasks, to ask how many lines or pages are finished since I saw them last. Not so, as I told you, was it in Belleisle. The days at Belleisle were all different, and only joined by a perfect love of the same object. Just to fill the hour—that is happiness. Fill my hour, ye gods, so that I shall not say, whilst I have done this, 'Behold, also, an hour of my life is gone,'—but rather, 'I have lived an hour.'"

We do not want factitious men, who can do any literary or professional feat, as, to write poems, or advocate a cause, or carry a measure, for money; or turn their ability indifferently in any particular direction by the strong effort of will. No; what has been best done in the world—the works of genius—cost nothing. There is no painful effort, but it is the spontaneous flowing of the thought. Shakespeare made his *Hamlet* as a bird weaves its nest. Poems have been written between sleeping and waking, irresponsibly. Fancy defines herself—

Forms that men spy
With the half-shut eye
In the beams of the setting sun, am I.

The masters painted for joy, and knew not that virtue had
gone out of them. They could not paint the like in cold
blood. The masters of English lyric wrote their songs so.
It was a fine efflorescence of fine powers; as was said of the
letters of the Frenchwomen—"the charming accident of their
more charming existence." Then the poet is never the poorer
for his song. A song is no song unless the circumstance is free
and fine. If the singer sing from a sense of duty or from
seeing no way of escape, I had rather have none. Those only
can sleep who do not care to sleep; and those only write or
speak best who do not too much respect the writing or the
speaking.

The same rule holds in science. The savant is often an
amateur. His performance is a memoir to the Academy on
fish-worms, tadpoles, or spiders' legs; he observes as other
academicians observe; he is on stilts at a microscope, and—
his memoir finished and read and printed—he retreats into
his routinary existence, which is quite separate from his
scientific. But in Newton, science was as easy as breathing;
he used the same wit to weigh the moon that he used to
buckle his shoes; and all his life was simple, wise, and majes-
tic. So was it in Archimedes—always self-same, like the sky. In
Linnæus, in Franklin, the like sweetness and equality—no
stilts, no tiptoe—and their results are wholesome and memorable to all men.

In stripping time of its illusions, in seeking to find what is
the heart of the day, we come to the quality of the moment,
and drop the duration altogether. It is the depth at which
we live, and not at all the surface extension, that imports.
We pierce to the eternity, of which time is the flitting surface;
and, really, the least acceleration of thought, and the least
increase of power of thought, make life to seem and to be of
vast duration. We call it time; but when that acceleration
and that deepening take effect, it acquires another and a
higher name.

There are people who do not need much experimenting;
who after years of activity, say, we knew all this before; who
love at first sight and hate at first sight; discern the affinities
and repulsions; who do not care so much for conditions as

others, for they are always in one condition, and enjoy themselves; who dictate to others, and are not dictated to; who in their consciousness of deserving success constantly slight the ordinary means of attaining it; who have self-existence and self-help; who are suffered to be themselves in society; who are great in the present; who have no talents, or care not to have them—being that which was before talent, and shall be after it, and of which talent seems only a tool—this is character, the highest name at which philosophy has arrived.

'Tis not important how the hero does this or this, but what he is. What he is will appear in every gesture and syllable. In this way the moment and the character are one.

'Tis a fine fable for the advantage of character over talent, the Greek legend of the strife of Jove and Phœbus. Phœbus challenged the gods, and said, "Who will outshoot the far-darting Apollo?" Zeus said, "I will." Mars shook the lots in his helmet, and that of Apollo leaped out first. Apollo stretched his bow and shot his arrow into the extreme west. Then Zeus arose, and with one stride cleared the whole distance, and said, "Where shall I shoot? there is no space left." So the bowman's prize was adjudged to him who drew no bow.

And this is the progress of every earnest mind; from the works of man and the activity of the hands to a delight in the faculties which rule them; from a respect to the works to a wise wonder at this mystic element of time in which he is conditioned; from local skills and the economy which reckons the amount of production *per* hour to the finer economy which respects the quality of what is done, and the right we have to the work, or the fidelity with which it flows from ourselves; then to the depth of thought it betrays, looking to its universality, or, that its roots are in eternity, not in time. Then it flows from character, that sublime health which values one moment as another, and makes us great in all conditions, and is the only definition we have of freedom and power.

Donald N. Michael

From CYBERNATION: THE SILENT CONQUEST
(1962)

INTRODUCTION

BOTH OPTIMISTS and pessimists often claim that automation is
simply the latest stage in the evolution of technological means
for removing the burdens of work. The assertion is mislead-
ing. There is a very good possibility that automation is so
different in degree as to be a profound difference in kind and
that it will pose unique problems for society, challenging our
basic values and the ways in which we express and enforce
them.*

In order to understand what both the differences and the
problems are and, even more, will be, we have to know something of the nature and use of automation and computers.
There are two important classes of devices. One class, usually
referred to when one speaks of "automation," is made up of
devices that automatically perform sensing and motor tasks,
replacing or improving on human capacities for performing
these functions. The second class, usually referred to when
one speaks of "computers," is composed of devices that perform, very rapidly, routine or complex logical and decision-
making tasks, replacing or improving on human capacities for
performing these functions.

Using these machines does not merely involve replacing
men by having machines do tasks that men did before. It is,
as John Diebold says, a way of "thinking as much as it is a
way of doing. . . . It is no longer necessary to think in terms
of individual machines, or even in terms of groups of machines; instead, for the first time, it is practical to look at an

* This paper makes the following assumptions in looking on the
next twenty years or so: *(1)* international relations will derive
from the same general conditions that pertain today; *(2)* the
weapons-systems industries will continue to support a major share
of our economy; *(3)* major discoveries will be made and applied
in other technologies, including psychology and medicine; *(4)*
trends in megalopolis living and in population growth will continue;
(5) no major shifts in underlying social attitudes and in public
and private goals will take place.

79

entire production or information-handling process as an integrated system and not as a series of individual steps."[1] For
example, if the building trades were to be automated, it
would not mean inventing machines to do the various tasks
now done by men; rather, buildings would be redesigned so
that they could be built by machines. One might invent an
automatic bricklayer, but it is more likely that housing would
be designed so that bricks would not be laid. Automation of
the electronics industry was not brought about through the
invention of automatic means for wiring circuits but through
the invention of essentially wireless—that is, printed—circuits
(though today there are automatic circuit wirers as well).

The two classes of devices overlap. At one pole are the
automatic producers of material objects and, at the other, the
sophisticated analyzers and interpreters of complex data. In
the middle zone are the mixed systems, in which computers
control complicated processes, such as the operations of an
oil refinery, on the basis of interpretations that they make
of data automatically fed to them about the environment.
Also in this middle zone are those routine, automatic, data-
processing activities which provide men with the bases for
controlling, or at least understanding, what is happening to a
particular environment. Processing of social-security data and
making straightforward tabulations of census information are
examples of these activities.*

Cybernated systems perform with a precision and a rapidity
unmatched in humans. They also perform in ways that would
be impractical or impossible for humans to duplicate. They can
be built to detect and correct errors in their own performance
and to indicate to men which of their components are producing the error. They can make judgments on the basis of
instructions programmed into them. They can remember and

---

* In order to eliminate the awkwardness of repeating the words
"automation" and "computers" each time we wish to refer to both
at the same time, and in order to avoid the semantic difficulties
involved in using one term or the other to mean both ends of the
continuum, we invent the term "cybernation" to refer to *both*
automation and computers. The word is legitimate at least to the
extent that it derives from "cybernetics," a term invented by Norbert Wiener to mean the processes of communication and control
in man and machines. He derived it from the Greek word for
"steersman." The theory and practice of cybernetics underlie all
systematic design and application of automation and computers.

search their memories for appropriate data, which either has been programmed into them along with their instructions or has been acquired in the process of manipulating new data. Thus, they can learn on the basis of past experience with their environment. They can receive information in more codes and sensory modes than men can. They are beginning to perceive and to recognize.

As a result of these characteristics, automation is being used to make and roll steel, mine coal, manufacture engine blocks, weave cloth, sort and grade everything from oranges to bank checks. More versatile automatic fabricators are becoming available, too:

> U.S. Industries announced . . . that it had developed what was termed the first general-purpose automation machine available to manufacturers as standard off-the-shelf hardware. . . . The new machine, called a TransfeRobot, sells for $2,500. . . . The Westclox Company of La Salle, Ill., has been using a TransfeRobot to oil clock assemblies as they pass on a conveyor belt. The machine oils eight precision bearings simultaneously in a second. At the Underwood Corporation typewriter plant in Hartford, the robot picks up, transfers and places a small typewriter component into a close-fitting nest for an automatic machine operation. In an automobile plant, the device feeds partly fabricated parts of a steering assembly to a trimming press and controls the press. The device consists basically of an arm and actuator that can be fitted with many types of fingers and jaws. All are controlled by a self-contained electronic brain.[2]

At the other end of the continuum, computers are being used rather regularly to analyze market portfolios for brokers; compute the best combination of crops and livestock for given farm conditions; design and "fly" under typical and extreme conditions rockets and airplanes before they are built; design, in terms of costs and traffic-flow characteristics, the appropriate angles and grades for complex traffic interchanges; keep up-to-date inventory records and print new stock orders as automatically computed rates of sales and inventory status indicate. Computers have also been programmed to write mediocre TV dramas (by manipulating segments of the plot), write music, translate tolerably if not perfectly from one language to another, and simulate some logical brain processes (so that the machine goes about solving puzzles—and making mistakes in the process—in the ways people do). Also, computers are programmed to play elaborate "games" by themselves or in collaboration with human beings. Among other reasons, these games are played to understand and plan more efficiently for the conduct of wars and the procedures for industrial and business aggrandizement. Through such games, involving a vast number of variables, and contingencies within which these variables act and interact, the best or most likely solutions to complex problems are obtained.

The utility and the applicability of computers are being continually enhanced. For example, after a few hours of training, nonspecialists can operate the smaller computers without the aid of programmers simply by plugging in prerecorded instruction tapes that tell the computer how to do specific tasks. Instruction-tape libraries can supply preprogrammed computer directions for everything from finding the cube root of a number to designing a bridge. When the machine is through with one task, its circuits can be easily cleared so that a new set of preprogrammed instructions can be plugged in by its businessman operator.

But the capabilities of computers already extend well beyond even these applications. Much successful work has been done on computers that can program themselves. For example, they are beginning to operate the way man appears to when he is exploring ways of solving a novel problem. That is, they apply and then modify, as appropriate, previous experiences with and methods of solution for what appear to be related problems. Some of the machines show originality and unpredictability. To take one example from a recent paper of Norbert Wiener:

> The present level of these learning machines is that they play a fair amateur game at chess but that in checkers they can show a marked superiority to the player who has programmed them after from 10 to 20 playing hours of working and indoctrination. They thus most definitely escape from the completely effective control of the man who has made them. Rigid as the repertory of factors may be which they are in a position to take into consideration, they do unquestionably—and so say those who have played with them—show originality, not merely in their tactics, which may be quite unforeseen, but even in the detailed weighting of their strategy.[3]

Another example of a machine the behavior of which is not completely controllable or predictable is the Perceptron, designed by Dr. Frank Rosenblatt. This machine can learn to recognize what it has seen before and to teach itself generalizations about what it recognizes. It can also learn to discriminate, and thereby to identify shapes similar to those it has seen before. Future versions will hear as well as see. It is not possible to predict the degree and quality of recognition that the machine will display as it is learning. It is designed to learn and discriminate in the same way that it is believed man may learn and discriminate; it has its own pace and style of learning, of refining its discriminations, and of making mistakes in the process.

It is no fantasy, then, to be concerned with the implications of the thinking machines. There is every reason to believe that within the next two decades machines will be available outside the laboratory that will do a credible job of original thinking, certainly as good thinking as that expected of most middle-level people who are supposed to "use their minds." There is no basis for knowing where this process will stop, nor, as Wiener has pointed out, is there any comfort in the assertion that, since man built the machine, he will always be smarter or more capable than it is.

> It may be seen that the result of a programming technique of [cybernation] is to remove from the mind of the designer and operator an effective understanding of many of the stages by which the machine comes to its conclusions and of what the real tactical intentions of many of its operations may be. This is highly relevant to the problem of our being able to foresee undesired consequences outside the frame of the strategy of the game while the machine is still in action and while intervention on our part may prevent the occurrence of these consequences. Here it is necessary to realize that human action is a feedback action. To avoid a disastrous consequence, it is not enough that some action on our part should be sufficient to change the course of the machine, because it is quite possible that we lack information on which to base consideration of such an action.[4]

The capabilities and potentialities of these devices are unlimited. They contain extraordinary implications for the emancipation and enslavement of mankind.

The opportunities for man's enhancement through the benefits of cybernation are generally more evident and more expected, especially in view of our proclivity to equate technological advances with progress and happiness. In the words of the National Association of Manufacturers:

> For the expanding, dynamic economy of America, the sky is indeed the limit. Now more than ever we must have confidence in America's capacity to grow. Guided by electronics, powered by atomic energy, geared to the smooth, effortless workings of automation, the magic carpet of our free economy heads for distant and undreamed horizons. Just going along for the ride will be the biggest thrill on earth![5]

But the somber and complex difficulties produced by cybernation, which already are beginning to plague some aspects of our society and economy, are only beginning to be recognized. Thus, although this paper will describe, first, the advantages of cybernation, which make its ever-expanding application so compelling, it will, on the whole, emphasize the less obvious, sometimes acutely uncomfortable, aspects of this development with which we must successfully contend if we are to enjoy the benefits of both cybernation and democracy.

THE ADVANTAGES OF CYBERNATION

IN RECENT YEARS deteriorating sales prospects, rising production costs, increased foreign competition, and lower profits have led business management to turn to our national talent for technological invention as the most plausible means of reducing costs and increasing productivity, whether the product is an engine block or tables of sales figures. And the government, faced with the need to process and understand rapidly increasing masses of numerical facts about the state of the nation and the world, is already using 524 computers and is the major customer for more of them.

What are the advantages of cybernated systems that make government and private enterprise turn to them to solve problems?

In the first place, in a competitive society a successfully cybernated organization often has economic advantages over a competitor using people instead of machines. As *U.S. News & World Report* says:

> In one line of business after another, the trend is the same. Companies are spending millions of dollars to mechanize their operations, boost output and cut costs. . . . Says an official of a big electrical company: "It is no longer a question of whether or not to automate, but rather it is how far to go and how fast to proceed. If you don't, your competition will."[6]

Not only must many organizations automate to compete, but the same principle probably holds for competing nations. We are by no means the only semicybernated society. Europe and Russia are well under way, and their machines and products compete with ours here and in the world market. The U.S.S.R. is making an all-out effort to cybernate as much of its planning-economic-industrial operation as it can.

In the second place, reducing the number of personnel in an organization reduces the magnitude of management's human-relations tasks, whether these be coping with overlong coffee breaks, union negotiations, human errors, or indifference.

In the third place, cybernation permits much greater rationalization of managerial activities. The computers can produce information about what is happening now, as well as continuously updated information about what will be the probable consequences of specific decisions based on present and extrapolated circumstances. The results are available in a multitude of detailed or simplified displays in the form of words, tables of figures, patterns of light, growth and decay curves, dial readings, and so on. In many situations, built-in feedback monitors the developing situation and deals with routine changes, errors, and needs with little or no intervention by human beings. This frees management for attention to more basic duties. There is, for example,

> . . . an automatic lathe . . . which gauges each part as it is produced and automatically resets the cutting tools to compensate for tool wear. In addition, when the cutting tools have been worn down to a certain predetermined limit, the machine automatically replaces them with sharp tools. The parts are automatically loaded onto the machine and are automatically unloaded as they are

finished. These lathes can be operated for 5 to 8 hours
without attention, except for an occasional check to
make sure that parts are being delivered to the loading
mechanism.[7]

Another example, combining built-in feedback with a display capability, adds further illumination:

> The Grayson-Robinson apparel chain, which has more
> than 100 stores throughout the country, receives print-
> punch tags daily from its stores and converts them to
> full-size punchcards. The complete merchandise and
> inventory control function is then handled on a com-
> puter. What styles are to be processed first are deter-
> mined at the computer center. During any given week
> about 60 per cent of the sales data are received and
> summarized. On the following Monday morning the
> remaining 40 per cent of the sales data are received.
> The computer can then begin running style reports im-
> mediately after the tickets have been converted to cards.
> By this time the company can run up style reports by
> departments and price lines in order to obtain the neces-
> sary merchandising information. The entire reporting
> job is completed by Wednesday afternoon of each week,
> including reports on all inactive stockpiles.[8]

Freeing management from petty distractions in these ways
permits more precise and better substantiated decisions,
whether they have to do with business strategy, government
economic policy, equipment-system planning, or military
strategy and tactics. Thus, management in business or government can have much better control both over the system
as it operates and over the introduction of changes into future
operations. Indeed, the changes themselves may be planned
in conformity with, and guided by, a strategy that is derived
from a computer analysis of the future environment.

In the fourth place, cybernation allows government and
industry much greater freedom in locating their facilities efficiently in relation to the accessibility of raw products, markets, transportation, and needed (or cheaper) human and
material resources. Distance is no longer a barrier to control
and coordination. The computers that control automated
processes need not be near the factories nor the data-process-
ing computers near their sources of information or users if
other considerations are more pressing. Widely dispersed

installations can be coordinated and controlled from still another place, and the dispersed units can interact with each other and affect one another's performance as easily, in many cases, as if they were all in the same place.

In the fifth place, some degree of cybernation is necessary to meet the needs of our larger population and to maintain or increase the rate of growth of the Gross National Product. An estimated 80,000,000 persons will be added to our population in the next twenty years. Beyond increases in productivity per man hour to be expected from the projected 20 per cent growth in the labor force during this same period, productive growth will have to be provided by machines.

If the criteria are control, understanding, and profits, there are strong reasons why government and business should want to, and indeed would have to, expand cybernation as rapidly as they can. The versatility of computers and automation is becoming better understood all the time by those who use them, even though, as with the human brain, most present users are far from applying their full potential. Cheap and general-purpose computers or modular components applicable to many types of automatic production and decision-making are now being manufactured. In good part, they are cheap because they themselves are produced by automated methods. Techniques for gathering the field data that serve as the "inputs" to the machines are being refined and themselves automated or semiautomated. For example, a large shoe distributor is planning to attach a prepunched IBM card to each shoe box. When a sale is made, the card is returned to a central facility to guide inventory adjustment, reordering, and sales recording and analysis. Techniques for quickly implementing the "outputs" from the machines are also being invented. Methods are being developed for systematically establishing the precise kind and degree of cybernation required in specific situations as well as the changes needed in the rest of the institution or organization using cybernation.

These are the advantages for management, for government, and for those parts of the work force whose status has been enhanced because of cybernation. But as cybernation advances, new and profound problems will arise for our society and its values. Cybernation presages changes in the social system so vast and so different from those with which we have traditionally wrestled that it will challenge to their roots our current perceptions about the viability of our way of life.

If our democratic system has a chance to survive at all, we shall need far more understanding of the consequences of cybernation. Even the job of simply preserving a *going* society will take a level of planning far exceeding any of our previous experiences with centralized control.

NOTES

[1] John Diebold, *Automation: Its Impact on Business and Labor,* National Planning Association, Planning Pamphlet No. 106, Washington, D.C., May, 1959, p. 3.

[2] "Multi-Purpose Automation Unit Is Sold 'Off the Shelf,'" *The New York Times,* June 23, 1961, p. 44.

[3] Norbert Wiener, "Some Moral and Technical Consequences of Automation," *Science,* CXXXI (May 6, 1960), p. 1356.

[4] Wiener, *op. cit.,* p. 1357.

[5] "Calling All Jobs," National Association of Manufacturers, New York, October, 1957, p. 21.

[6] "When Machines Have Jobs—and Workers Do Not," *U.S. News & World Report,* L (February 6, 1961), p. 76.

[7] Statement by Walter Reuther; see *Automation and Technological Change,* 84th Congress, First Session, USGPO, 1959, p. 99.

[8] Statement by James A. Suffridge; see *New Views on Automation,* 86th Congress, Second Session, USGPO, 1960, p. 591.

Robert Sherman Townes

PROBLEM FOR EMMY
(1952)

EMMY lived—we all used that word—in a great Room that had once been the University's ROTC armory. The walls had been painted pale gray, and a few partitions and glass cubicles had been set up, but the shape and vast reach of the old armory remained unchanged. Emmy almost filled the width of one end, standing a good fifteen feet high and coming out into the Room over twenty feet to the edge of the heavy carpeting. To the casual eye Emmy was no more than several huge gray-enameled steel boxes with panels of tiny lights, a few switches, one large red light. It would have been difficult to explain to an outsider, when Emmy was silent, the reverent hush of the white-clad servants who attended her day and night.

Emmy had a much longer name—the Manndenker-Golemacher Electronic Calculator Implemented Model M-VII— but those who worked for her and for whom she worked had shortened all that to just Emmy. Not alone from a need for brevity, but also because of the strong sense of personality that pervaded the immediate area of the great mechanism. Most of us who worked in the Room fell into the way of thinking of Emmy as a person; a clever, reasonable, amiable person. We talked to her, patted her approvingly after a particularly intricate problem was solved through her miles of wire and thousands of tubes. We even kept our voices muted in her softly whirring presence.

The head of the University's Department of Cybernetics (the new science that had sprung up in the forties to build and rule such machines) was a thickset, heavy-maned research fellow, Dr. Adam Golemacher. On the foundation begun by his predecessor, Manndenker, he had erected a structure of ever-widening improvements, until Emmy was acknowledged to be the top electronic calculator of the country. The star, as it were. The awe which I, Dichter, his assistant, so often felt before Emmy never rose in Dr. G. To him she was a massive equation of comprehended elements; one million, two hundred and fifty thousand pieces of inert matter assembled under his direction, activated by the city power supply to turn over certain mathematical functions too lengthy for human time limits. This and no more. Dr. G. knew Emmy far too well to be familiar with her.

But I had had no part in Emmy's creation. When I joined the staff in the Room, the machine was a performing entity. A complete, handsome thing, for all its size, trim and tidy in the sleek steel housing. The walls nearby were muted with smartly dotted soundproofing that made a fine setting for Emmy. I liked this shipshape, cleanly place. The salary was not high, but Adam Golemacher was one of those men who educate with their mere presence. It was said everywhere that mattered that he knew more of this intricate and exquisite science than any man alive; and I had good reason to believe it.

In his absurdly tiny office, bare as a monk's cell but for the big photograph of Einstein on one sterile wall, Dr. Gole-macher passed final judgment on the problems to be presented for Emmy's study. Many industrial and scientific organizations submitted requests for help. Dr. G., his big, dry hands roving like chunky lions through the thick jungle of his gray hair, would riffle through these tenders, tossing most of them aside—onto the floor, that is—with some sort of contemptuous remark such as, "Piffle-paffle, a cretin child could work this out with blocks in an hour." Then the rejected problems were sent back with stiff printed notes, for all the world like editors' rejection slips.

Now and then the old man's startlingly young black eyes would crackle at some one of the problems. Threading through its preliminaries, he would catch the spoor of some elusive question that was basically exciting. Then he would usually go on far past the desired matter. Since the client paid a flat fee of five hundred dollars an hour for Emmy's services and seemed never disposed (through mystified humility, I always assumed) to argue the bills, Dr. G. charged the extra as a contribution to science. Thus many a plastics manufacturer or bridge builder stored up, unbeknownst to himself, extra pearls in heaven.

When a problem was finally selected it was sent to the mathematicians—perhaps better, The Mathematicians. In keeping with the temple-like hush of the Room and our acolytish attendance on Emmy, there was something hieratic about these twelve men. They sat in two rows of six white desks, with small adding machines and oceans of paper before them, bent over, muttering to themselves, dressed in white (no one seemed to know quite why we all wore white), like the priests of a new logarithmic cult. Each of these men had a home life of his own, parents and past, individual dreams and lusts. But in the sweeping reaches of the Room (they sat at the far end from Emmy), drenched in the sunlight from the great windows, they were as alike as gears. And gears they were, which set in motion the infinitely faster thought trains of Emmy.

It was their function to translate problems into language Emmy could grasp. The calculator, like all others, used binary rather than decimal numbers. The Mathematicians arranged the data in the form of marks on a tape that fed into the machine. This was the longest part of the operation of any problem. With the constant tinkering improvements of Dr.

Golemacher, it was slowly becoming less and less difficult, more—vestigial. The Mathematicians knew this, of course, and one could often see, in a hard look or a wry word, their feral hatred of the great machine that was devouring the days of their lives in order to make their lives useless.

Dr. Golemacher did not encourage any of these humanizations of the machine. He regarded them as an insult to his reason—and to his handiwork. Such personification savored to him of the sensational Sunday press. He was firmly convinced that all reporters were liars. None of the bright-eyed young physics majors sent us by the feature editors ever got past me.

We kept a full staff of some twenty men who did nothing but clean and repair the machine. In their white coveralls from ankle to throat, they looked like a lot of swearing bunnies. And there was a lot of swearing to be done over Emmy, muted though it was. The myriad parts needed constant supervision, and even with that, breakdowns occurred at bad moments. There were even breakdowns that could not be explained; nothing would prove mechanically or electrically wrong, yet the soft clickings and the twinkling lights would offer patterns that were erratic, meaningless, and untrue. The men would say that it was just one of the old girl's bad days. Dr. Golemacher would roar, "One side, fumblers-bumblers!" and bare his arms and look furiously for a tangible trouble spot. But in the end, only a rest of a day or two would restore the machine to perfect working order.

There was one April morning, all silvery and aglow from a fine rain, when Emmy seemed to be looking and behaving especially well. I started up the switches that would bring the power into the cells. The black-coated cylinders that were her memory (for this one problem's course) hummed, the great encyclopedia of permanent memory on plastic slips stood at the ready. I slowly fed in the data on an especially complex problem of a Midwestern plane maker. Emmy was being asked to consider several sets of conditions, weigh them, and select the best; that is, the cheapest and most efficient. The answer would eventually be typed out by Emmy's typewriter in her special blue ink. Later, rendered down into practical factors, it would be presented as a package from the oracle to the plane manufacturer—who would be awed.

But on that morning I could not, I believe, be awed; there

was too much April. Perched on my high white stool, I fed
the problem's many factors into Emmy's colossal scheme of
connections—so like my own ten billion God-given neurons.
Within the humming machine electronic "synapses," know-
able and unmysterious, digested reams of figures in a fraction
of a second. These were summed and integrated, canceled
and compared in the flick of an eyelid. On the panel the rows
and rows of tiny red and white lights made a visible pattern
of the mathematics, like Bach played on an enormous switch-
board.

Outside the great windows, the campus was burgeoning.
A calfish undergraduate was mawking over a full-bosomed
coed; April was in the set of her body, her movements, and
sure acceptance of his bumbling tribute. The trees showed
tiny green flames along the black boughs. It was no day to
spend with a machine. In spite of Dr. Golemacher's strict
rule about unnecessary noise in the Room, I hummed softly
to myself—a bit of old nursery tune. (I am not well up on
the jolly popular things one hears around.) Suddenly the
error bell rang out sharply. The big red light flashed on and
off hectically. *Error. Error.* I was taken completely off guard.
There had seemed to be no flaw in the problem data as I
handed them on to Emmy. Yet the harsh bell was announcing
some serious mistake which the machine could not absorb.

I moved quickly to shut off the power. With my hand on
the switch for the first section, I happened to glance at the
twinkling panel. For a moment I did not quite grasp what I
saw. Even when I did, reason and training fought against it
for me. My hand on the switch was cold and sweating. There
could be no mistaking it; the machine was not at work on the
problem at all. Most of the rows of tiny lights were wholly
dark. The remaining few were pulsing off and on in a definite
rhythm: the rhythm of the little tune I had been humming:
"London Bridge Is Falling Down."

While I stared foolishly at the lights, one of The Mathematicians, believed to be a young female, approached, instantly caught the melody in the winking lights, and looked
at me severely.

"Very droll. But what will Dr. G. Say?" Then with a wee
spark of feminine curiosity, "However do you do it?"

"*I'm* not doing it. *It's* doing it," I almost wailed.

She was not a frail woman. She gasped, stiffened in her
starchy smock, and marched off for Dr. Golemacher. I turned

to Emmy. Before I quite knew what I was saying I muttered, "Now see what you've got us into," and fetched her case a swift kick. It hurt my ankle. The lights at once snapped off. When Dr. G. arrived there was no trace of the irrelevance. He did not bother to be incredulous. Me, he might have suspected ("You do not channel your imagination, Dichter; you waste it in fuzzy dreaming"); but he knew his Mathematicians. He came up at once with an explanation.

"You admit you were humming, Dichter." (I got the Prussian drillmaster frown here.) "Well, then, the machine picked up sympatheic vibrations," and so on, and so on. And that was that. It was a normal April morning again. The plane problem could get along, as it did, without any further hitch.

Problems came in steadily, always more difficult. Dr. G., roughly jolly, reveled in them as they become tougher. Under his wizard attentions, Emmy's "implementation" came ever nearer human ability. Cells sensitive to color, light, and heat, voices, music, and the invisible world of waves that permeate the universe were added and integrated to the thousands of miles of wire and tons of steel and glass. Dr. Golemacher even kept an eye on work in the brainwave fields, so that one day this area of energy might be explored for Emmy. She stood in the Room, growing up all the time. She had no self, no sentience, but we who moved about went like people seen in dreams or scenic wallpapers. We were hushed, minute, secret. The cleaners were overcareful with their cloths and applied cleaning pastes like beauticians. The repairmen used their tools with the respectful nicety of surgeons.

When Emmy got the job from the telescope at Palomar, we were besieged by the press. Dr. Golemacher shut himself away; I had to go through the endlessly amusing play on "Dr. Dichter" that had plagued me since I took my first degree. Newsmen, like scientists, have a somewhat elementary sense of humor. But Emmy was news. Taking the scraps of material grouped together at the observatory, Emmy mulled them over, then reached a finger into far space and unerringly pointed out the hulk of a dead star stumbling blindly among the burning suns. Once or twice Emmy broke down completely as she tried to pry along the alleys of space and find out just where we were in the shifting cosmos. Then Dr. G. would nurse and tease the great mechanism, "prescribe" rest, and bully her all at once. And back to the job she always went, running fingers along the edge of the fourth dimension itself.

But always we had to frame the question in detail. She could only give an answer or not give an answer. All her tubes could not match the billions of neurons, the zipping synapses of the human brain. She was so much more than we, and so much less.

Autumn came to the campus as burning wood smoke and those young people who always seem to turn up every year. To Emmy, September was an involved problem for a paint manufacturer. The Mathematicians and some color chemists had set up the problem on the tape. I was feeding in the data, taking the separate answers and refeeding them for a conclusion. Outside, the greens were dying off bravely in their not-care show of red and gold. Someone—perhaps I—had left open a color-sensitive cell that faced the open window. Suddenly there was the red error signal, the alarm bell. I looked up at the lights fearfully. There was no tune. It was worse than that. The problem had ceased to operate. Emmy's lights, all of them, were pulsing gently. There was a lazy, brooding, *pleased* quality in that play of lights. Like the gurgling of a baby. On an impulse I slammed shut the cover of the cell facing the out of doors. The pulsing died away; the paint maker's problem began to course through the machine again. This time I did not send for Dr. Golemacher.

But he knew there was something wrong. Perhaps I was too diffident with Emmy. Perhaps, as he watched me at work one day, he caught a flick of mystery in my eye. He was observant as well as brilliant. In his unusually solicitous inquires after my health of mornings I sensed the physician rather than the co-worker. I knew I must regain my crispness or be offered humiliating suggestions of a year's leave "for nerves."

I made a point of watching when some large-scale overhauling of the machine's vitals was afoot. Seeing the matter-of-fact pieces and parts being taken away and replaced with others from prosaic cartons helped me back to a human-operator-of-a-machine state of mind. I was firm with myself. These bits of metal and glass were assembled like a super-Erector set; they did wholly predictable things, marvelous only in their mass but not in their conception—the last was for man, and for man alone.

Thus I was reassured. All went well until late December. After that I no longer had my job.

A week before Christmas, Dr. Golemacher and I had started to put the machine up for the holidays. The campus was silent (the students who do not go home or away for the holidays are apt to be a quiet lot). The Mathematicians were away from their monkish desks. Only a few maintenance men remained; they were in the basement playing cards. It was a pale Friday afternoon; a touch of snow hung in the wan sky.

In the chill vastness of the Room, unattended, lit by a tired sun, Emmy should have looked awesome and cold; instead she looked lonesome and cold. Dr. G. went about securing the dials, flipping the few switches, checking buttons and levers. Suddenly the machine gave a start, a great grunt. A few scattered lights flittered on the panel. Even Dr. G. was taken off guard. He laughed gruffly, with a barely perceptible undertone of relief.

"Nothing. Nothing at all. Just passed in front of a foto cell with this white coat. That's all."

There was an unusual quality of camaraderie in the old man's manner as we went on with the job. Some of the deep loneliness of the Room, perhaps. Soon everything was secured. No current was flowing into the machine, except for the radiant-heating pipes to prevent freezing. We gave everything one last check. I happened to put my hand on the steel panel where the switches were—

Impossible. There was a definite humming—the sound of the machine in operation, although all the switches were clearly off.

Dr. G. was as quick as ever. A wiring error, a leak from somewhere; someone was going to catch hell. His big face was all abstract irritation. But then he saw the lights.

Adam Golemacher was not a dreamy man, but he had built most of Emmy. And that was surely no job for a dead spirit or tight mind. Any mathematician is alert to eternity. No builder ever loses the feel from his fingers of what he has built. Looking up at the lights, Dr. Golemacher clutched my arm. He who disliked personal contact clung to me. The chill silence of the Room became ominous. The tiny lights were flickering on and off in a slow, fumbling series of patterns that seemed to make no sense.

With a grand show of relief I said (too loudly, I found, as

the words crashed tinnily in the big chamber), "Well, we can
be thankful at least that it's no more nursery rhymes. I never
did—"

"Quiet, Dichter, and look there."

Now I could not mistake the pattern; perhaps I had really
known at once and my mind had played for time—time that
was running away. The pattern was simple:

> One and one is two.
> Two and two is four.
> Three and three is six.

—the little sums set forth haltingly, as a child would make
them with marbles. A very small child. But Emmy could do
"sums" beyond the reach of any human brain. Emmy could
do anything . . . *that she was told.*

Dr. Golemacher's heavy face was tired, pinched; the brilliant eyes were filling with sadness. I was taking longer to
understand. The little lights went on with the tables. At seven
times nine they stuttered a bit and came up with sixty-one.
The red light shone weakly; the alarm whispered. Carefully
the lights made up sixty-three and continued.

"Always had trouble with that one myself," the old man
murmured, but he did not smile. We stood side by side before the machine; we seemed to want to be close together.

When the tables ended, the simple tables, there was a halt.
No more advanced ones began. The lights went dark; but
deep within, the illicit power was humming faintly, ponder-
ingly. Dr. Golemacher waited as though he knew what he
was waiting for. I had never noticed before how very old he
was. It had never shown before. Outside, the bare trees stood
like ironwork in the dim, snowy sunlight. The machine
whirred again. A high-pitched sound, wholly unfamiliar.

None of the lights flickered. The keys of the typing attach-
ment at our elbows began to tremble. They jumped, fell
back, jammed, fell back, rose up again. After a while of this,
they began to type out something. The words were slow and
far apart at first, then closer, then hurried. The white tape
rolled from the glass box, looped on the floor at our feet.
First I saw the terrible look in Adam Golemacher's eyes.
Then I saw the words. Over and over again was written in
Emmy's own blue ink, WHO AM I   WHO AM I   WHO AM I   WHO
AM I

Robert Frost

THE BEAR
  (1928)

The bear puts both arms around the tree above her
And draws it down as if it were a lover
And its choke cherries lips to kiss good-bye,
Then lets it snap back upright in the sky.
Her next step rocks a boulder on the wall
(She's making her cross-country in the fall).
Her great weight creaks the barbed-wire in its staples
As she flings over and off down through the maples,
Leaving on one wire tooth a lock of hair.
Such is the uncaged progress of the bear.
The world has room to make a bear feel free;
The universe seems cramped to you and me.
Man acts more like the poor bear in a cage
That all day fights a nervous inward rage,
His mood rejecting all his mind suggests.
He paces back and forth and never rests
The toe-nail click and shuffle of his feet,
The telescope at one end of his beat,
And at the other end the microscope,
Two instruments of nearly equal hope,
And in conjunction giving quite a spread.
Or if he rests from scientific tread,
'Tis only to sit back and sway his head
Through ninety-odd degrees of arc, it seems,
Between two metaphysical extremes.
He sits back on his fundamental butt
With lifted snout and eyes (if any) shut,
(He almost looks religious but he's not),
And back and forth he sways from cheek to cheek,
At one extreme agreeing with one Greek,
At the other agreeing with another Greek
Which may be thought, but only so to speak.
A baggy figure, equally pathetic
When sedentary and when peripatetic.

Walt Whitman

WHEN I HEARD THE LEARN'D ASTRONOMER
(1865)

When I heard the learn'd astronomer,
When the proofs, the figures, were ranged in columns
    before me,
When I was shown the charts and diagrams, to add, divide,
    and measure them,
When I sitting heard the astronomer where he lectured with
    much applause in the lecture-room,
How soon unaccountable I became tired and sick,
Till rising and gliding out I wandered off by myself,
In the mystical moist night-air, and from time to time
Looked up in perfect silence at the stars.

Part II:

THE MACHINE AS FRIEND

Francis Bacon

THE HOUSE OF SALOMON
(1624)

"God bless thee, my son; I will give thee the greatest jewel I have. For I will impart unto thee, for the love of God and men, a relation of the true state of Salomon's House. Son, to make you know the true state of Salomon's House, I will keep this order. First, I will set forth unto you the end of our foundation. Secondly, the preparations and instruments we have for our works. Thirdly, the several employments and functions whereto our fellows are assigned. And fourthly, the ordinances and rites which we observe.

"The End of our Foundation is the knowledge of Causes, and secret motions of things; and the enlarging of the bounds of Human Empire, to the effecting of all things possible.

"The Preparations and Instruments are these. We have large and deep caves of several depths: the deepest are sunk six hundred fathom; and some of them are digged and made under great hills and mountains: so that if you reckon together the depth of the hill and the depth of the cave, they are (some of them) above three miles deep. For we find that the depth of a hill, and the depth of a cave from the flat, is the same thing; both remote alike from the sun and heaven's beams, and from the open air. These caves we call the Lower Region. And we use them for all coagulations, indurations, refrigerations, and conservations of bodies. We use them likewise for the imitation of natural mines; and the producing also of new artificial metals, by compositions and materials which we use, and lay there for many years. We use them also sometimes (which may seem strange), for curing of some diseases, and for prolongation of life in some hermits that choose to live there, well accommodated of all things necessary; and indeed live very long; by whom also we learn many things.

"We have burials in several earths, where we put divers cements, as the Chineses do their porcellain. But we have them in greater variety, and some of them more fine. We have also great variety of composts, and soils, for the making of the earth fruitful.

"We have high towers; the highest about half a mile in

height; and some of them likewise set upon high mountains; so that the vantage of the hill with the tower is in the highest of them three miles at least. And these places we call the Upper Region: accounting the air between the high places and the low, as a Middle Region. We use these towers, according to their several heights and situations, for insolation, refrigeration, conservation; and for the view of divers meteors; as winds, rain, snow, hail; and some of the fiery meteors also. And upon them, in some places, are dwellings of hermits, whom we visit sometimes, and instruct what to observe.

"We have great lakes both salt and fresh, whereof we have use for the fish and fowl. We use them also for burials of some natural bodies: for we find a difference in things buried in earth or in air below the earth, and things buried in water. We have also pools, of which some do strain fresh water out of salt; and others by art do turn fresh water into salt. We have also some rocks in the midst of the sea, and some bays upon the shore, for some works wherein is required the air and vapour of the sea. We have likewise violent streams and cataracts, which serve us for many motions: and likewise engines for multiplying and enforcing of winds, to set also on going divers motions.

"We have also a number of artificial wells and fountains, made in imitation of the natural sources and baths; as tincted upon vitriol, sulphur, steel, brass, lead, nitre, and other minerals. And again we have little wells for infusions of many things, where the waters take the virtue quicker and better than in vessels or basons. And amongst them we have a water which we call Water of Paradise, being, by that we do to it, made very sovereign for health, and prolongation of life.

"We have also great and spacious houses, where we imitate and demonstrate meteors; as snow, hail, rain, some artificial rains of bodies and not of water, thunders, lightnings; also generations of bodies in air; as frogs, flies, and divers others.

"We have also certain chambers, which we call Chambers of Health, where we qualify the air as we think good and proper for the cure of divers diseases, and preservation of health.

"We have also fair and large baths, of several mixtures, for the cure of diseases, and the restoring of man's body from arefaction: and others for the confirming of it in strength of sinews, vital parts, and the very juice and substance of the body.

"We have also large and various orchards and gardens, wherein we do not so much respect beauty, as variety of ground and soil, proper for divers trees and herbs: and some very spacious, where trees and berries are set whereof we make divers kinds of drinks, besides the vineyards. In these we practise likewise all conclusions of grafting and inoculating, as well of wild-trees as fruit-trees, which produceth many effects. And we make (by art) in the same orchards and gardens, trees and flowers to come earlier or later than their seasons; and to come up and bear more speedily than by their natural course they do. We make them also by art greater much than their nature; and their fruit greater and sweeter and of differing taste, smell, colour, and figure, from their nature. And many of them we so order, as they become of medicinal use.

"We have also means to make divers plants rise by mixtures of earths without seeds; and likewise to make divers new plants, differing from the vulgar; and to make one tree or plant turn into another.

"We have also parks and inclosures of all sorts of beasts and birds, which we use not only for view or rareness, but likewise for dissections and trials; that thereby we may take light what may be wrought upon the body of man. Wherein we find many strange effects; as continuing life in them, though divers parts, which you account vital, be perished and taken forth; resuscitating of some that seem dead in appearance; and the like. We try also all poisons and other medicines upon them, as well of chirurgery as physic. But art likewise, we make them greater or taller than their kind is; and contrariwise dwarf them, and stay their growth: we make them more fruitful and bearing than their kind is; and contrariwise barren and not generative. Also we make them differ in colour, shape, activity, many ways. We find means to make commixtures and copulations of different kinds; which have produced many new kinds, and them not barren, as the general opinion is. We make a number of kinds of serpents, worms, flies, fishes, of putrefaction; whereof some are advanced (in effect) to be perfect creatures, like beasts or birds; and have sexes, and do propagate. Neither do we this by chance, but we know beforehand of what matter and commixture what kind of those creatures will arise.

"We have also particular pools, where we make trials upon fishes, as we have said before of beasts and birds.

"We have also places for breed and generation of those kinds of worms and flies which are of special use; such as are with you your silk-worms and bees.

"I will not hold you long with recounting of our brew-houses, bake-houses, and kitchens, where are made divers drinks, breads, and meats, rare and of special effects. Wines we have of grapes; and drinks of other juice of fruits, of grains, and of roots: and of mixtures with honey, sugar, manna, and fruits dried and decocted. Also of the tears or woundings of trees, and of the pulp of canes. And these drinks are of several ages, some to the age or last of forty years. We have drinks also brewed with several herbs, and roots, and spices; yea with several fleshes, and white meats; whereof some of the drinks are such, as they are in effect meat and drink both: so that divers, especially in age, do desire to live with them, with little or no meat or bread. And above all, we strive to have drinks of extreme thin parts, to insinuate into the body, and yet without all biting, sharpness, or fretting; insomuch as some of them put upon the back of your hand will, with a little stay, pass through to the palm, and yet taste mild to the mouth. We have also waters which we ripen in that fashion, as they become nourishing; so that they are indeed excellent drink; and many will use no other. Breads we have of several grains, roots, and kernels; yea and some of flesh and fish dried; with divers kinds of leavenings and seasonings: so that some do extremely move appetites; some do nourish so, as divers do live of them, without any other meat; who live very long. So for meats, we have some of them so beaten and made tender and mortified, yet without all corrupting, as a weak heat of the stomach will turn them into good chylus, as well as a strong heat would meat otherwise prepared. We have some meats also and breads and drinks, which taken by men enable them to fast long after; and some other, that used make the very flesh of men's bodies sensibly more hard and tough, and their strength far greater than otherwise it would be.

"We have dispensatories, or shops of medicines. Wherein you may easily think, if we have such variety of plants and living creatures more than you have in Europe (for we know what you have), the simples, drugs, and ingredients of medicines, must likewise be in so much the greater variety. We have them likewise of divers ages, and long fermentations. And for their preparations, we have not only all manner of exquisite distillations and separations, and especially by gentle heats and percolations through divers strainers, yea and substances; but also exact forms of composition, whereby they incorporate almost, as they were natural simples.

"We have also divers mechanical arts, which you have not; and stuffs made by them; as papers, linen, silks, tissues; dainty works of feathers of wonderful lustre; excellent dyes, and many others; and shops likewise, as well for such as are not brought into vulgar use amongst us as for those that are. For you must know that of the things before recited, many of them are grown into use throughout the kingdom; but yet if they did flow from our invention, we have of them also for patterns and principals.

"We have also furnaces of great diversities, and that keep great diversity of heats; fierce and quick; strong and constant; soft and mild; blown, quiet; dry, moist; and the like. But above all, we have heats in imitation of the sun's and heavenly bodies' heats, that pass divers inequalities and (as it were) orbs, progresses, and returns, whereby we produce admirable effects. Besides, we have heats of dungs, and of bellies and maws of living creatures, and of their bloods and bodies; and of hays and herbs laid up moist; of lime unquenched; and such like. Instruments also which generate heat only by motion. And farther, places for strong insolations; and again, places under the earth, which by nature or art yield heat. These divers heats we use, as the nature of the operation which we intend requireth.

"We have also perspective-houses, where we make demonstrations of all lights and radiations; and of all colours; and out of things uncoloured and transparent, we can represent unto you all several colours; not in rain-bows, as it is in gems and prisms, but of themselves single. We represent also all multiplications of light, which we carry to great distance, and make so sharp as to discern small points and lines; also all colorations of light: all delusions and deceits of the sight, in figures, magnitudes, motions, colours: all demonstrations of shadows. We find also divers means, yet unknown to you, of producing of light originally from divers bodies. We procure means of seeing objects afar off; as is the heaven and remote places; and represent things near as afar off, and things afar off as near; making feigned distances. We have also helps for the sight, far above spectacles and glasses in use. We have also glasses and means to see small and minute bodies perfectly and distinctly; as the shapes and colours of small flies and worms, grains and flaws in gems, which cannot otherwise be seen; observations in urine and blood, not otherwise to be seen. We make artificial rain-bows, halos, and circles about light. We represent also all manner of reflexions, refractions, and multiplications of visual beams of objects.

"We have also precious stones of all kinds, many of them of great beauty, and to you unknown; crystals likewise; and glasses of divers kinds; and amongst them some of metals vitrificated, and other materials besides those of which you make glass. Also a number of fossils, and imperfect minerals, which you have not. Likewise loadstones of prodigious virtue; and other rare stones, both natural and artificial.

"We have also sound-houses, where we practise and demonstrate all sounds, and their generation. We have harmonies which you have not, of quarter-sounds, and lesser slides of sounds. Divers instruments of music likewise to you unknown, some sweeter than any you have; together with bells and rings that are dainty and sweet. We represent small sounds as great and deep; likewise great sounds extenuate and sharp; we make divers tremblings and warblings of sounds, which in their original are entire. We represent and imitate all articulate sounds and letters, and the voices and notes of beasts and birds. We have certain helps which set to the ear do further the hearing greatly. We have also divers strange and artificial echos, reflecting the voice many times, and as it were tossing it: and some that give back the voice louder than it came; some shriller, and some deeper; yea, some rendering the voice differing in the letters or articulate sound from that they receive. We have also means to convey sounds in trunks and pipes, in strange lines and distances.

"We have also perfume-houses; wherewith we join also practices of taste. We multiply smells, which may seem strange. We imitate smells, making all smells to breathe out of other mixtures than those that give them. We make divers imitations of taste likewise, so that they will deceive any man's taste. And in this house we contain also a confiture-house; where we make all sweet-meats, dry and moist, and divers pleasant wines, milks, broths, and sallets, in far greater variety than you have.

"We have also engine-houses, where are prepared engines and instruments for all sorts of motions. There we imitate and practise to make swifter motions than any you have, either out of your muskets or any engine that you have; and to make them and multiply them more easily, and with small force, by wheels and other means: and to make them stronger, and more violent that yours are; exceeding your greatest cannons and basilisks. We represent also ordnance and instruments of war, and engines of all kinds: and likewise new mixtures and compositions of gun-powder, wildfires burning in water, and unquenchable. Also fire-works of all variety both for pleasure and use. We imitate also flights of birds; we have some degrees of flying in the air; we have ships and boats for going under water, and brooking of seas; also swimming-girdles and supporters. We have divers curious clocks, and other like motions of return, and some perpetual motions. We imitate also motions of living creatures, by images of men, beasts, birds, fishes, and serpents. We have also a great number of other various motions, strange for equality, fineness, and subtilty.

"We have also a mathematical house, where are represented all instruments, as well as geometry as astronomy, exquisitely made.

"We have also houses of deceits of the senses; where we represent all manner of feats of juggling, false apparitions, impostures, and illusions; and their fallacies. And surely you will easily believe that we that have so many things truly natural which induce admiration, could in a world of particulars deceive the senses, if we would disguise those things and labour to make them seem more miraculous. But we do hate all impostures and lies: insomuch as we have severely forbidden it to our fellows, under pain of ignominy and fines, that they do not shew any natural work or thing, adorned or swelling; but only pure as it is, and without all affectation of strangeness.

"These are (my son) the riches of Salomon's House.

"For the several employments and offices of our fellows; we have twelve that sail into foreign countries, under the names of other nations (for our own we conceal); who bring us the books, and abstracts, and patterns of experiments of all other parts. These we call Merchants of Light.

"We have three that collect the experiments which are in all books. These we call Depredators.

"We have three that collect the experiments of all mechanical arts; and also of liberal sciences; and also of practices which are not brought into arts. These we call Mystery-men.

"We have three that try new experiments, such as themselves think good. These we call Pioners or Miners.

"We have three that draw the experiments of the former four into titles and tables, to give the better light for the drawing of observations and axioms out of them. These we call Compilers.

"We have three that bend themselves, looking into the experiments of their fellows, and cast about how to draw out of them things of use and practice for man's life, and knowledge as well for works as for plain demonstration of causes, means of natural divinations, and the easy and clear discovery of the virtues and parts of bodies. These we call Dowry-men or Benefactors.

"Then after divers meetings and consults of our whole number, to consider of the former labours and collections, we have three that take care, out of them, to direct new experiments, of a higher light, more penetrating into nature than the former. These we call Lamps.

"We have three others that do execute the experiments so directed, and report them. These we call Inoculators.

"Lastly, we have three that raise the former discoveries by experiments into greater observations, axioms, and aphorisms. These we call Interpreters of Nature.

"We have also, as you must think, novices and apprentices, that the succession of the former employed men do not fail; besides a great number of servants and attendants, men and women. And this we do also: we have consultations, which of the inventions and experiences which we have discovered shall be published, and which not: and take all an oath of secrecy, for the concealing of those which we think fit to keep secret: though some of those we do reveal sometimes to the state, and some not.

"For our ordinances and rites: we have two very long and fair galleries: in one of these we place patterns and samples of all manner of the more rare and excellent inventions: in the other we place the statua's of all principal inventors. There we have the statua of your Columbus, that discovered the West Indies: also the inventor of ships: your monk that was the inventor of ordnance and of gunpowder: the inventor of music: the inventor of letters: the inventor of printing: the inventor of observations of astronomy: the inventor of works in metal: the inventor of glass: the inventor of silk of the worm: the inventor of wine: the inventor of corn and bread: the inventor of sugars: and all these by more certain tradition than you have. Then have we divers inventors of our own, of excellent works; which since you have not seen, it were too long to make descriptions of them; and besides, in the right understanding of those descriptions you might easily err. For upon every invention of value we erect a statua to the inventor, and give him a liberal and honourable reward. These statua's are some of brass; some of marble and touch-stone; some of cedar and other special woods gilt and adorned: some of iron; some of silver; some of gold.

"We have certain hymns and services, which we say daily, of laud and thanks to God for his marvellous works: and forms of prayers, imploring his aid and blessing for the illumination of our labours, and the turning of them into good and holy uses.

"Lastly, we have circuits or visits of divers principal cities of the kingdom; where, as it cometh to pass, we do publish such new profitable inventions as we think good. And we do also declare natural divinations of diseases, plagues, swarms of hurtful creatures, scarcity, tempests, earthquakes, great inundations, comets, temperature of the year, and divers other things; and we give counsel thereupon what the people shall do for the prevention and remedy of them."

And when he had said this, he stood up; and I, as I had been taught, kneeled down; and he laid his right hand upon my head, and said; "God bless thee, my son, and God bless this relation which I have made. I give thee leave to publish it for the good of other nations; for we here are in God's bosom, a land unknown." And so he left me; having assigned a value of about two thousand ducats, for a bounty to me and my fellows. For they give great largesses where they come upon all occasions.

[THE REST WAS NOT PERFECTED.]

Carl Sandburg

THE HAMMER
(1910)

> I have seen
> The old gods go
> And the new gods come.
>
> Day by day
> And year by year
> The idols fall
> And the idols rise.
>
> Today
> I worship the hammer.

Adam Smith

THE DIVISION OF LABOUR
(1776)

EVERY BODY must be sensible how much labour is facilitated and abridged by the application of proper machinery. It is unnecessary to give any example. I shall only observe, therefore, that the invention of all those machines by which labour is so much facilitated and abridged seems to have been originally owing to the division of labour. Men are much more likely to discover easier and readier methods of attaining any object, when the whole attention of their minds is directed towards that single object, than when it is dissipated among a great variety of things. But in consequence of the division of labour, the whole of every man's attention comes naturally to be directed towards some one very simple object. It is naturally to be expected, therefore, that some one or other of those who are employed in each particular branch of labour should soon find out easier and readier methods of performing their own particular work, wherever the nature of it admits of such improvement. A great part of the machines made use of in those manufactures in which labour is most subdivided, were originally the inventions of common workmen, who, being each of them employed in some very simple operation, naturally turned their thoughts towards finding out easier and readier methods of performing it. Whoever has been much accustomed to visit such manufactures must frequently have been shewn very pretty machines, which were the inventions of such workmen, in order to facilitate and quicken their own particular part of the work. In the first fire-engines, a boy was constantly employed to open and shut alternately the communication between the boiler and the cylinder, according as the piston either ascended or descended. One of those boys, who loved to play with his companions, observed that, by tying a string from the handle of the valve which opened this communication to another part of the machine, the valve would open and shut without his assistance, and leave him at liberty to divert himself with his play-fellows. One of the greatest improvements that has been made upon this machine, since it was first invented, was in this manner the discovery of a boy who wanted to save his own labour.

All the improvements in machinery, however, have by no means been the inventions of those who had occasion to use the machines. Many improvements have been made by the ingenuity of the makers of the machines, when to make them became the business of a peculiar trade; and some by that of those who are called philosophers or men of speculation, whose trade it is not to do any thing, but to observe every thing; and who, upon that account, are often capable of combining together the powers of the most distant and dissimilar objects. In the progress of society, philosophy or speculation becomes, like every other employment, the principal or sole trade and occupation of a particular class of citizens. Like every other employment too, it is subdivided into a great number of different branches, each of which affords occupation to a peculiar tribe or class of philosophers; and this subdivision of employment in philosophy, as well as in every other business, improves dexterity, and saves time. Each individual becomes more expert in his own peculiar branch, more work is done upon the whole, and the quantity of science is considerably increased by it.

It is the great multiplication of the productions of all the different arts, in consequence of the division of labour, which occasions, in a well-governed society, that universal opulence which extends itself to the lowest ranks of the people. Every workman has a great quantity of his own work to dispose of beyond what he himself has occasion for; and every other workman being exactly in the same situation, he is enabled to exchange a great quantity of his own goods for a great quantity, or, what comes to the same thing, for the price of a great quantity of theirs. He supplies them abundantly with what they have occasion for, and they accommodate him as amply with what he has occasion for, and a general plenty diffuses itself through all the different ranks of the society.

Observe the accommodation of the most common artificer or day-labourer in a civilized and thriving country, and you will perceive that the number of people of whose industry a part, though but a small part, has been employed in procuring him this accommodation, exceeds all computation. The woollen coat, for example, which covers the day-labourer, as coarse and rough as it may appear, is the produce of the joint labour of a great multitude of workmen. The shepherd, the sorter of the wool, the wool-comber or carder, the dyer, the scribbler, the spinner, the weaver, the fuller, the dresser, with many others, must all join their different arts in order to complete even this homely production. How many merchants and carriers, besides, must have been employed in transporting the materials from some of those workmen to others who often live in a very distant part of the country! How much commerce and navigation in particular, how many ship-builders, sailors, sail-makers, rope-makers, must have been employed in order to bring together the different drugs made use of by the dyer, which often come from the remotest corners of the world! What a variety of labour too is necessary in order to produce the tools of the meanest of those workmen! To say nothing of such complicated machines as the ship of the sailor, the mill of the fuller, or even the loom of the weaver, let us consider only what a variety of labour is requisite in order to form that very simple machine, the shears with which the shepherd clips the wool. The miner, the builder of the furnace for smelting the ore, the feller of the timber, the burner of the charcoal to be made use of in the smelting-house, the brick-maker, the brick-layer, the workmen who attend the furnace, the mill-wright, the forger, the smith, must all of them join their different arts in order to produce them. Were we to examine, in the same manner, all the different parts of his dress and household furniture, the coarse linen shirt which he wears next his skin, the shoes which cover his feet, the bed which he lies on, and all the different parts which compose it, the kitchen-grate at which he prepares his victuals, the coals which he makes use of for that purpose, dug from the bowels of the earth, and brought to him perhaps by a long sea and a long land carriage, all the other utensils of his kitchen, all the furniture of his table, the knives and forks, the earthen or pewter plates upon which he serves up and divides his victuals, the different hands employed in preparing his bread and his beer, the glass window which lets in the heat and the light, and keeps out the wind and the rain, with all the knowledge and art requisite for preparing that beautiful and happy invention, without which these northern parts of the world could scarce have afforded a very comfortable habitation, together with the tools of all the different workmen employed in producing those different conveniences; if we examine, I say, all these things, and consider what a variety of labour is employed about each of them, we shall be sensible that without the assistance and co-operation of many thousands, the very meanest person in a civilized country could not be provided, even according to, what we very falsely imagine, the easy and simple manner in which he is commonly accommodated. Compared, indeed, with the more extravagant luxury of the great, his accommodation must no doubt appear extremely simple and easy; and yet it may be true, perhaps, that the accommodation of an European prince does not always so much exceed that of an industrious and frugal peasant, as the accommodation of the latter exceeds that of many an African king, the absolute master of the lives and liberties of ten thousand naked savages.

Samuel Miller

MECHANIC ARTS
   (1803)

THE PROGRESS of civilized man in the mechanic arts, during the last hundred years, has been astonishingly great. To attempt a review, in detail, even of the principal inventions, discoveries and improvements, which have taken place, during the period in question, in this boundless field for the exertion of genius and enterprise, would swell this section into many volumes. But happily the minds of most readers are so conversant with many of the objects which demand attention, in this department of the present work, that such minuteness of detail is as unnecessary as it is impossible.

The modern discoveries in *Mechanical Philosophy* have led to great and important improvements in the mechanic arts. The subserviency of those discoveries to the progress of many branches of art will readily appear from the perusal of the chapter which relates to them. That they have contributed, and will probably yet contribute, in a considerable degree, to the abridgement of labour, to the convenience and profit of artists, and to the excellence and beauty of manufactures, is too obvious to require particular explanation.

The great discoveries which the philosophers of the last century made in *Chemistry* may also be considered as rendering very distinguished service to the mechanic arts. On the manufacture of all *metallic* and *earthen* wares, the improvements in chemistry have shed important light; and indeed to all the arts in the different processes of which heat, solution, composition, distillation, fermentation, and precipitation are necessary, chemical philosophy has furnished valuable aid.

Never were manufactures carried on upon so *large a scale* as during the eighteenth century, especially toward the close of it. The number of hands, and the amount of capital employed in various branches of manufacture in Europe, may be pronounced, without hesitation, greatly to exceed the largest establishments of any former times.

It may also be asserted that manufactures in general were never carried on with so much expedition and cheapness, or with so much elegance of workmanship, as at the close of the period under review. It is true, these circumstances have led to an increased *slightness*, and the want of *durability*, particularly in some articles of modern manufacture; but in many more cases, a great improvement in *quality*, as well as in *elegance*, has taken place.

The *division* and *abridgement of labour* were carried to a greater length in the course of the last age than in any preceding period. The influence of both these circumstances in promoting the mechanic arts, will be readily appreciated by every intelligent reader.

But besides these general remarks, it will be proper to take notice of some of the principal inventions and improvements of the mechanical kind, by which the last age is distinguished.

The different kinds of machinery for *Carding* and *Spinning Cotton*, which modern times have produced, have proved a source of incalculable advantage to manufacturers, and do honour to the age. Less than forty years ago, the only machine much used for reducing cotton wool into yarn, was the *One-thread wheel.* Other methods indeed, had been thought of, and proposed for promoting a more easy and expeditious process; but without any extensive or permanent success. At length, about the year 1767, Mr. JAMES HARGRAVE, an English weaver, constructed a machine, by means of which any number of threads, from twenty to eighty, might be spun at once, and for which he obtained a patent. This machine is called a *Jenny*, and deservedly holds a high place among modern inventions. The astonishing abridgement of labour which it produces has been too much and generally celebrated to require illustration here. Soon after the invention of this machine, Mr. HARGRAVE contrived a new method of *carding* cotton, more easy and expeditious than the old way of carding by the hand, which was now found inadequate to the rapid progress and large demands of the improved mode of spinning. He was succeeded by several other ingenious artists, who laboured with success, and who produced that expeditious plan of carding, by what are commonly called *Cylinder-cards,* which is now so extensively and profitably practised.

The next and most remarkable improvements in this kind of machinery were made by Mr. ARKWRIGHT, afterwards Sir RICHARD ARKWRIGHT, also of Great-Britain. He laid before the public his new method of spinning cotton, in 1768, for which he obtained a patent in 1769. In 1775 he also obtained patents for several engines which he had constructed to prepare the materials for spinning. The result of his different inventions is a combination of machinery, impelled by horses, water, or steam, according to circumstances, by which cotton is *carded, roved* and *spun* with wonderful expedition, and with great exactness and equality.[1]

The effects produced by these splendid improvements, in extending the cotton manufactures of Great-Britain, and in rendering them a source of national wealth and aggrandizement, are generally known. The number of cotton mills erected within a few years past; the great number of hands to which they afford employment; the immense capitals devoted to them; and their great productiveness, present a spectacle altogether unparalleled in history.

The first British *Calicoes* were made in Lancashire, about the year 1772. The manufacture of *Muslins* was first successfully introduced into that country in 1781. Both these branches of manufacture, which were before chiefly confined to India, have lately gained an extension, and assumed a consequence which must render their introduction a most important era in the history of Great-Britain.

Machines for carding and spinning cotton were introduced into several parts of the United States during the last fifteen years of the century under review. But, like most other enterprises in the manufacturing line, undertaken in our country, they have not been pursued either so extensively or so profitably as could be wished.

In this connection it will be proper to take some notice of two American inventions, for facilitating the making of wool and cotton *Cards*. About sixteen or seventeen years ago, a machine was invented in Massachusetts, for cutting and bending wire in a state completely prepared for *sticking* cards.[2] Before this time the cards used in the United States were imported from Europe. Ever since a sufficient quantity has been manufactured in our own country to supply its demands, and, at a late period, for exportation to a considerable amount. In 1797, Mr. AMOS WHITTEMORE, of Cambridge, in Massachusetts, invented a machine, which, by a simple operation, bends, cuts, and sticks card teeth, by the aid of which a dozen pairs of cards can be furnished in less time than was formerly required to make a single pair.[3]

Allied to the inventions above enumerated are the improvements in the art of *Weaving* which modern times have produced. Among these, perhaps none is of more importance than the *Flying Shuttle*, lately introduced by the artists of Great-Britain. Previous to the introduction of this contrivance, when wide cloth was woven it was necessary to employ two or more hands to execute the work. The same task can now be executed by one person, and with much more convenience and expedition than formerly.

It was before remarked that *Steam Engines* were scarcely at all known prior to the eighteenth century. To the honour of inventing and perfecting this kind of machinery the artists of Great-Britain are entitled. The honour particularly due to Messrs. NEWCOMEN, BEIGHTON, and WATT, on this subject, has been acknowledged in a former chapter. The force of *Steam* has been applied, during the period under review, to the turning of mills for almost every purpose; and there is no doubt that the machines moved by this agent are the most powerful ever formed by the art of man.[4]

In the erection of *Bridges*, modern artists have displayed unprecedented boldness and enterprise. The first bridge constructed of *cast iron* was produced in the eighteenth century. This was erected over the river Severn, in Shropshire, South-Britain, in 1779, by Mr. A. DARLEY, an ingenious iron-master, assisted by the exertions of Mr. J. WILKINSON, of the same profession. The second *iron* bridge was constructed on a larger scale, over the same river, in 1796, upon a new plan, by Mr. THELFORD. A third, on a still larger and more daring scale, was built over the river Wear, in Durham, a short time afterwards, by ROWLAND BURDON, ESQ. To these may be added the *wooden* bridges, of several kinds, and on various new constructions, which have been invented in the course of a few years past, both in Europe and America, and which have proved sources of great public utility.

In the construction of *Mills*, improvements no less remarkable and important have been made, within the period in question. Of these, some have arisen from the new light lately thrown upon the laws of *hydraulics;* and others from the ingenuity and enterprise of practical artists. The numerous experiments and discoveries, and the learned writings which have been given to the world, in the course of the century, on this subject, by DESAGULIERS, EMERSON, SMEATON, BARKER, and BURNS, of Great-Britain; by BELIDOR, DE PARCIEUX, and others, of France; by BERNOULLI, of Switzerland; by LAMBERT and KARSTNER, of Germany; and by

ELVIUS, of Sweden, make a most interesting part of the mechanical history of the age.

Equally worthy of attention are the successive inventions and improvements of modern artists, in the construction of all kinds of *Wheel Carriages*. To enumerate these, and to attempt to give a list of their authors, would be an endless task. Suffice it to say, that the superiority of modern wheel-carriages over those possessed by our predecessors, in lightness, elegance, beauty of form, and convenience, is very great, and constitutes one of the mechanical honours of the age.

In the art of *Coining* several important inventions have been produced, in the course of the last century, which are worthy of being remembered. Probably the most conspicuous and valuable of these is that by Mr. BOULTON, an artist near Birmingham, in Great-Britain. "He has lately constructed a most magnificent apparatus for coining, which has cost him some thousand pounds. The whole machinery is moved by an improved steam-engine, which rolls the copper for half-pence finer than copper has before been rolled for making money; it works the coupoirs or screw-presses for cutting out the circular pieces of copper, and coins both the faces and edges of the money at the same time, with such superior excellence, and cheapness of workmanship, as well as with marks of such powerful machinery, as must totally prevent clandestine imitation, and, in consequence, save many lives from the hand of the executioner. By this machinery four boys, of ten or twelve years of age, are capable of striking thirty thousand guineas in an hour, and the machine itself keeps an unerring account of the pieces struck."[5]

Several modern improvements in the art of *Printing* deserve a place in this imperfect list. The first worthy of being mentioned is the *Stereotype*[6] plan of printing, which has lately become so fashionable, especially in France. This plan was first invented in 1725, by Mr. GED, a goldsmith, of Edinburgh, who, among other books, printed a very neat edition of *Sallust*,[7] in his new method. Owing, however, either to some defect in the plan, or to the want of skill in the execution of his specimen, Mr. GED's invention seems to have attracted but little notice. In 1782 Mr. ALEXANDER TILLOCH, of Great-Britain, revived, or rather re-discovered this art; for he is said to have been ignorant of GED's contrivance till long after he had announced his own. The subsequent year he took out a patent for it, in conjunction with Mr. ANDREW FOULIS, printer to the University of Glasgow. About the year 1789 M. DIDOT, of France, seems to have invented, a third time, this valuable art, and to have contrived several important improvements, which render this mode much more convenient and useful than that of any of his predecessors.[8] The *Stereotype* plan of printing is most happily calculated to secure accuracy in numerical tables, and in books of a similar kind. Indeed, for publishing all works of classical character, extensive sale, and permanent demand, it is an invaluable acquisition. The beautiful editions of several Greek and Roman classics, which have been executed in this manner, by the French artist above mentioned, are well known to be favourable specimens of this far-famed improvement.

In a considerable degree resembling the *Stereotype,* is the *Logographic* mode of printing, an invention announced in 1783, by Mr. H. JOHNSON, of Great-Britain. In this invention the types for printing, instead of answering to *single letters,* are made to correspond to *whole words;* a circumstance which points out the etymology of the name. The advantages of this new mode are said to be these: that the compositor has less charged upon his memory than in the common way; that he is much less liable to error; that he saves time, inasmuch as the type of each word is as easily and as readily set as that of a single letter; that the distribution afterwards is more simple, easy and expeditious; and that no extraordinary expense, nor greater number of types is required in this than in the common mode of printing.[9]

Another improvement in the art of printing, which belongs to the last age, is the kind of impression called *Fac-simile,* or forming the types in such a manner as precisely to resemble the manuscript intended to be copied. The first approach to this method of printing was the Medicean Virgil, printed at Florence, in 1741. This, however, though an approximation to the plan, was by no means, strictly speaking, what is now meant by *fac-simile* printing, as the resemblance of the manuscript was not complete. The first great work of this kind was the New Testament, of the Alexandrian MS. in the British Museum, published by Dr. WOIDE, in 1786, which exhibits its prototype to a degree of similarity scarcely credible. Since that time, a few other works, of considerable extent, have been published on the same plan, particularly Dr. KIPLING's edition of the four Gospels and the Acts of the Apostles, according to the MS. of BEZA. But, for the most part, the practice in question has been confined to manuscripts of small extent, and to objects of especial curiosity.[10]

The art of forming *types*, for printing, has also received considerable improvement in the course of the eighteenth century. Among the numerous authors of these, the celebrated JOHN BASKERVILLE, an English artist, deserves particular notice. The diligence, zeal, and success with which he applied himself to improve the mode of founding types, and to give them a more beautiful form, are well known; as well as the numerous editions which he was enabled to give of important works, particularly the Latin classics, in a style of elegance far surpassing every thing of the kind which had before issued from the press. Various inventions, to abridge labour in the business of letter-foundery, have also been made within this period; of these, perhaps, few are entitled to be mentioned with more respect than that of Mr. APOLLOS KINSLEY, an ingenious American, who is said to have devised a method of abbreviating, to an astonishing degree the necessary process in this manufacture.[11]

The discoveries made within a few years past in the philosophy of *Tanning* have greatly facilitated the process, and promoted the interests of that important art. For these the public are indebted to Dr. MACBRIDE, Messrs. FAY, SEGUIN, DESMOND, and several others.

The still more numerous and radical improvements which late years have produced in the art of *Brewing* are no less worthy of notice. The successive investigations, and valuable writings of Sir ROBERT MURRAY, M. COMBRUNE, Mr. RICHARDSON, Mr. KER, and Mr. LONG, on this subject, are worthy of respectful notice in marking the progress of the age under review.

In the art of *Bleaching*, also, important discoveries and improvements were made, in the course of the last age, especially toward the close of it. The speculations and experiments of Drs. HOME and BLACK, and Mr. WATT, of Great-Britain; and of Messrs. CHAPTAL, BERTHOLLET, PAJOT DE CHARMES, and BEAUME, of France; besides those of many other chemists and practical artists, have contributed to place this art, so interesting to manufacturers, entirely on a new footing, within a few years past. Instead of the old process, which ordinarily employed a number of weeks, and even several months, recent discoveries have furnished means of reducing cloth to a state of beautiful whiteness in a few hours.

In the art of *Dyeing* no less signal progress has been made within a few years. The learned investigations and laborious experiments which have been successively instituted for the improvement of this art, by DUFAY, HELLOT, MACQUER, D'APLIGNY, and BERTHOLLET, of France; and by Messrs. DELAVAL and HENRY, and Dr. BANCROFT,[12] and others, of Great-Britain, are very honourably displayed in their respective works, and have been productive of great utility to several of the manufacturing classes of the community.

In the eighteenth century the first *Porcelain ware* ever manufactured in Europe was produced. The account of the invention is curious. JOHN FREDERICK BÖTTGER, a German, about the year 1706, believed, or pretended, that he had learned the art of transmuting various substances into gold, from a goldsmith at Berlin. He went into Saxony, and was allowed all the requisite materials, and every assistance necessary for prosecuting his operations, by certain persons who thought proper to encourage him. For several years he laboured in vain. At last, imputing his want of success to the crucibles not being of a proper quality, he attempted to make these vessels himself, of a hard and durable kind; and in this attempt he accidentally produced porcelain.[13] The manufacture of this article was afterwards extended to France, Italy, and Great-Britain. But of all the countries of Europe, France produces porcelain in the greatest quantity, and of the best quality.

For many of the improvements lately made in several of the manufactures last mentioned, we are much indebted to modern *Chemistry*. The important aid furnished to these, and a multitude of other mechanical operations, by the facts and principles brought to light in the course of recent chemical inquiries, is too well known to require explanation.

The manufacture of *Metallic Wares*, in modern times, has made astonishing progress, both in extent and refinement. In Great-Britain especially, those branches of the mechanic arts which belong to metallic substances, and particularly the manufactures of *Iron,* have received the greatest degree of improvement. The workmen, of that country, in this department of art, have been enabled, within a few years past, by various inventions and discoveries, to unite rapidity of execution, elegance of form and polish, excellence of quality, and cheapness of price, in their manufactures, to a degree without example in the history of human ingenuity.

But to recite the mechanical inventions and improvements which belong to the period under review would be a task almost without limits. To this class belong the ingenious experiments and valuable discoveries of Mr. WEDGWOOD, in the art of *Pottery,* and in various kinds of manufactures in *Clay;* the invention of a new and more durable kind of *Stucco* than had ever been used before, by Mr. HIGGINS; the numerous improvements which have been made in the composition and manufacture of *Glass;* the almost countless new plans for improving the construction of *Lamps,* by ARGAND and others; the various modes proposed for rendering *Stoves* and *Fireplaces* more economical and comfortable, by FRANKLIN, RITTENHOUSE, RUMFORD, and PEALE; the new degrees of perfection to which *Clocks* and other *Chronometers* have been carried;[14] the invention of new vegetable materials for the formation of *Paper,* more plentiful, and easy of access than those of which alone it had been before made;[15] the method of *renovating old paper,* by a chemical process, cleansing it from all foreign matter, discharging the ink, and rendering it again fit to receive new impressions; the methods which have been devised for *multiplying copies* of prints and manuscripts, with ease, expedition, and cheapness; the various plans for *cutting Nails,* instead of the old and tedious method of forming them on the anvil, besides a multitude of others, scarcely, if at all, less important, which time would fail to enumerate.

Finally, the effects of the various improvements which have been introduced into every department of the mechanic arts, during the last age, in promoting the conveniency, cheapness, and elegance of *living,* will readily occur to the most careless observer. No one will say that it indicates undue partiality to our own times to assert, that at no period of the world was the *art of living,* especially the comforts and conveniences of domestic life, ever on so advantageous a footing as at present. Ancient writers, indeed, have given highly coloured pictures of the magnificence and sensuality which reigned at different times, in *Greece* and *Rome;* and in more modern days we read many descriptions of luxury which superficial thinkers would suppose to indicate much greater plenty, comfort, and spendour, than are now commonly enjoyed. But they are, for the most part, descriptions of plenty without taste, and of luxury without enjoyment. When we compare the ancient modes of living, with the dress,[16] the furniture, the equipage, the conveniences of travelling, and the incomparably greater ease with which the same amount of comfortable accommodation may be obtained at present, none can hesitate to give a decided preference, in all these respects, to modern times. Perhaps it would not be extravagant to say that many of the higher orders of mechanics and day labourers now wear better clothes, and live, not more plentifully, but in some respects more conveniently, more neatly, and with more true taste, than many princes and kings were in the habit of doing two centuries ago, and in a manner quite as pleasant as multitudes of a rank far superior to themselves, at a later period. In short, the remarkable and unprecedented union of neatness and simplicity, cheapness and elegance, which has been exhibited, in the art of living, within the last thirty or forty years, is, at once, a testimony of the rapid improvement of the mechanic arts, and one of the most unquestionable points in which we may claim a superiority over our predecessors.

NOTES

[1] Sir RICHARD ARKWRIGHT was bred a barber; and was, in the early part of his life, in very low circumstances. He rose in fortune and in fame rapidly; and, in 1793, died at his manufactory in Derbyshire, leaving property to the amount of £500,000 sterling, or 2,225,000 dollars. HARDIE's *Biographical Dictionary*.

[2] Two persons claimed the invention of this machine, viz. FOSTER and M'CLINCH. The latter had his machine first in use, being more of a practical mechanic; but it was said that he had privately obtained a sight of FOSTER's work, who first planned the machinery. As it is not easy to ascertain the precise truth of this question, so it is of no importance to the public to which of these gentlemen the honour belongs.

[3] In September, 1799, WILLIAM WHITTEMORE and Co. commenced the manufacture of cards with this machine, in Cambridge. There are now twenty-three machines of this kind in operation at the same manufactory, which are able to furnish *two hundred dozen pairs* of cards, on an average, every week.

[4] One of these engines, as improved by Mr. WATT, and employed for draining the deep mines of Cornwall, works a pump of eighteen inches diameter, and upwards of 100 fathom, or 600 feet high, at the rate of ten to twelve strokes, of seven feet long each, in a minute, and with one-fifth part of the fuel that a common engine would take to do the same work. The power of this engine may be more easily comprehended by saying that it can raise a weight equal to 81,000 lbs. eighty feet high in a minute,

which is equal to the combined action of 200 good horses. See *Botanic Garden, Additional Notes,* p. 155, New-York edition.

⁵ DARWIN's *Botanic Garden,* part i. canto 1, note.

⁶ This word, which M. DIDOT of France, seems to have first employed, is derived from the Greek words, ϛερεος, *solidus,* and τυπσ; *typus,* denoting that the types are soldered, or otherwise connected together.

⁷ In the title page of this edition there are the following words, viz., *Edinburghi: Gulielmus Ged, aurifaber Edinensis, non typis mobilibus, ut vulga fieri solet: sed tabellis seu laminis fusis, excudebat.*

⁸ The *Stereotype* mode of printing adopted by DIDOT is as follows. The page is first set up in moveable types; a mould or impression is then taken of the page with any suitable plastic material; and afterwards as many solid pages are cast from the mould as may be wanted. The plan adopted by GED and others seems to have been different. After setting up the page with moveable types, they soldered them together, and thus formed a permanent page, from which as many copies might be stricken as were desired. The comparative merits of these different plans will readily present themselves to the intelligent reader.

⁹ *Encyclopædia,* Art. *Logography.*

¹⁰ *Monthly Review,* of London, vol. xii. N. S. p. 241.

¹¹ *American Review, and Literary Journal,* vol. i. No. 1.

¹² *Experimental Researches concerning the Philosophy of Permanent Colours,* by E. BANCROFT, M.D. &C., 1794.

¹³ *Monthly Review,* vol. vi. N. S. p. 545.

¹⁴ Among the several improvers of *Time-keepers,* during the last age, HARRISON, ARNOLD, and KENDALL were before mentioned as deserving particular praise. The first named was bred a carpenter, and began by making wooden clocks. It is unnecessary to add that by the force of his genius he rose to the highest eminence as an artist.

¹⁵ There is a particular reference here to the discovery of the Rev. Mr. SENGER, of Germany, that a certain aquatic plant, called by LINNAEUS *Conferva Rivularis,* is capable of being manufactured into paper, of as excellent a quality as that made of rags, and at less expense. The same discovery was made a short time afterwards by ROBERT R. LIVINGSTON, Esq. late Chancellor of the State of New-York, and now Minister Plenipotentiary to the French Republic, without any knowledge of what Mr. SENGER had done; and indeed some time before the German discovery had been communicated to the public. It has been also ascertained that paper of an excellent quality may be made of common *Straw,* and that, in a state of mixture with other materials, even *Saw-dust* is useful in fabricating the same substance.

¹⁶ When the author speaks of the superiority of modern *dress* to the ancient, he wishes to be understood not as asserting that it

is superior in its *form:* this he is persuaded would not be in all respects true: the full and flowing garments of the Greeks were probably, more healthful, as well as more graceful; but in the *texture, conveniency,* and *cheapness* of dress, it is presumed later fashions have greatly the advantage.

James Reynolds(?)

From EQUALITY: A HISTORY OF LITHCONIA
(1802)

THE whole island may be compared to a city spread over a large garden: not a spot can be seen but what is in a high state of cultivation. Every district is divided into as many fields as is thought convenient and advantageous for culture, and numbered from one upwards: each field is entered into a book—on one page the crops and management, and on the other produce. The management for each succeeding year is determined at the annual meeting of each district; a matter which is easily settled, as the approved routine of crops is always preferred, except in a certain limited number of fields, reserved for experiments. . . .

Any man who finds out a method of making the soil produce more abundantly may, if he pleases, be exempt from work. He who invents a machine, to facilitate or expedite labor, has the same reward. Here are no idle disputes about the propriety of introducing machines into practice: no vain fears of depriving the poor of work, and of the means of subsistence. Every man is convinced that he who can make useful labor more easy and expeditious, or who makes three grains of wheat to grow where there were only two, augments the number of the enjoyments of every Lithconian, and deserves the applause of his country. Therefore, no country in the world has such excellent tools, or perfect machinery, as are to be found here. Nothing excites ridicule so much as a man laboring with a bad instrument, or machine out of repair. On the other hand, nothing seems to give a Lithconian so much pleasure, as the sight of a dextrous workman, using an excellent machine.

THE PUSHBUTTON CORNUCOPIA
(1959)

AT five-thirty one frosty Indiana morning last week, Farmer Warren North, forty-five, rolled out of bed to get at his chores. After a hearty breakfast (orange juice, cereal, bacon and eggs), he left his twelve-room white frame and fieldstone house, walked briskly to the barnyard. In the early morning mist the low-lying white barn, surmounted by five giant blue-black silos, rode the frozen prairie like an ocean liner. Like a rumble of surf came the hungry bellowing of 400 white-faced Herefords and the grunting of 500 Hampshire hogs, waiting at row on row of troughs to be fed. In the barn, North stepped up to an instrument panel as intricate as a ship's, began pushing buttons and pulling switches. All around, the barn came to vibrant life. From one silo dropped ground corn, from another silage, from a third shelled corn.

By pushing other buttons, Farmer North shot in supplementary vitamins, mineral and hormone nutrients. Then he cut in the big noisemaker. In a channel in front of the silos a snakelike auger began to turn. As it writhed, it propelled the feed up a steep incline and sent it tumbling out through a conduit that passed directly over 330 feet of feed troughs. At regular intervals, trapdoors automatically distributed the individual animal's feed. When all the animals on one side of a trough had been fed, the traps changed position, shunted feed to the animals waiting on the other side.

Ten minutes later, Farmer North was through with a job that would have taken five men half a day working with buckets and pitchforks. He was ready to indulge his hobby. He returned to his farmhouse and poured himself another cup of coffee. While it cooled, he read a story on the "farm problem" in the *Wall Street Journal*. Carrying his cup and a cigarette, he walked into his living room, forty feet long and beige-carpeted wall to wall. It was dominated at the far end by a two-story pipe organ flanked by two electronic organs and a grand piano. Farmer North sat down at the console, and after running through a few warm-up chords and arpeggios, began to play Johann Sebastian Bach's chorale, *Jesu, Joy of Man's Desiring*.

SYMBOL AND EXAMPLE

Farmer North is a symbol—and a prime example—of the profound changes that have been wrought in United States agriculture by mechanization and automation, plus the new use of fertilizers. In the last twenty years, farming has changed more radically than in the previous two centuries. Once farmers used to dole out fertilizer thinking only of how much it cost them. Now they pour it on by the carload, confident of getting back bigger profits at harvesttime. Farm use of fertilizer has risen in twenty years from 1,500,000 tons to 6,200,000 tons. To handle the huge increase in crops, farmers have had to mechanize almost every farm job. From 1938 to 1958, farmers more than trebled their ownership of tractors, to 4,700,000 (an average 1½ per commercial farm). Since 1945 they have increased their number of newer work-saving machinery by 1,200 per cent—mostly with machines that had not even been invented in 1938. Farmers have invested $17.5 billion in 1,040,000 combines, 745,000 cornpickers, 590,000 pickup hay balers, 255,000 field forage harvesters, and other machinery. They spend $1.5 billion for gasoline and oil each year just to keep the equipment going.

Now farmers are taking the big step from mechanization to automation in the raising of animals and fowl; they are copying the assembly-line techniques of industry and bringing animals indoors. Once man felt he could not provide an environment for animals as good as nature's. Now he knows he can do a whole lot better. Behind him, giving him confidence, are ever-new discoveries in antibiotics, hormones, climate control, nutrition and plant and animal genetics.

. . . The result of all this is that farm productivity is soaring at a rate that once nobody believed possible. From 1938 through 1957, overall farm labor productivity rose at an annual average rate of 4.7 per cent (2.2 per cent for the rest of the economy). Even more significant, productivity is increasing at an accelerating rate. Last year, it jumped 8 per cent, as much as the increase for the decade 1920-1930. . . . Last year, with farmers paid $620 million to put land in the soil bank, the planted acreage was reduced to the smallest since 1919. But the yield was 11 per cent greater than in the previous record year of 1957. This year, in many crops, the United States is headed for even bigger surpluses. The 1959 wheat harvest was forecast last week at 1.2 billion bushels.

This will add 200 million bushels to the record 1.3 billion bushel wheat carryover expected this July 1. . . .

IN THE BOX

For Farmer North, the revolution in farming came at precisely the right time. Twenty years ago Warren North could not afford a pair of new work shoes; he did his chores in an overshoe and a boot. Today, by taking full advantage of all the scientific advances, plus an amount of hard work that would have broken a weaker man, North is comfortably a millionaire. But he remembers every struggling step of the way. . . . He was one of the first in Indiana to use fertilizer on wheat, pioneered with hybrid corn in 1937. His yield rose from 50 bushels to 65 bushels and ultimately 100 bushels per acre. He made up his own mind. When the experts said Russian hard wheat would not grow in his area, he planted Russian hard wheat. His yield went from 30 bushels to 42 bushels per acre.

BIGGER AND BIGGER

He developed a passion for the latest in machinery. He bought his first tractor in 1933 for $550. Gradually he went in for bigger and more expensive models. By 1950 he was paying $3,000 for a tractor. Later he paid $4,800 apiece for three more. In 1952 he bought a $5,500 combine, decided he had made a good deal when the price rose to $8,000. He early realized that to make costly equipment pay he had to have more land to operate it more of the time. He bought [his sister] Wanda's 90 acres, partly to save the land from going to another buyer, inherited twenty-five acres from his grandmother. The rest he picked up at steadily rising market prices from other farmers. Year by year he mortgaged and paid off, mortgaged and paid off. Gradually his property line stretched out to enclose 300 acres, then 500, then two years ago 1,000 acres of the finest land in northern Indiana—worth $500 an acre. When his land got ahead of his equipment, he switched from four-blade to six-blade plows to cut plowing time by one-third.

By 1957 Warren North had all the land he wanted. The question was how he could best use it. He was selling grain and feeding hogs and some cattle. He decided that raising grain did not pay enough and that he had to go in for mass production of livestock, use all his grain for his own animals. Through the years North had kept a tight rein on his wage outlay. He employed only two year-round hired hands, plus two part-time men in summer. But the going wage in his area had gone up from $100 to $180 a month, plus a house, utilities, and so on. "I figured even if I could get more men they would not be any account."

THE DRIVE TO AUTOMATE

For the same reason that inspired many an industrialist faced with similar cost-price squeeze, North decided to automate his livestock feeding, bought glass-lined steel Harvestore silos, developed by the A. O. Smith Corporation of Milwaukee, Wisconsin, for $55,000. Hermetically sealed to prevent decay, the silos permitted him to store corn and silage as soon as cut, thereby giving it all the feed value of green produce. Since the corn did not have to be dried to bone hardness as in ordinary storage, it would also be easily digestible. (Around Warren North, in a more primitive cycle, many farmers still followed the traditional and inefficient practice of feeding dried corn to cattle, running in hogs to pick out undigested kernels from the manure, then letting chickens clean up.)

North spent another $75,000 on equipment to go with the silos. The result is that he can swiftly raise his livestock feeding output without more capital. By turning his animals over three times a year, he is already running at the rate of 1,200 head of cattle, 1,500 hogs a year. Depending on the market outlook, he can increase this to 1,800 cattle and 4,000 hogs with no additional labor.

Last year *Prairie Farmer*, the leading Midwestern farm magazine (circulation 415,000), was so impressed by North that it held its annual farm progress show on his farm. Two hundred tents were set up. In two days 215,000 visitors tramped over the place to see how he does it. Said Jim Thomson, managing editor of *Prairie Farmer*: "North is one of America's great farmers." Actually, what Warren North has done is also being done by many another:

RUSSELL CASE, thirty-six, who twenty years ago helped his father and grandfather operate a scrubby one-hundred-acre place, now has two farms totaling 2,500 acres near West Mansfield, Ohio. It takes eight mobile radios to keep the two dozen trucks, nineteen tractors, six combines, and assorted other mechanical gear shuttling back and forth to harvest crops worth $150,000.

C. E. BENZEL cultivates an 180-acre irrigated farm outside Alliance, Nebraska, which last year produced 625 tons of beet sugar. Using the latest in mechanical planters, thinners, and harvesters, Benzel and six helpers do the work of thirty migratory workers.

BILL FARR has just installed an automated $200,000 feed mill, one hundred feet high and sixty feet long, to prepare food for the 10,000 cattle he fattens on his feed lots near Greeley, Colorado. Truckloads of corn, barley, dry beet pulp, dehydrated alfalfa, protein mix, et cetera, are ground and mixed into eight different types of feed to give the maximum weight gain to cattle at different age levels. In addition to antibiotics and minerals, Farr also adds tranquilizers to make the animals eat more, avoid threshing around and bruising their flesh en route to the slaughterhouse. . . .

FEWER FARMS

Where all this is leading to is obvious to farm experts. The number of farmers will steadily drop as more mechanization and automation increase the investment needed to farm. Economists of the Department of Agriculture estimate that the 3,100,000 commercial farms of 1954 may well be 2,000,-000 by 1975. But they see rising prices for land and even used equipment making it easy for farmers to sell out at good prices. Those who stay in will have bigger markets. In 1940 each United States farmer fed himself and ten others. He now feeds twenty others. In 1975 experts expect it will be about forty-two. Increasing agricultural efficiency will make the job easier and more profitable.

Whether the United States can much longer afford the huge surpluses being piled up by this efficiency is doubted by most farm experts. Even if the support scandal continues, there is something for United States taxpayers to be cheerful about. Rising efficiency keeps down the cost of food. The mountainous grain surplus currently is causing a buildup in cattle breeding—pointing to an eventual price break.

For the world, the enormous success of Farmer North and thousands like him may be even more significant. The new methods have proved just as successful abroad as in the United States. For example, in England, Farmer Anthony

Fisher tried his hand at dairying. After his herd died of foot-and-mouth disease he was about ready to quit. Hearing about the United States system of raising broilers, he wrote to Ralston Purina Company to get free brochures on how to do it. He started out with two hundred birds. Now his output has grown to one million a year. The broiler king of England, he has one packing plant, plans another to process his chickens and those of his imitators. The broiler is fast becoming as cheap and popular in England as in the United States.

Thus the new methods of mechanization and automation developed by the United States farmer can show the world how to solve the food shortages brought on by the explosion in population. In the next decade, the most important United States export may well be the lessons that Farmer North and others learned down on the farm.

George R. Price

THE TEACHING MACHINE
(1959)

One of the most interesting developments in educational techniques, invented by B. F. Skinner, professor of psychology at Harvard University, is a simple machine which embodies a provocative idea.

VERY QUIETLY, ALMOST UNNOTICED amid the fanfare over thermonuclear weapons, earth satellites, and moon probes, an important new invention has made its appearance. It is the teaching machine, so simple in its basic form that a child could build one in a grade-school carpentry shop, and yet of such significance that it may rank with the great educational advances of recent years.

The new machine is the invention of Professor B. F. Skinner of Harvard, a brilliant and original psychologist. His specialty is the psychology of learning, and in his laboratory in Harvard's Memorial Hall, pigeons play ping-pong and the piano, rats balance balls on their noses like seals, and other animals perform other amazing feats that possibly no one before has ever been able to train members of their species to do.

It was only a few years ago that Skinner turned his attention to problems of human education, but the result has been a series of devices that have already been tested for teaching such diverse subjects as algebra, German, psychology, spelling, physics, grammar, and reading.

One of the simplest of these, designed according to Skinner's principles by Harvard education instructor Douglas Porter, is being used by a third-grade spelling student. Ostensibly, it is simply a shallow box with a narrow window across the top, and a lever mechanism to move a worksheet from front to back. But what it and its slightly more complex relatives promise to do is nothing less than to solve or alleviate some of the most pressing problems of present-day education.

Take the problem of teacher shortages, for example. The machines can free teachers from many burdensome chores and thereby give them more time to teach more students.

What about students who don't want to learn? Children using the machines look as serious and work as hard as young Russians—and they enjoy it, too. Second-grade spelling students, allowed to go ahead at their own speed, finished nine weeks' work in five. Fourth-graders studying arithmetic, that most hated of all elementary school subjects, like it so much some even want to work through recess.

Juvenile delinquency? Even here the machines may help. Experiments on teaching delinquent children by machine are only just beginning, but results so far are encouraging. Here's the remark of a delinquent boy learning algebra by machine, as he finds himself, for the first time in his life, doing well in a school subject: "Just think, all this time I'm good at algebra, and I never knew it."

The teaching machines may, in fact, get at the root problem involved in the great central controversy between education for excellence and education for "life adjustment." Skinner's view is that the change in emphasis away from unpleasant drill subjects and toward easier and pleasanter studies, which has occurred in America during the past seventy or eighty years, was not wholly a matter of free choice by teachers and boards of education. A century ago, he points out, students were customarily beaten into working hard to master Latin declensions and geometric proofs, and those who still would not or could not learn were promptly dropped from school. But when corporal punishment was outlawed and schools undertook to educate the entire population, it became impossible to enforce the old, hard drilling in the old-fashioned way. Hence the goals of education had to change.

But the startling hope that the teaching machines offer is to provide a new and better source of motivation to make children work hard—as their great-grandparents did from terror of the birch rod—and at the same time make their study so pleasant and effective that even the dull ones can learn hard subjects without frustration. Thus American education would be able to achieve its proper goal of educating *all* students *both* for life adjustment and for excellence.

But how can a box with a window in the top and a lever at the side accomplish so much? Actually, the critical feature is not the machine itself, but the written teaching *program* that is inserted into the machine and followed by the student. In the Porter machine the program is printed on the worksheet; in other teaching machines it appears on discs, cards, or tapes. The program is the medium through which the human being doing the actual teaching communicates with the student; and the machine, as we shall see, is only a device to help the student follow the program systematically.

A Teaching Machine Program
(Adapted from Harvard's "Natural Sciences 114")

Directions: Cover the column of answers at the right. Fill in the missing word(s) in the first question in writing. Immediately expose the top answer in the right hand column. Mark your answer with a check or cross, grading yourself as correct if your answer is substantially equivalent to a given answer, even if not identical. Continue in this way through the list of questions, grading yourself on each question before you go on to the next.

1. Performing animals are sometimes trained with rewards. A hungry animal can be rewarded with＿＿＿＿＿.

                                                              food

2. The trainer rewards the animal for a good performance by giving it food＿＿＿＿＿it has performed correctly.

                                                      when, if, after

3. Reward and performance occur in the temporal order:
   (1)_____, (2)_____.

   (1) performance (2) reward

4. Food given to a hungry animal is not a reward for a response unless it is given_____.

   after the response

5. The reward *does not* act as a stimulus to_____the response.

   elicit, cause, produce

6. A reward simply makes it more_____that an animal will behave in the same way.

   probable, likely

7. If an animal is not rewarded for a response, future responses will become less_____.

   probable, likely, frequent

8. To make sure an animal will perform at the right time, the trainer_____it for the desired behavior frequently.

   rewards

9. A technical term for reward is *reinforcement*. To reward an organism with food is to_____it with food.

   reinforce

10. Reinforcing a response produces an increase in the _____that the response will occur again.

    probability, likelihood

To understand clearly just why the combination of program plus machine achieves its remarkable results, we must start at the beginning with the basic laws of learning, and see how they are obeyed in Skinner's animal-training work and how they are violated in virtually every school in the world. Then we can return to the machines themselves for a closer look at the how and why of their operation.

The best way to introduce "Skinnerian" learning theory is through the actual teaching-machine program used in "Natural Science 114," a course taught at Harvard by Skinner himself in collaboration with Dr. James Holland. Excerpts from the program are printed in the box above, and the reader can get a little of the feel of using a teaching machine by working through the program. It will be seen that it is something like taking a written examination, except that the questions are leading questions designed to give away the answers, and that one learns immediately after answering each question whether he is correct or not.

REINFORCEMENT

The essence of Skinnerian animal training is to reinforce (reward) an animal promptly for each small step of progress as it approaches closer and closer to the behavior desired. Using old-fashioned methods, we may spend hours trying to teach a dog to "heel" or lie still at command. But Skinner can set a pigeon in the middle of a bare floor and *in five minutes* teach it to walk in a figure eight, just by making signals and tossing food pellets at the proper moments.

This process of training through small steps is called *shaping*: the trainer shapes the animal's behavior through his reinforcements as a sculptor shapes a mass of clay. If we reward a pigeon only when it spontaneously executes a figure eight, we may wait months; and then it may be more months before it does it again (since the food will have reinforced only the final step in the figure eight). Instead, Skinner guides the pigeon through the figure eight, first reinforcing it for any motion, then only for any walking in a curved line, then only as it adjusts its path closer and closer to the desired final pattern.

Few homes are provided with pigeons, but readers with dogs may want to try out Skinner's instructions for training a dog to touch some object such as the handle on a low cupboard door. This is the basic rule: *Whenever* the dog does the thing you want it to do, reinforce *immediately*. Within one second if possible, sound a signal, and then toss a piece of food on the floor. The signal acts as a *bridging stimulus* that bridges the gap in time between the behavior to be reinforced and the reward of eating the food.

Here's the procedure: Prepare pieces of food small enough so that your dog can eat thirty or forty without satiation. In addition, provide yourself with a signaling device. The snap of a metal "cricket" is a good signal.

The first stage in the training is to teach your dog to associate the signal with food. Begin by tossing a few pieces of food on the floor one at a time about a minute apart. When he is eating each piece without delay, start pairing the signal with the food. Sound the signal, and immediately afterwards toss the food on the floor. Wait thirty seconds or more, and repeat. Continue doing this until he has several times in a row responded to the signal by immediately hurrying to the spot where you have been tossing the food.

Now you are ready to start reinforcing your dog for approaching the cupboard. If he sits and does nothing, begin by rewarding him for any motion however slight. The instant he moves, sound the signal, and then toss the food. Then reinforce him only for a stronger motion; and keep raising your requirements. Soon he will be moving around actively. Now start reinforcing him only when he turns toward the cupboard. When he is doing this consistentlsy, begin to reward him for approaching it; and finally reinforce him only as he goes nearer and nearer to the handle.

According to Skinner, once the dog has learned to respond to the specific goal, the rest of the training period should take only about five minutes, even if you are just a beginner.

Now let's summarize Skinner's rules of training, and then see to what extent they are followed in American schools: Rule 1. Reinforce desired behavior as promptly as possible. Rule 2. Reinforce as frequently as possible. Rule 3. Shape behavior into the desired form through a series of small steps. Rule 4. Reinforce by rewarding rather than punishing, as far as possible, and especially avoid harsh punishments. (Nobody has yet succeeded in teaching a pigeon to play the piano by beating it.)

Such are the principles, but clearly all four are violated in most of the world's schools: (1) Reinforcement is usually delayed. Thus a student turns in his homework, and two days later gets it back with a grade on it. (2) Reinforcement is quite infrequent. Only a very few of the innumerable small steps in learning are reinforced through being graded or through receiving a teacher's approval in a classroom recitation. (3) Reinforcement is applied to large blocks of complex behavior instead of to the tiny, separate steps in learning—like rewarding a pigeon when he happens to walk in a figure eight, instead of guiding him into it. (4) Finally, though corporal punishment has vanished from most American schools, the main motivation toward proper behavior is still fear. Thus a student sits at his desk filling in his workbook in order to avoid the teacher's displeasure, a bad grade, a talk with the principal, or an unfavorable report to his parents.

NEW MOTIVATIONS

What new motivations and rewards can be provided? Fortunately, there's no need to toss boys and girls candy rewards, as one tosses meat to a dog. Skinner suggests that it is naturally rewarding for a human being to learn and to solve problems correctly. Let us recall how young children love to ask questions all day long. And let us also recall how serious little children are in their play. Thus, four-year-olds playing house may smile, but they usually are not silly or giddy. Play is their way of learning, and the true business of a child is to learn. Hence it should be fun for a child to learn, and it is not surprising that children using the teaching machines are usually very serious and absorbed in their work, yet find it fun.

Now let's take another look at the machines themselves. In the simple Porter-type machines used by the spelling students, one question at a time is exposed through the window, and the lever will move the worksheet in only one direction. After the student has written his answer, he operates the lever to move the question and his answer under a transparent strip of glass or plastic across the upper part of the window where he can still read them, but cannot change his answer. Simultaneously, the correct answer comes into view in the lower part of the window. He compares his answer with the correct one and grades himself with a check or cross, and then goes on to the next question.

How does this system fit in with Skinner's four rules of training? Clearly, the first requirement is met—reinforcement is prompt. Second, reinforcement is frequent since the machine tirelessly reinforces the student for each correct response—just as though he had an infinitely patient private tutor. Third, the program is designed so that the steps are gradual and easy, to guide the student to knowledge and understanding. And fourth, reinforcement is mainly by reward (the pleasure of answering correctly) rather than by punishment (the small pain of being told the answer is incorrect), since the questions are so simple that most are answered correctly. Thus, all four requirements are fully met—and the results with the machines indicate that it is indeed true that no other motivation is necessary to make a person study hard than the reward of finding out, as soon as he has answered a question, that his answer is correct.

But a possible objection comes to mind: This method of teaching is no doubt fine for animals, but isn't it too mechanical for a human being? Does a human being really need to be rewarded for each tiny step he takes in learning? After all, Newton and Einstein and other great thinkers of the past didn't need a machine standing by them to keep telling them they were correct.

Of course, there is some truth to this. Human beings do work long and arduously for distant rewards. But for a child the ability to sacrifice the present for the future is limited, and too many bright diversions lure him away from his studies.

Furthermore, we can be sure that Einstein and Newton *did* have a sort of machine that kept reinforcing them by telling them they were correct. Great mathematicians develop an aesthetic sense by which they can recognize almost infallibly when they are on the right track, and thus at each completed step in their reasoning they taste the pleasure of accomplishment. In fact, any man who is successful in his work gets this sort of satisfaction in his daily activities. But the average schoolchild never attains sufficient mastery of a subject to make him feel enough pleasure in his own reasoning to carry him on to further studies.

REWARDING THE STUDENT

At the beginning of his life a child is generously rewarded for each tiny accomplishment, as his parents smile at him, praise him, or fondle him for his cunning efforts to walk or talk. Later, as he plays in nursery school or kindergarten, learning is its own reward and—like Einstein and Newton— his behavior is frequently reinforced by the pleasure of accomplishment as he recognizes the excellence of his imitation of a railroad train or a doctor. But then when he is dumped into school, the rewards for learning drop off and the frustrations mount up. "Many the hardships, few the joys" in studying (as Walt Whitman said of the soldier's life), so that many a student emerges from the school system with a deep distaste for everything educational.

In short, the teaching machines have nothing at all to do with treating a child like an animal. On the contrary. Their function would be to make learning as rewarding in schools and colleges as it is for infants and preschool tots. Then all children, and not just those especially fortunate in their parents, teachers or heredity, would feel pleasure in intellectual achievement and be raised to a level where they would continue their education of their own accord. Thus, the bright promise the machines offer is to reconcile the aims of the "progressivists," some of whom believe all children should be educated to an equal level with as little pain as possible, and the "traditionalists," who believe children should work hard and learn as much as possible.

What other types of teaching machine are there besides the Porter machines? About a dozen different types have been built—at Harvard, the University of Georgia, the University of Kentucky and elsewhere—including machines with phonograph records for foreign-language instruction, and a fascinating electrified device for the nursery-school set, who match pictures and press buttons. The machines used by the Harvard and Radcliffe students in Natural Science 114 operate like the Porter machines, with the added feature that a question not answered correctly is automatically presented again and again until the student gets it right.

FUTURE MACHINES

What will future teaching machines be like? There may be two main types. One might be simple and inexpensive like the Porter machine (which probably could be mass produced to sell for around $5), so that every student could keep one at his desk for class work plus another at home to help on homework. The other would be a more complex and expensive "ideal" machine. This would have a control by which the students could make the machine automatically skip a certain fraction of the questions, to make the program more difficult or more gradual as he preferred; and when he made an error, the machine would automatically switch to a special subprogram designed to clarify the point on which he'd floundered.

And here's a third feature, suggested by Dr. Thomas F. Gilbert, a leading teaching-machine researcher currently working at Harvard with Skinner: After a student has been answering questions rapidly and perfectly for a few minutes, the machine may display a message saying, for example, "You have been doing very well. Perhaps you would like to learn some interesting information about Diophantus of Alexandria, who made important discoveries about the type of equation you are working on now. If so, press the button marked 'Branch.' If not, press the button marked 'Continue.'"

How well do students learn, using the present machines? Much more work is needed before we can have a final answer to this question, but the comparisons thus far made do indicate that most students learn better and faster with the

machines and enjoy their work more. And, of course, the
future machines and programs should be still better.

What about teachers? Right now it takes a great deal of
extra work to prepare a program and begin teaching by machine. But the belief is that after the programs and procedures have been well worked out, the machines will make
life far easier for teachers and give them much more time to
give individual attention to students. . . .

Isaac Asimov

ROBBIE
(1950)

"NINETY-EIGHT—ninety-nine—*one hundred.*" Gloria withdrew
her chubby little forearm from before her eyes and stood for
a moment, wrinkling her nose and blinking in the sunlight.
Then, trying to watch in all directions at once, she withdrew
a few cautious steps from the tree against which she had been
leaning.

She craned her neck to investigate the possibilities of a
clump of bushes to the right and then withdrew farther to
obtain a better angle for viewing its dark recesses. The quiet
was profound except for the incessant buzzing of insects and
the occasional chirrup of some hardy bird, braving the midday
sun.

Gloria pouted, "I bet he went inside the house, and I've
told him a million times that that's not fair."

With tiny lips pressed together tightly and a severe frown
crinkling her forehead, she moved determinedly toward the
two-story building up past the driveway.

Too late she heard the rustling sound behind her, followed
by the distinctive and rhythmic clump-clump of Robbie's
metal feet. She whirled about to see her triumphing companion emerge from hiding and make for the home-tree at
full speed.

Gloria shrieked in dismay. "Wait, Robbie! That wasn't
fair, Robbie! You promised you wouldn't run until I found

you." Her little feet could make no headway at all against Robbie's giant strides. Then, within ten feet of the goal, Robbie's pace slowed suddenly to the merest of crawls, and Gloria, with one final burst of wild speed, dashed pantingly past him to touch the welcome bark of home-tree first.

Gleefully, she turned on the faithful Robbie, and with the basest of ingratitude, rewarded him for his sacrifice, by taunting him cruelly for a lack of running ability.

"Robbie can't run," she shouted at the top of her eight-year-old voice. "I can beat him any day. I can beat him any day." She chanted the words in a shrill rhythm.

Robbie didn't answer, of course—not in words. He pantomimed running, instead, inching away until Gloria found herself running after him as he dodged her narrowly, forcing her to veer in helpless circles, little arms outstretched and fanning at the air.

"Robbie," she squealed, "stand still!"—And the laughter was forced out of her in breathless jerks.

—Until he turned suddenly and caught her up, whirling her round, so that for her the world fell away for a moment with the blue emptiness beneath, and green trees stretching hungrily downward toward the void. Then she was down in the grass again, leaning against Robbie's leg and still holding a hard metal finger.

After a while, her breath returned. She pushed uselessly at her disheveled hair in vague imitation of one of her mother's gestures and twisted to see if her dress were torn.

She slapped her hand against Robbie's torso, "Bad boy! I'll spank you!"

And Robbie cowered, holding his hands over his face so that she had to add: "No, I won't Robbie, I won't spank you. But anyway, it's my turn to hide now because you've got longer legs and you promised not to run till I found you."

Robbie nodded his head—a small parallelepiped with rounded edges and corners attached to a similar but much larger parallelepiped that served as torso by means of a short, flexible stalk—and obediently faced the tree. A thin, metal film descended over his glowing eyes and from within his body came a steady, resonant ticking.

"Don't peek now—and don't skip any numbers," warned Gloria, and scurried for cover.

With unvarying regularity, seconds were ticked off, and at the hundredth, up went the eyelids, and the glowing red of Robbie's eyes swept the prospect. They rested for a moment on a bit of colorful gingham that protruded from behind a boulder. He advanced a few steps and convinced himself that it was Gloria who squatted behind it.

Slowly, remaining always between Gloria and home-tree, he advanced on the hiding place, and when Gloria was plainly in sight and could no longer even theorize to herself that she was not seen, he extended one arm toward her, slapping the other against his leg so that it rang again. Gloria emerged sulkily.

"You peeked!" she exclaimed, with gross unfairness. "Besides I'm tired of playing hide-and-seek. I want a ride."

But Robbie was hurt at the unjust accusation, so he seated himself carefully and shook his head ponderously from side to side.

Gloria changed her tone to one of gentle coaxing immediately, "Come on, Robbie. I didn't mean it about the peeking. Give me a ride."

Robbie was not to be won over so easily, though. He gazed stubbornly at the sky, and shook his head even more emphatically.

"Please, Robbie, please give me a ride." She encircled his neck with rosy arms and hugged tightly. Then, changing moods in a moment, she moved away. "If you don't I'm going to cry," and her face twisted appallingly in preparation.

Hardhearted Robbie paid scant attention to this dreadful possibility, and shook his head a third time. Gloria found it necessary to play her trump card.

"If you don't," she exclaimed warmly, "I won't tell you any more stories, that's all. Not one!"

Robbie gave in immediately and unconditionally before this ultimatum, nodding his head vigorously until the metal of his neck hummed. Carefully, he raised the little girl and placed her on his broad, flat shoulders.

Gloria's threatened tears vanished immediately and she crowed with delight. Robbie's metal skin, kept at a constant temperature of seventy by the high resistance coils within, felt nice and comfortable, while the beautifully loud sound her heels made as they bumped rhythmically against his chest was enchanting.

"You're an air-coaster, Robbie, you're a big silver air-coaster. Hold out your arms straight. —You *got* to, Robbie, if you're going to be an air-coaster."

The logic was irrefutable. Robbie's arms were wings catching the air currents and he was a silver 'coaster.

Gloria twisted the robot's head and leaned to the right. He banked sharply. Gloria equipped the coaster with a motor that went "Br-r-r" and then with weapons that went "Powie" and "Sh-sh-shshsh." Pirates were giving chase, and the ship's blasters were coming into play. The pirates dropped in a steady rain.

"Got another one. —Two more," she cried.

Then "Faster, men," Gloria said pompously, "we're running out of ammunition." She aimed over her shoulder with undaunted courage, and Robbie was a blunt-nosed spaceship zooming through the void at maximum acceleration.

Clear across the field he sped, to the patch of tall grass on the other side, where he stopped with a suddenness that evoked a shriek from his flushed rider, and then tumbled her onto the soft green carpet.

Gloria gasped and panted, and gave voice to intermittent whispered exclamations of "That was *nice!*"

Robbie waited until she had caught her breath, and then pulled gently at a lock of hair.

"You want something?" said Gloria, eyes wide in an apparently artless complexity that fooled her huge "nursemaid" not at all. He pulled the curl harder.

"Oh, I know. You want a story."

Robbie nodded rapidly.

"Which one?"

Robbie made a semicircle in the air with one finger.

The little girl protested, "*Again?* I've told you Cinderella a million times. Aren't you tired of it? —It's for babies."

Another semicircle.

"Oh, well," Gloria composed herself, ran over the details of the tale in her mind (together with her own elaborations, of which she had several) and began:

"Are you ready? Well—once upon a time there was a beautiful little girl whose name was Ella. And she had a terribly cruel stepmother and two very ugly and *very* cruel stepsisters and—"

Gloria was reaching the very climax of the tale—midnight was striking and everything was changing back to the shabby originals lickety-split, while Robbie listened tensely with burning eyes—when the interruption came.

"Gloria!"

It was the high-pitched sound of a woman who has been calling not once, but several times; and had the nervous tone of one in whom anxiety was beginning to overcome impatience.

"Mamma's calling me," said Gloria, not quite happily. "You'd better carry me back to the house, Robbie."

Robbie obeyed with alacrity, for somehow there was that in him which judged it best to obey Mrs. Weston, without as much as a scrap of hesitation. Gloria's father was rarely home in the daytime except on Sunday—today, for instance— and when he was, he proved a genial and understanding person. Gloria's mother, however, was a source of uneasiness to Robbie and there was always the impulse to sneak away from her sight.

Mrs. Weston caught sight of them the minute they rose above the masking tufts of long grass and retired inside the house to wait.

"I've shouted myself hoarse, Gloria," she said, severely, "Where were you?"

"I was with Robbie," quavered Gloria. "I was telling him Cinderella, and I forgot it was dinnertime."

"Well, it's a pity Robbie forgot, too." Then, as if that reminded her of the robot's presence, she whirled upon him. "You may go, Robbie. She doesn't need you now." Then, brutally, "And don't come back till I call you."

Robbie turned to go, but hesitated as Gloria cried out in his defense: "Wait, Mamma, you got to let him stay. I didn't finish Cinderella for him. I said I would tell him Cinderella and I'm not finished."

"Gloria!"

"Honest and truly, Mamma, he'll stay so quiet, you won't even know he's here. He can sit on the chair in the corner, and he won't say a word—I mean he won't *do* anything. Will you, Robbie?"

Robbie, appealed to, nodded his massive head up and down once.

"Gloria, if you don't stop this at once, you shan't see Robbie for a whole week."

The girl's eyes fell, "All right! But Cinderella is his favorite story and I didn't finish it. —And he likes it so much."

The robot left with a disconsolate step, and Gloria choked back a sob.

George Weston was comfortable. It was a habit of his to be comfortable on Sunday afternoons. A good, hearty dinner below the hatches; a nice soft, dilapidated couch on which to sprawl; a copy of the *Times;* slippered feet and shirtless chest—how could anyone *help* but be comfortable?

He wasn't pleased, therefore, when his wife walked in. After ten years of married life, he still was so unutterably foolish as to love her, and there was no question that he was always glad to see her—still, Sunday afternoons just after dinner were sacred to him, and his idea of solid comfort was to be left in utter solitude for two or three hours. Consequently, he fixed his eye firmly upon the latest reports of the Lefebre-Yoshida expedition to Mars (this one was to take off from Lunar Base and might actually succeed) and pretended she wasn't there.

Mrs. Weston waited patiently for two minutes, then impatiently for two more, and finally broke the silence.

"George!"

"Humpph?"

"George, I say! *Will* you put down that paper and look at me?"

The paper rustled to the floor, and Weston turned a weary face toward his wife, "What is it, dear?"

"You know what it is, George. It's Gloria and that terrible machine."

"What terrible machine?"

"Now, don't pretend you don't know what I'm talking about. It's that robot Gloria calls Robbie. He doesn't leave her for a moment."

"Well, why should he? He's not supposed to. And he certainly isn't a terrible machine. He's the best darn robot money can buy, and I'm damned sure he set me back half a year's income. He's worth it, though—darn sight cleverer than half my office staff."

He made a move to pick up the paper again, but his wife was quicker and snatched it away.

"You listen to *me*, George. I won't have my daughter entrusted to a machine—and I don't care how clever it is. It has no soul, and no one knows what it may be thinking. A child just isn't *made* to be guarded by a thing of metal."

Weston frowned, "When did you decide this? He's been with Gloria two years now, and I haven't seen you worry till now."

"It was different at first. It was a novelty; it took a load off me, and—and it was a fashionable thing to do. But now I don't know. The neighbors—"

"Well, what have the neighbors to do with it? Now, look. A robot is infinitely more to be trusted than a human nursemaid. Robbie was constructed for only one purpose really—to be the companion of a little child. His entire 'mentality' has been created for the purpose. He just can't help being faithful and loving and kind. He's a machine—*made so*. That's more than you can say for humans."

"But something might go wrong. Some—some—" Mrs. Weston was a bit hazy about the insides of a robot, "some little jigger will come loose and the awful thing will go berserk and—and—" She couldn't bring herself to complete the quite obvious thought.

"Nonsense," Weston denied, with an involuntary nervous shiver. "That's completely ridiculous. We had a long discussion at the time we bought Robbie about the First Law of Robotics. You *know* that it is impossible for a robot to harm a human being; that long before enough can go wrong to alter that First Law, a robot would be completely inoperable. It's a mathematical impossibility. Besides, I have an engineer from U. S. Robots here twice a year to give the poor gadget a complete overhaul. Why there's no more chance of anything at all going wrong with Robbie than there is of you or I suddenly going looney—considerably less, in fact. Besides, how are you going to take him away from Gloria?"

He made another futile stab at the paper, and his wife tossed it angrily into the next room.

"That's just it, George! She won't play with anyone else. There are dozens of little boys and girls that she should make friends with, but she won't. She won't go *near* them unless I make her. That's no way for a little girl to grow up. You want her to be normal, don't you? You want her to be able to take her part in society?"

"You're jumping at shadows, Grace. Pretend Robbie's a dog. I've seen hundreds of children who would rather have their dog than their father."

"A dog is different, George. We *must* get rid of that horrible thing. You can sell it back to the company. I've asked, and you can."

"You've *asked?* Now look here, Grace, let's not go off the deep end. We're keeping the robot until Gloria is older, and

I don't want the subject brought up again." And with that he walked out of the room in a huff.

Mrs. Weston met her husband at the door two evenings later. "You'll have to listen to this, George. There's bad feeling in the village."

"About what?" asked Weston. He stepped into the washroom and drowned out any possible answer by the splash of water.

Mrs. Weston waited. She said, "About Robbie."

Weston stepped out, towel in hand, face red and angry, "What are you talking about?"

"Oh, it's been building up and building up. I've tried to close my eyes to it, but I'm not going to any more. Most of the villagers consider Robbie dangerous. Children aren't allowed to go near our place in the evenings."

"We trust *our* child with the thing."

"Well, people aren't reasonable about these things."

"Then to hell with them."

"Saying that doesn't solve the problem. I've got to do my shopping down there. I've got to meet them every day. And it's even worse in the city these days when it comes to robots. New York has just passed an ordinance keeping all robots off the streets between sunset and sunrise."

"All right, but they can't stop us from keeping a robot in our home. —Grace, this is one of your campaigns. I recognize it. But it's no use. The answer is still No! We're keeping Robbie!"

And yet he loved his wife—and what was worse, his wife knew it. George Weston, after all, was only a man—poor thing—and his wife made full use of every device which a clumsier and more scrupulous sex has learned, with reason and futility, to fear.

Ten times in the ensuing week, he cried, "Robbie stays— and that's *final!*" and each time it was weaker and accompanied by a louder and more agonized groan.

Came the day, at last, when Weston approached his daughter guiltily and suggested a "beautiful" visivox show in the village.

Gloria clapped her hands happily, "Can Robbie go?"

"No, dear," he said, and winced at the sound of his voice, "they won't allow robots at the visivox—but you can tell him all about it when you get home." He stumbled all over the last few words and looked away.

Gloria came back from town bubbling over with enthusiasm, for the visivox had been a gorgeous spectacle indeed.

She waited for her father to maneuver the jet-car into the sunken garage, "Wait till I tell Robbie, Daddy. He would have liked it like anything. —Especially when Francis Fran was backing away so-o-o quietly, and backed right into one of the Leopard-Men and had to run." She laughed again, "Daddy, are there really Leopard-Men on the Moon?"

"Probably not," said Weston absently. "It's just funny make-believe." He couldn't take much longer with the car. He'd have to face it.

Gloria ran across the lawn. "Robbie. —Robbie!"

Then she stopped suddenly at the sight of a beautiful collie which regarded her out of serious brown eyes as it wagged its tail on the porch.

"Oh, what a nice dog!" Gloria climbed the steps, approached cautiously and patted it. "Is it for me, Daddy?"

Her mother had joined them. "Yes, it is, Gloria. Isn't it nice—soft and furry. It's very gentle. It *likes* little girls."

"Can he play games?"

"Surely. He can do any number of tricks. Would you like to see some?"

"Right away. I want Robbie to see him, too. —*Robbie!*" She stopped, uncertainly, and frowned, "I'll bet he's just staying in his room because he's mad at me for not taking him to the visivox. You'll have to explain to him, Daddy. He might not believe me, but he knows if you say it, it's so."

Weston's lips grew tighter. He looked toward his wife but could not catch her eye.

Gloria turned precipitously and ran down the basement steps, shouting as she went, "Robbie— Come and see what Daddy and Mamma brought me. They brought me a dog, Robbie."

In a minute she had returned, a frightened little girl. "Mamma, Robbie isn't in his room. Where is he?" There was no answer, and George Weston coughed and was suddenly extremely interested in an aimlessly drifting cloud. Gloria's voice quavered on the verge of tears, "Where's Robbie, Mamma?"

Mrs. Weston sat down and drew her daughter gently to her, "Don't feel bad, Gloria. Robbie has gone away, I think."

"Gone *away?* Where? Where's he gone away, Mamma?"

"No one knows, darling. He just walked away. We've looked and we've looked and we've looked for him, but we can't find him."

"You mean he'll never come back again?" Her eyes were round with horror.

"We may find him soon. We'll keep looking for him. And meanwhile you can play with your nice new doggie. Look at him! His name is Lightning and he can—"

But Gloria's eyelids had overflown. "I don't want the nasty dog—I want Robbie. I want you to find me Robbie." Her feelings became too deep for words, and she spluttered into a shrill wail.

Mrs. Weston glanced at her husband for help, but he merely shuffled his feet morosely and did not withdraw his ardent stare from the heavens, so she bent to the task of consolation, "Why do you cry, Gloria? Robbie was only a machine, just a nasty old machine. He wasn't alive at all."

"He was *not* no machine!" screamed Gloria, fiercely and ungrammatically. "He was a *person* just like you and me and he was my *friend.* I want him back. Oh, Mamma, I want him back."

Her mother groaned in defeat and left Gloria to her sorrow.

"Let her have her cry out," she told her husband. "Childish griefs are never lasting. In a few days she'll forget that awful robot ever existed."

But time proved Mrs. Weston a bit too optimistic. To be sure, Gloria ceased crying, but she ceased smiling, too, and the passing days found her ever more silent and shadowy. Gradually, her attitude of passive unhappiness wore Mrs. Weston down and all that kept her from yielding was the impossibility of admitting defeat to her husband.

Then, one evening, she flounced into the living room, sat down, folded her arms, and looked boiling mad.

Her husband stretched his neck in order to see her over his newspaper, "What now, Grace?"

"It's that child, George. I've had to send back the dog to-day. Gloria positively couldn't stand the sight of him, she said. She's driving me into a nervous breakdown."

Weston laid down the paper and a hopeful gleam entered his eye, "Maybe—Maybe we ought to get Robbie back. It might be done, you know. I can get in touch with—"

"No!" she replied, grimly. "I won't hear of it. We're not

giving up that easily. My child shall *not* be brought up by a robot if it takes years to break her of it."

Weston picked up his paper again with a disappointed air. "A year of this will have me prematurely gray."

"You're a big help, George," was the frigid answer. "What Gloria needs is a change of environment. Of course she can't forget Robbie here. How can she when every tree and rock reminds her of him? It is really the *silliest* situation I have ever heard of. Imagine a child pining away for the loss of a robot."

"Well, stick to the point. What's the change in environment you're planning?"

"We're going to take her to New York."

"The city! In August! Say, do you know what New York is like in August? It's unbearable.".

"Millions do bear it."

"They don't have a place like this to go to. If they didn't have to stay in New York, they wouldn't."

"Well, *we* have to. I say we're leaving now—or as soon as we can make the arrangements. In the city, Gloria will find sufficient interests and sufficient friends to perk her up and make her forget that machine."

"Oh, Lord," groaned the lesser half, "those frying pavements!"

"We have to," was the unshaken response. "Gloria has lost five pounds in the last month and my little girl's health is more important to me than your comfort."

"It's a pity you didn't think of your little girl's health before you deprived her of her pet robot," he muttered—but to himself.

Gloria displayed immediate signs of improvement when told of the impending trip to the city. She spoke little of it, but when she did, it was always with lively anticipation. Again, she began to smile and to eat with something of her former appetite.

Mrs. Weston hugged herself for joy and lost no opportunity to triumph over her still skeptical husband.

"You see, George, she helps with the packing like a little angel, and chatters away as if she hadn't a care in the world. It's just as I told you—all we need do is substitute other interests."

"Hmpph," was the skeptical response, "I hope so."

Preliminaries were gone through quickly. Arrangements were made for the preparation of their city home, and a couple were engaged as housekeepers for the country home. When the day of the trip finally did come, Gloria was all but her old self again, and no mention of Robbie passed her lips at all.

In high good humor the family took a taxi-gyro to the airport (Weston would have preferred using his own private 'gyro, but it was only a two-seater with no room for baggage) and entered the waiting liner.

"Come, Gloria," called Mrs. Weston. "I've saved you a seat near the window so you can watch the scenery."

Gloria trotted down the aisle cheerily, flattened her nose into a white oval against the thick clear glass, and watched with an intentness that increased as the sudden coughing of the motor drifted backward into the interior. She was too young to be frightened when the ground dropped away as if let through a trapdoor and she herself suddenly became twice her usual weight, but not too young to be mightily interested. It wasn't until the ground had changed into a tiny patchwork quilt that she withdrew her nose, and faced her mother again.

"Will we soon be in the city, Mamma?" she asked, rubbing her chilled nose, and watching with interest as the patch of moisture which her breath had formed on the pane shrank slowly and vanished.

"In about half an hour, dear." Then, with just the faintest trace of anxiety, "Aren't you glad we're going? Don't you think you'll be very happy in the city with all the buildings and people and things to see. We'll go to the visivox every day and see shows and go to the circus and the beach and—"

"Yes, Mamma," was Gloria's unenthusiastic rejoinder. The liner passed over a bank of clouds at the moment, and Gloria was instantly absorbed in the unusual spectacle of clouds underneath one. Then they were over clear sky again, and she turned to her mother with a sudden mysterious air of secret knowledge.

"*I* know why we're going to the city, Mamma."

"Do you?" Mrs. Weston was puzzled. "Why, dear?"

"You didn't tell me because you wanted it to be a surprise, but *I* know." For a moment, she was lost in admiration at her own acute penetration, and then she laughed gaily. "We're going to New York so we can find Robbie, aren't we? —With detectives."

The statement caught George Weston in the middle of a drink of water, with disastrous results. There was a sort of strangled gasp, a geyser of water, and then a bout of choking coughs. When all was over, he stood there, a red-faced, water-drenched and very, very annoyed person.

Mrs. Weston maintained her composure, but when Gloria repeated her question in a more anxious tone of voice, she found her temper rather bent.

"Maybe," she retorted, tartly. "Now sit and be still, for Heaven's sake."

New York City, A.D. 1998, was a paradise for the sight-seer more than ever in its history. Gloria's parents realized this and made the most of it.

On direct orders from his wife, George Weston arranged to have his business take care of itself for a month or so, in order to be free to spend the time in what he termed "dissipating Gloria to the verge of ruin." Like everything else Weston did, this was gone about in an efficient, thorough, and businesslike way. Before the month had passed, nothing that could be done had not been done.

She was taken to the top of the half-mile tall Roosevelt Building, to gaze down in awe upon the jagged panorama of rooftops that blended far off in the fields of Long Island and the flatlands of New Jersey. They visited the zoos where Gloria stared in delicious fright at the "real live lion" (rather disappointed that the keepers fed him raw steaks instead of human beings, as she had expected), and asked insistently and peremptorily to see "the whale."

The various museums came in for their share of attention, together with the parks and the beaches and the aquarium. She was taken halfway up the Hudson in an excursion steamer fitted out in the archaism of the mad twenties. She traveled into the stratosphere on an exhibition trip, where the sky turned deep purple and the stars came out and the misty earth below looked like a huge concave bowl. Down under the waters of the Long Island Sound she was taken in a glass-walled subsea vessel, where in a green and waver-ing world, quaint and curious sea-things ogled her and wiggled suddenly away.

On a more prosaic level, Mrs. Weston took her to the department stores where she could revel in another type of fairyland.

In fact, when the month had nearly sped, the Westons were convinced that everything conceivable had been done to take Gloria's mind once for all off the departed Robbie —but they were not quite sure they had succeeded.

The fact remained that wherever Gloria went, she displayed the most absorbed and concentrated interest in such robots as happened to be present. No matter how exciting the spectacle before her, nor how novel to her girlish eyes, she turned away instantly if the corner of her eye caught a glimpse of metallic movement.

Mrs. Weston went out of her way to keep Gloria away from all robots.

And the matter was finally climaxed in the episode at the Museum of Science and Industry. The Museum had announced a special "children's program" in which exhibits of scientific witchery scaled down to the child mind were to be shown. The Westons, of course, placed it upon their list of "absolutely."

It was while the Westons were standing totally absorbed in the exploits of a powerful electromagnet that Mrs. Weston suddenly became aware of the fact that Gloria was no longer with her. Initial panic gave way to calm decision and, enlisting the aid of three attendants, a careful search was begun.

Gloria, of course, was not one to wander aimlessly, however. For her age, she was an unusually determined and purposeful girl, quite full of the maternal genes in that respect. She had seen a huge sign on the third floor, which had said, "This Way to the Talking Robot." Having spelled it out to herself and having noticed that her parents did not seem to wish to move in the proper direction, she did the obvious thing. Waiting for an opportune moment of parental distraction, she calmly disengaged herself and followed the sign.

The Talking Robot was a *tour de force*, a thoroughly impractical device, possessing publicity value only. Once an hour, an escorted group stood before it and asked questions of the robot engineer in charge in careful whispers. Those the engineer decided were suitable for the robot's circuits were transmitted to the Talking Robot.

It was rather dull. It may be nice to know that the square
of fourteen is one hundred ninety-six, that the temperature
at the moment is 72 degrees Fahrenheit, and the air-
pressure 30.02 inches of mercury, that the atomic weight
of sodium is 23, but one doesn't really need a robot for
that. One especially does not need an unwieldy, totally
immobile mass of wires and coils spreading over twenty-five
square yards.

Few people bothered to return for a second helping, but
one girl in her middle teens sat quietly on a bench waiting
for a third. She was the only one in the room when Gloria
entered.

Gloria did not look at her. To her at the moment, another
human being was but an inconsiderable item. She saved her
attention for this large thing with the wheels. For a moment,
she hesitated in dismay. It didn't look like any robot she had
ever seen.

Cautiously and doubtfully she raised her treble voice,
"Please, Mr. Robot, sir, are you the Talking Robot, sir?"
She wasn't sure, but it seemed to her that a robot that actually
talked was worth a great deal of politeness.

(The girl in her mid-teens allowed a look of intense concentration to cross her thin, plain face. She whipped out a
small notebook and began writing in rapid pot-hooks.)

There was an oily whir of gears and a mechanically
timbred voice boomed out in words that lacked accent and
intonation, "I—am—the—robot—that—talks."

Gloria stared at it ruefully. It *did* talk, but the sound
came from inside somewheres. There was no *face* to talk to.
She said, "Can you help me, Mr. Robot, sir?"

The Talking Robot was designed to answer questions,
and only such questions as it could answer had ever been
put to it. It was quite confident of its ability, therefore, "I—
can—help—you."

"Thank you, Mr. Robot, sir. Have you seen Robbie?"

"Who—is Robbie?"

"He's a robot, Mr. Robot, sir," she stretched to tiptoes.
"He's about so high, Mr. Robot, sir, only higher, and he's very
nice. He's got a head, you know. I mean you haven't but he
has, Mr. Robot, sir."

The Talking Robot had been left behind, "A—robot?"

"Yes, Mr. Robot, sir. A robot just like you, except he can't
talk, of course, and—looks like a real person."

"A—robot—like—me?"

"Yes, Mr. Robot, sir."

To which the talking robot's only response was an erratic splutter and an occasional incoherent sound. The radical generalization offered it, that is, its existence, not as a particular object, but as a member of a general group, was too much for it. Loyally, it tried to encompass the concept and half a dozen coils burned out. Little warning signals were buzzing.

(The girl in her mid-teens left at that point. She had enough for her Physics-1 paper on "Practical Aspects of Robotics." . . .)

Gloria stood waiting, with carefully concealed impatience, for the machine's answer when she heard the cry behind her of "There she is!" and recognized that cry as her mother's.

"What are you doing here, you bad girl?" cried Mrs. Weston, anxiety dissolving at once into anger. "Do you know you frightened your mamma and daddy almost to death? Why did you run away?"

The robot engineer had also dashed in, tearing his hair, and demanding who of the gathering crowd had tampered with the machine. "Can't anybody read signs?" he yelled. "You're not allowed in here without an attendant."

Gloria raised her grieved voice over the din: "I only came to see the talking Robot, Mamma. I thought he might know where Robbie was because they're both robots." And then, as the thought of Robbie was suddenly brought forcefully home to her, she burst into a sudden storm of tears. "And I *got* to find Robbie, Mamma. I *got* to."

Mrs. Weston strangled a cry, and said, "Oh, good Heavens. Come home, George. This is more than I can stand."

That evening, George Weston left for several hours, and the next morning he approached his wife with something that looked suspiciously like smug complacence.

"I've got an idea, Grace."

"About what?" was the gloomy, uninterested query.

"About Gloria."

"You're not going to suggest buying back that robot?"

"No, of course not."

"Then go ahead. I might as well listen to you. Nothing *I've* done seems to have done any good."

"All right. Here's what I've been thinking. The whole trouble with Gloria is that she thinks of Robbie as a *person* and not as a *machine*. Naturally, she can't forget him. Now, if we managed to convince her that Robbie was nothing more than a mess of steel and copper in the form of sheets and wires with electricity its juice of life, how long would her longings last. It's the psychological attack, if you see my point."

"How do you plan to do it?"

"Simple. Where do you suppose I went last night? I persuaded Robertson of U. S. Robots and Mechanical Men, Inc., to arrange for a complete tour of his premises tomorrow. The three of us will go, and by the time we're through, Gloria will have it drilled into her that a robot is *not* alive."

Mrs. Weston's eyes widened gradually, and something glinted in her eyes that was quite like sudden admiration, "Why, George, that's a *good* idea."

And George Weston's vest buttons strained. "Only kind I have," he said.

Mr. Struthers was a conscientious General Manager and naturally inclined to be a bit talkative. The combination, therefore, resulted in a tour that was fully explained, perhaps even overabundantly explained, at every step. However, Mrs. Weston was not bored. Indeed, she stopped him several times and begged him to repeat his statements in simpler language so that Gloria might understand. Under the influence of this appreciation of his narrative powers, Mr. Struthers expanded genially and became ever more communicative, if possible.

George Weston, himself, showed a gathering impatience.

"Pardon me, Struthers," he said, breaking into the middle of a lecture on the photoelectric cell, "haven't you a section of the factory where only robot labor is employed?"

"Eh? Oh, yes! Yes, indeed!" He smiled at Mrs. Weston. "A vicious circle in a way, robots creating more robots. Of course, we are not making a general practice out of it. For one thing, the unions would never let us. But we can turn out a very few robots using robot labor exclusively, merely as a sort of scientific experiment. You see," he tapped his pince-nez into one palm argumentatively, "what the labor unions don't realize—and I say this as a man who has always been very sympathetic with the labor movement in general—is that the advent of the robot, while involving some dislocation to begin with, will, inevitably—"

"Yes, Struthers," said Weston, "but about that section of the factory yau speak of—may we see it? It would be very interesting, I'm sure."

"Yes! Yes, of course!" Mr. Struthers replaced his pince-nez in one convulsive movement and gave vent to a soft cough of discomfiture. "Follow me, please."

He was comparatively quiet while leading the three through a long corridor and down a flight of stairs. Then, when they had entered a large well-lit room that buzzed with metallic activity, the sluices opened and the flood of explanation poured forth again.

"There you are!" he said with pride in his voice. "Robots only! Five men act as overseers, and they don't even stay in this room. In five years, that is, since we began this project, not a single accident has occurred. Of course, the robots here assembled are comparatively simple, but . . ."

The General Manager's voice had long died to a rather soothing murmur in Gloria's ears. The whole trip seemed rather dull and pointless to her, though there *were* many robots in sight. None were even remotely like Robbie, though, and she surveyed them with open contempt.

In this room, there weren't any people at all, she noticed. Then her eyes fell upon six or seven robots busily engaged at a round table halfway across the room. They widened in incredulous surprise. It was a big room. She couldn't see for sure, but one of the robots looked like—looked like —*it was!*

"*Robbie!*" Her shriek pierced the air, and one of the robots about the table faltered and dropped the tool he was holding. Gloria went almost mad with joy. Squeezing through the railing before either parent could stop her, she dropped lightly to the floor a few feet below, and ran toward her Robbie, arms waving and hair flying.

And the three horrified adults, as they stood frozen in their tracks, saw what the excited little girl did not see— a huge, lumbering tractor bearing blindly down upon its appointed track.

It took split-seconds for Weston to come to his senses, and those split-seconds meant everything, for Gloria could not be overtaken. Although Weston vaulted the railing in a wild attempt, it was obviously hopeless. Mr. Struthers signaled wildly to the overseers to stop the tractor, but the overseers were only human and it took time to act.

It was only Robbie that acted immediately and with precision.

With metal legs eating up the space between himself and his little mistress he charged down from the opposite direction. Everything then happened at once. With one sweep of an arm, Robbie snatched up Gloria, slackening his speed not one iota, and, consequently, knocking every breath of air out of her. Weston, not quite comprehending all that was happening, felt, rather than saw, Robbie brush past him, and came to a sudden bewildered halt. The tractor intersected Gloria's path half a second after Robbie had, rolled on ten feet farther and came to a grinding, long-drawn-out stop.

Gloria regained her breath, submitted to a series of passionate hugs on the part of both her parents and turned eagerly toward Robbie. As far as she was concerned, nothing had happened except that she had found her friend.

But Mrs. Weston's expression had changed from one of relief to one of dark suspicion. She turned to her husband, and, despite her disheveled and undignified appearance, managed to look quite formidable, "*You* engineered this, *didn't* you?"

George Weston swabbed at a hot forehead with his handkerchief. His hand was unsteady, and his lips could curve only into a tremulous and exceedingly weak smile.

Mrs. Weston pursued the thought, "Robbie wasn't designed for engineering or construction work. He couldn't be of any use to them. You had him placed there deliberately so that Gloria would find him. You know you did."

"Well, I did," said Weston. "But, Grace, how was I to know the reunion would be so violent? And Robbie has saved her life; you'll have to admit that. You *can't* send him away again."

Grace Weston considered. She turned toward Gloria and Robbie and watched them abstractedly for a moment. Gloria had a grip about the robot's neck that would have asphyxiated any creature but one of metal, and was prattling nonsense in half-hysterical frenzy. Robbie's chrome-steel arms (capable of bending a bar of steel two inches in diameter into a pretzel) wound about the little girl gently and lovingly, and his eyes glowed a deep, deep red.

"Well," said Mrs. Weston, at last, "I guess he can stay with us until he rusts."

Walter Van Tilburg Clark

THE PORTABLE PHONOGRAPH
(1941)

THE RED SUNSET, with narrow, black cloud strips like threats across it, lay on the curved horizon of the prairie. The air was still and cold, and in it settled the mute darkness and greater cold of night. High in the air there was wind, for through the veil of the dusk the clouds could be seen gliding rapidly south and changing shapes. A queer sensation of torment, of two-sided, unpredictable nature, arose from the stillness of the earth air beneath the violence of the upper air. Out of the sunset, through the dead, matted grass and isolated weed stalks of the prairie, crept the narrow and deeply rutted remains of a road. In the road, in places, there were crusts of shallow, brittle ice. There were little islands of an old oiled pavement in the road too, but most of it was mud, now frozen rigid. The frozen mud still bore the toothed impress of great tanks, and a wanderer on the neighboring undulations might have stumbled, in this light, into large, partially filled-in and weed-grown cavities, their banks channeled and beginning to spread into badlands. These pits were such as might have been made by falling meteors, but they were not. They were the scars of gigantic bombs, their rawness already made a little natural by rain, seed, and time. Along the road, there were rakish remnants of fence. There was also, just visible, one portion of tangled and multiple barbed wire still erect, behind which was a shelving ditch with small caves, now very quiet and empty, at intervals in its back wall. Otherwise there was no structure or remnant of a structure visible over the dome of the darkling earth, but only, in sheltered hollows, the darker shadows of young trees trying again.

Under the wuthering arch of the high wind a V of wild geese fled south. The rush of their pinions sounded briefly, and the faint, plaintive notes of their expeditionary talk. Then they left a still greater vacancy. There were the smell and expectation of snow, as there is likely to be when the wild geese fly south. From the remote distance, towards the red sky, came faintly the protracted howl and quick yap-yap of a prairie wolf.

North of the road, perhaps a hundred yards, lay the parallel and deeply intrenched course of a small creek, lined with leafless alders and willows. The creek was already silent under ice. Into the bank above it was dug a sort of cell, with a single opening, like the mouth of a mine tunnel. Within the cell there was a little red of fire, which showed dully through the opening, like a reflection or a deception of the imagination. The light came from the chary burning of four blocks of poorly aged peat, which gave off a petty warmth and much acrid smoke. But the precious remnants of wood, old fence posts and timbers from the long-deserted dugouts, had to be saved for the real cold, for the time when a man's breath blew white, the moisture in his nostrils stiffened at once when he stepped out, and the expansive blizzards paraded for days over the vast open, swirling and settling and thickening, till the dawn of the cleared day when the sky was thin blue-green and the terrible cold, in which a man could not live for three hours unwarmed, lay over the uniformly drifted swell of the plain.

Around the smoldering peat, four men were seated cross-legged. Behind them, traversed by their shadows, was the earth bench, with two old and dirty army blankets, where the owner of the cell slept. In a niche in the opposite wall were a few tin utensils which caught the glint of the coals. The host was rewrapping in a piece of daubed burlap four fine leather-bound books. He worked slowly and very carefully, and at last tied the bundle securely with a piece of grass-woven cord. The other three looked intently upon the process, as if a great significance lay in it. As the host tied the cord, he spoke. He was an old man, his long, matted beard and hair gray to nearly white. The shadows made his brows and cheekbones appear gnarled, his eyes and cheeks deeply sunken. His big hands, rough with frost and swollen by rheumatism, were awkward but gentle at their task. He was like a prehistoric priest performing a fateful ceremonial rite. Also, his voice had in it a suitable quality of deep, reverent despair, yet perhaps at the moment, a sharpness of selfish satisfaction.

"When I perceived what was happening," he said, "I told myself, 'It is the end. I cannot take much; I will take these.'"

"Perhaps I was impractical," he continued. "But for myself, I do not regret, and what do we know of those who will come after us? We are the doddering remnant of a race of mechanical fools. I have saved what I love; the soul of what was good in us is here; perhaps the new ones will make a strong enough beginning not to fall behind when they become clever."

He rose with slow pain and placed the wrapped volumes in the niche with his utensils. The others watched him with the same ritualistic gaze.

"Shakespeare, the Bible, *Moby Dick*, *The Divine Comedy*," one of them said softly. "You might have done worse, much worse."

"You will have a little soul left until you die," said another harshly. "That is more than is true of us. My brain becomes thick, like my hands." He held the big, battered hands, with their black nails, in the glow to be seen.

"I want paper to write on," he said. "And there is none."

The fourth man said nothing. He sat in the shadow farthest from the fire, and sometimes his body jerked in its rags from the cold. Although he was still young, he was sick, and coughed often. Writing implied a greater future than he now felt able to consider.

The old man seated himself laboriously, and reached out, groaning at the movement, to put another block of peat on the fire. With bowed heads and averted eyes, his three guests acknowledged his magnanimity.

"We thank you, Doctor Jenkins, for the reading," said the man who had named the books.

They seemed then to be waiting for something. Doctor Jenkins understood, but was loath to comply. In an ordinary moment he would have said nothing. But the words of *The Tempest*, which he had been reading, and the religious attention of the three made this an unusual occasion.

"You wish to hear the phonograph," he said grudgingly.

The two middle-aged men stared into the fire, unable to formulate and expose the enormity of their desire.

The young man, however, said anxiously, between suppressed coughs, "Oh, please," like an excited child.

The old man rose again in his difficult way, and went to the back of the cell. He returned and placed tenderly upon the packed floor, where the firelight might fall upon it, an old portable phonograph in a black case. He smoothed the top with his hand, and then opened it. The lovely green-felt-covered disk became visible.

"I have been using thorns as needles," he said. "But tonight, because we have a musician among us"—he bent his head to the young man, almost invisible in the shadow—"I will use a steel needle. There are only three left."

The two middle-aged men stared at him in speechless adoration. The one with the big hands, who wanted to write, moved his lips, but the whisper was not audible.

"Oh, don't!" cried the young man, as if he were hurt. "The thorns will do beautifully."

"No," the old man said. "I have become accustomed to the thorns, but they are not really good. For you, my young friend, we will have good music tonight."

"After all," he added generously, and beginning to wind the phonograph, which creaked, "they can't last forever."

"No, nor we," the man who needed to write said harshly. "The needle, by all means."

"Oh, thanks," said the young man. "Thanks," he said again in a low, excited voice, and then stifled his coughing with a bowed head.

"The records, though," said the old man when he had finished winding, "are a different matter. Already they are very worn. I do not play them more than once a week. One, once a week, that is what I allow myself.

"More than a week I cannot stand it; not to hear them," he apologized.

"No, how could you?" cried the young man. "And with them here like this."

"A man can stand anything," said the man who wanted to write, in his harsh, antagonistic voice.

"Please, the music," said the young man.

"Only the one," said the old man. "In the long run, we will remember more that way."

He had a dozen records with luxuriant gold and red seals. Even in that light the others could see that the threads of the records were becoming worn. Slowly he read out the titles and the tremendous dead names of the composers and the artists and the orchestras. The three worked upon the names in their minds, carefully. It was difficult to select from such a wealth what they would at once most like to remember. Finally, the man who wanted to write named Gershwin's "New York."

"Oh, no," cried the sick young man, and then could say nothing more because he had to cough. The others understood him, and the harsh man withdrew his selection and waited for the musician to choose.

The musician begged Doctor Jenkins to read the titles again, very slowly, so that he could remember the sounds. While they were read, he lay back against the wall, his eyes closed, his thin, horny hand pulling at his light beard, and listened to the voices and the orchestras and the single instruments in his mind.

When the reading was done he spoke despairingly. "I have forgotten," he complained; "I cannot hear them clearly.

"There are things missing," he explained.

"I know," said Doctor Jenkins. "I thought that I knew all of Shelley by heart. I should have brought Shelley."

"That's more soul than we can use," said the harsh man. "*Moby Dick* is better.

"By God, we can understand that," he emphasized.

The Doctor nodded.

"Still," said the man who had admired the books, "we need the absolute if we are to keep a grasp on anything.

"Anything but these sticks and peat clods and rabbit snares," he said bitterly.

"Shelley desired an ultimate absolute," said the harsh man. "It's too much," he said. "It's no good; no earthly good."

The musician selected a Debussy nocturne. The others considered and approved. They rose to their knees to watch the Doctor prepare for the playing, so that they appeared to be actually in an attitude of worship. The peat glow showed the thinness of their bearded faces, and the deep lines in them, and revealed the condition of their garments. The other two continued to kneel as the old man carefully lowered the needle onto the spinning disk, but the musician suddenly drew back against the wall again, with his knees up, and buried his face in his hands.

At the first notes of the piano the listeners were startled. They stared at each other. Even the musician lifted his head in amazement, but then quickly bowed it again, strainingly, as if he were suffering from a pain he might not be able to endure. They were all listening deeply, without movement. The wet, blue-green notes tinkled forth from the old machine, and were individual, delectable presences in the cell. The individual, delectable presence swept into a sudden tide of unbearably beautiful dissonance, and then continued fully the swelling and ebbing of that tide, the dissonant inpourings, and the resolutions, and the diminishments, and the little, quiet wavelets of interlude lapping between. Every sound was piercing and singularly sweet. In all the men except the musician, there occurred rapid sequences of tragically heightened recollection. He heard nothing but what was there. At the final, whispering disappearance, but moving quietly so that the others would not hear him and look at him, he let his head fall back in agony, as if it were drawn there by the hair, and clenched the fingers of one hand over his teeth. He sat that way while the others were silent, and until they began to breathe again normally. His drawn-up legs were trembling violently.

Quickly Doctor Jenkins lifted the needle off, to save it and not to spoil the recollection with scraping. When he had stopped the whirling of the sacred disk, he courteously left the phonograph open and by the fire, in sight.

The others, however, understood. The musician rose last, but then abruptly, and went quickly out at the door without saying anything. The others stopped at the door and gave their thanks in low voices. The Doctor nodded magnificently.

"Come again," he invited, "in a week. We will have the 'New York.'"

When the two had gone together, out toward the rimed road, he stood in the entrance, peering and listening. At first, there was only the resonant boom of the wind overhead, and then far over the dome of the dead, dark plain, the wolf cry lamenting. In the rifts of clouds the Doctor saw four stars flying. It impressed the Doctor that one of them had just been obscured by the beginning of a flying cloud at the very moment he heard what he had been listening for, a sound of suppressed coughing. It was not nearby, however. He believed that down against the pale alders he could see the moving shadow.

With nervous hands he lowered the piece of canvas which served as his door, and pegged it at the bottom. Then quickly and quietly, looking at the piece of canvas frequently, he slipped the records into the case, snapped the lid shut, and carried the phonograph to his couch. There, pausing often to stare at the canvas and listen, he dug earth from the wall and disclosed a piece of board. Behind this there was a deep hole in the wall, into which he put the phonograph. After a moment's consideration, he went over and reached down his bundle of books and inserted it also. Then, guardedly, he once more sealed up the hole with the board and the earth. He also changed his blankets, and the grass-stuffed sack which served as a pillow, so that he could lie facing the entrance. After carefully placing two more blocks of peat upon the fire, he stood for a long time watching the stretched canvas, but it seemed to billow naturally with the first gusts of a lowering wind. At last he prayed, and got in under his blankets, and closed his smoke-smarting eyes. On the inside of the bed, next the wall, he could feel with his hands the comfortable piece of lead pipe.

Part III:

**THE MACHINE AS A
THING OF BEAUTY**

Paul Engle

POETRY IN A MACHINE AGE
(1937)

THE most evident quality of poetry is intensity—a certain verbal exaggeration. It is that which distinguishes it from prose and from plain speech. It is that which emphasizes what is being said. It is the basis of the pleasure afforded by verse. This intensity is not elaborate description or the piling-up of adjectives. It may be the opposite—a reducing of what is said to its simplest terms, as in the following couplet from Robert Frost:

> I often see flowers from a passing car
> That are gone before I can tell what they are.

Or it may be the bare statement of a fact which, although it has nothing at all added, expresses the fact imaginatively, as does MacLeish's calling of the ocean "that endless silence, edged with unending sound." Or the intensification may be achieved by symbol and figurative language. In these lines from *John Brown's Body* the image is completely obvious and clear:

> Jack Ellyat turned away from the window now,
> The frosty sleighbell of winter was in his ears,
> He saw the new year, a child in a buffalo-robe.

The image may be far more subtle, as the lines from the German poet Rilke in which he describes a visit to a small church in prerevolutionary Russia where he found God crouching in a corner like a wounded and captured animal. Whatever the means of intensification may be, it is always a heightening of the voice, although that may involve a lowering of its sound. It is a lifting of the words like a hand's gesture.

When the vowels and consonants of a line of verse are so skillfully arranged in relation to the sense and to each other that the line seems to vibrate like a taut wire, it is the contribution that this tautness makes to the transference of a certain feeling from one mind into another mind which is important. The sound of the line considered by itself is of

169

less value, however pleasant it may be, than the function it has of emphasizing the meaning through the force of its sound. In this passage from *Conquistador* the swing of the lines makes clearer the feeling in the mind of the writer, thinking of the armored Spaniards who came in their pride and were killed by stone and arrow:

> Those with the glaze in their eyes and the fine bearing:
> The born leaders of men: the resonant voices:
> They give them the lands for their tombs: they call it
>   *America*.

It is the mood of the mind, and the accuracy with which the verse reproduces it—the attitude toward a thing and not the thing itself—which is the real concern of poetry. Bettors on horse races call this attitude a hunch because it has not been reached rationally, but intuitively. It is for the telling about these hunches that rhythms and forms of verse exist. It is Carl Sandburg writing "See the trees lean to the wind's way of learning" instead of "See the wind bend the trees."

If a poet's business, then, is to communicate his own mind in an intelligible and intensified language, how is the saying that a poet is "representative of his times" to be explained? What is a man like who is, in his verse, representative of today? How has living in a machine age affected the position of a poet who is trying to tell about the excitements in his head?

A poet cannot repudiate his age. If he tries to do so, even his repudiation will belong to it. He is a part of all his environment, both that which he unconsciously takes in, as his eyes automatically acknowledge that what confronts them, and that which he consciously acquires, as in the study of folklore and psychiatry. Being so integrated to his age, when he comes to talk about his own character in verse, what he says has not only the individual accent of his own voice but also the larger intonation of his times.

Three forces which belong particularly to the twentieth century have altered the conditions of writing poetry: machinery, psychology, and sociology.

The change that machinery has brought is more than a new collection of sights and sounds and smells, although these are relevant. It is partly the mechanizing of daily acts—the substitution of button-pushing and switch-throwing for acquired skills. But it is far more the revelation of new worlds of power and movement. It is the hands extended, in making an article, to elaborate machines, the nimble fingers losing their genius to the thousand-times more nimble parts of loom and drill press. It is the eye magnified by intricately cut glass, and the ear amplified by the radio, made more sensitive than that of any forest-living creature.

A poet today, seeking for a way to express a great force, will think as readily of compressed steam in a cylinder as of the tides; of an electrical current rather than the strength of an animal. The fact of a human voice thrown out through the air by a machine and being made audible half the world away by another machine is exciting to the imagination. The purring cat's-head of a dynamo has as great possibilities for becoming as familiarly used in verse as the traditional plow, itself a machine. One of the largest conceptions possible in poetry now is the airplane—man catapulted through space by his own creation.

The machine must not be worshiped as god or devil, nor must it be damned, save when it is misused as in the deadly instruments of war. The poet must accept it as part of his world in the way that the author of *John Brown's Body* has urged:

> Out of John Brown's strong sinews the tall skyscrapers
>   grow,
> Out of his heart the chanting buildings rise,
> Rivet and girder, motor and dynamo,
> Pillar of smoke by day and fire by night,
> The steel-faced cities reaching at the skies,
> The whole enormous and rotating cage
> Hung with hard jewels of electric light. . . .
> If you at last must have a word to say,
> Say neither, in their way,
> "It is a deadly magic and accursed,"
> Nor "It is blest," but only, "It is here."

The necessary thing is to combine the new machinery with the old—plows, spinning wheels, ships, and wagons. The new is an immensely speeded-up addition to these. Poetry has previously drawn most of its images from nature. It must now draw a greater number from machines, as they displace part of nature in our experience. This is not to imply that poetry must be filled with the whir and clatter of a factory, although it should be at times. The autumnal flight of birds and the turn and pound of a driving wheel should both move through the verse of our time.

Equally with the aspects of nature, machines may be merely described or their relation to men indicated. Or they may be converted into symbols and images as Macknight Black does in "Reciprocating Engine" from his book of poems, *Machinery:*

> The arc of a balance-wheel
> Flows like a curved rush of swallows, come over a
>   hill. . . .
> Things lost come again in sudden new beauty.
> Look long on an engine. It is sweet to the eyes.

In these from "Smoke and Steel," Sandburg describes the union of the blood of men and the smoke of fires in the making of steel:

>   A bar of steel—it is only
> Smoke at the heart of it, smoke and the blood of a man.
> A runner of fire ran in, ran out, ran somewhere else,
> And left—smoke and the blood of a man
> And the finished steel, chilled and blue.

Ultimately the machine must be transformed into a generalized term, as in Auden's looking at something: "As the hawk sees it or the helmeted airman." In these lines from Stephen Spender the machine no longer stands outside the inner motivation of the poem, nor is it merely described. It is an integral part of the original mood and the writing.

> More beautiful and soft than any moth
> With burring furred antennae feeling its huge path
> Through dusk, the air-liner with shut-off engines
> Glides over suburbs and the sleeves set trailing tall
> To point the wind. Gently, broadly, she falls,
> Scarcely disturbing charted currents of air.

The poem convinces you that it was as natural for Spender to write so sympathetically of an airplane as it was for Keats to write of a Grecian urn, or Shelley of the west wind.

The knowledge that the air around him swarms with words and music on radio waves, with the sun's energy and an infinitude of light-waves bearing the appearances of objects, is as important to a poet as it is fascinating. The roaring flame of blast furnaces at night may have for him the same burning terror that the sun has by day. The problem of using science and machines in verse has so far been their impersonality, their lack of human association. We were accustomed to windmills but not to dynamos. We were familiar with a horse-drawn plow but not with tractors, and besides there was an ancient tradition for using the plow and the windmill in poetry. But this is changing. It begins with the child. He plays now with miniature airplanes, streamlined trains, and a multitude of mechanical devices. He sees them represented in the funnies. They will not be strange to him when he grows up. He may have his childhood recalled by the sight, not of a certain flower remembered from his mother's garden, but by the sight of a certain airplane with a distinctive wing—if any model will last that long.

It is often complained that machines, being inanimate, can never even partly displace animate nature in poetry. They saw that such a nature image as that in the line "But thine eternal summer shall not fade" can never be replaced by an image from science or machinery. There are two replies to this.

In the first place, much of the nature used in poetry is just as nonliving as machines; a season's change is weather as well as plants; and Wordsworth's "something far more deeply interfused" was actually fused with rock and sun as well as daffodils. The traditional comparison of a man's old age to the setting sun shows how an inanimate object may, by long association, acquire the aspect of life. And yet surely the running-down and disrepair of an old machine are more definite images of a man's age, and far more contemporary ones. In the second place, as with the example of the sun above, machines may by constant familiarity acquire that semblance of a life which inanimate objects of nature have long had.

There are many city dwellers today for whom a machine and impersonal environment are far more real and understandable than a nature environment. Nature for them is something kept behind cages in parks or used as an escape from city heat; a place where empty beer cans are thrown on Sunday. The nature tradition of poetry will in time seem for them unreal and irrelevant—as lifeless as machine poetry now seems to many. Their life will have to be expressed in its hard and daily terms, in steel and motor. The clouds are there, over the city, but they are bringers of gutter-streams and coolers of hot apartment-house roofs rather than nourishers of crops and growing things.

There is one further consideration. Machinery may not serve precisely the same purpose in poetry that nature does, and therefore will not be substituted directly for it. Its function may be to reveal a portion of human life which thus far the use of nature has not been able to reveal, in doing which it will not compete with nature but rather complement and complete it. One specific example of this is the difficulty of expressing man's social relationships in verse by means of the traditional forms and images. It may be that the highly complex and perfectly unified parts of machines, the relationship between separate but interacting machines, and the power that operates through all of them will express social terms and the unity and interaction of social life far better than can anything drawn from nature. With that increasing sympathy for society which will come with understanding, there will rise a stronger motivation to write poetry which deals with specific social and political questions. Anything that affects the lives of men is fit subject for poetry. If the life of this century is going to be one of social unrest and profound efforts to adjust the machine to society, or our social and economic system to a machine age, then poetry will be unavoidably concerned, at least in part, with that unrest. . . .

Emily Dickinson

I LIKE TO SEE IT LAP THE MILES
(c. 1862)

> I like to see it lap the miles,
> And lick the valleys up,
> And stop to feed itself at tanks;
> And then, prodigious, step

Around a pile of mountains,
And, supercilious, peer
In shanties by the sides of roads;
And then a quarry pare

To fit its sides, and crawl between,
Complaining all the while
In horrid, hooting stanza;
Then chase itself down hill

And neigh like Boanerges;
Then, punctual as a star,
Stop—docile and omnipotent—
At its own stable door.

Walt Whitman

TO A LOCOMOTIVE IN WINTER
  (1876)

Thee for my recitative.
Thee in the driving storm even as now, the snow, the winter-
    day declining,
Thee in thy panoply, thy measur'd dual throbbing and thy
    beat convulsive,
The black cylindric body, golden brass and silvery steel,
Thy ponderous side-bars, parallel and connecting rods, gy-
    rating, shuttling at thy sides,
Thy metrical, now swelling pant and roar, now tapering in
    the distance,
Thy great protruding head-light fix'd in front,
Thy long, pale, floating vapor-pennants, tinged with delicate
    purple,
The dense and murky clouds out-belching from thy smoke-
    stack,
Thy knitted frame, thy springs and valves, the tremulous
    twinkle of thy wheels,
Thy train of cars, behind, obedient, merrily following,

Through gale or calm, now swift, now slack, yet steadily
    careering;
Type of the modern—emblem of motion and power—pulse of
    the continent,
For once come serve the Muse and merge in verse, even as
    here I see thee,
With storm and buffeting gusts of wind and falling snow,
By day thy warning ringing bell to sound its notes,
By night thy silent signal lamps to swing.

Fierce-throated beauty!
Roll through my chant with all thy lawless music, thy swing-
    ing lamps at night,
Thy madly-whistled laughter, echoing, rumbling like an earth-
    quake, rousing all,
Law of thyself complete, thine own track firmly holding,
(No sweetness debonair of tearful harp or glib piano thine,)
Thy trills of shrieks by rock and hills return'd,
Launch'd o'er the prairies wide, across the lakes,
To the free skies unpent and glad and strong.

Carl Sandburg

PRAYERS OF STEEL
(1918)

Lay me on an anvil, O God.
Beat me and hammer me into a crowbar.
Let me pry loose old walls.
Let me lift and loosen old foundations.

Lay me on an anvil, O God.
Beat me and hammer me into a steel spike.
Drive me into the girders that hold a skyscraper together.
Take red-hot rivets and fasten me into the central
    girders.
Let me be the great nail holding a skyscraper through
    blue nights into white stars.

Macknight Black

MACHINERY
(1929)

> Slow, salt machinery
> Of oceans laboring on blackened reefs
> Is not more constant than the racing steel
> Of engines leaping to their thrusts;
> In neither is there sign
> Of power's beginning or its end.
> Here wheels, like breakers, pile
> And pound on stillness; polished tons
> Of matter beat the shaken air.
> This flood, like floods of water, hurls
> A mindless rhythm through the mind;
> It chants of wholeness unremembered,
> Ancient as bloodless toil.

Stephen Spender

THE EXPRESS
(1933)

> After the first powerful, plain manifesto
> The black statement of pistons, without more fuss
> But gliding like a queen, she leaves the station.
> Without bowing and with restrained unconcern
> She passes the houses which humbly crowd outside,
> The gasworks, and at last the heavy page
> Of death, printed by gravestones in the cemetery.
> Beyond the town, there lies the open country
> Where, gathering speed, she acquires mystery,
> The luminous self-possession of ships on ocean.
> It is now she begins to sing—at first quite low
> Then loud, and at last with a jazzy madness—
> The song of her whistle screaming at curves,

Of deafening tunnels, brakes, innumerable bolts.
And always light, aerial, underneath
Retreats the elate meter of her wheels.
Steaming through metal landscape on her lines,
She plunges new eras of wild happiness,
Where speed throws up strange shapes, broad curves
And parallels clean like trajectories from guns.
At last, further than Edinburgh or Rome,
Beyond the crest of the world, she reaches night
Where only a low stream-line brightness
Of phosphorus on the tossing hills is light.
Ah, like a comet through flame, she moves entranced,
Wrapt in her music no bird song, no, nor bough
Breaking with honey buds, shall ever equal.

Stephen Spender

THE LANDSCAPE NEAR AN AERODROME
(1933)

More beautiful and soft than any moth
With burring furred antennae feeling its huge path
Through dusk, the air liner with shut-off engines
Glides over suburbs and the sleeves set trailing tall
To point the wind. Gently, broadly, she falls,
Scarcely disturbing charted currents of air.

Lulled by descent, the travelers across sea
And across feminine land indulging its easy limbs
In miles of softness, now let their eyes trained by
    watching
Penetrate through dusk the outskirts of this town
Here where industry shows a fraying edge.
Here they may see what is being done.

Beyond the winking masthead light
And the landing ground, they observe the outposts
Of work: chimneys like lank black fingers

Or figures, frightening and mad: and squat buildings
With their strange air behind trees, like women's faces
Shattered by grief. Here where few houses'
Moan with faint light behind their blinds,
They remark the unhomely sense of complaint, like a
    dog
Shut out, and shivering at the foreign moon.

In the last sweep of love, they pass over fields
Behind the aerodrome, where boys play all day
Hacking dead grass: whose cries, like wild birds,
Settle upon the nearest roofs
But soon are hid under the loud city.

Then, as they land, they hear the tolling bell
Reaching across the landscape of hysteria,
To where, louder than all those batteries
And charcoaled towers against that dying sky,
Religion stands, the Church blocking the sun.

Part IV:

THE MACHINE AS ENEMY

Samuel Butler

DARWIN AMONG THE MACHINES
(1863)

[To the Editor of the *Press*, Christchurch, New Zealand, 13 June, 1863.]

Sir—There are few things of which the present generation is more justly proud than of the wonderful improvements which are daily taking place in all sorts of mechanical appliances. And indeed it is matter for great congratulation on many grounds. It is unnecessary to mention these here, for they are sufficiently obvious; our present business lies with considerations which may somewhat tend to humble our pride and to make us think seriously of the future prospects of the human race. If we revert to the earliest primordial types of mechanical life, to the lever, the wedge, the inclined plane, the screw and the pulley, or (for analogy would lead us one step further) to that one primordial type from which all the mechanical kingdom has been developed, we mean to the lever itself, and if we then examine the machinery of the *Great Eastern*, we find ourselves almost awestruck at the vast development of the mechanical world, at the gigantic strides with which it has advanced in comparison with the slow progress of the animal and vegetable kingdom. We shall find it impossible to refrain from asking ourselves what the end of this mighty movement is to be. In what direction is it tending? What will be its upshot? To give a few imperfect hints towards a solution of these questions is the object of the present letter.

We have used the words "mechanical life," "the mechanical kingdom," "the mechanical world" and so forth, and we have done so advisedly, for as the vegetable kingdom was slowly developed from the mineral, and as in like manner the animal supervened upon the vegetable, so now in these last few ages an entirely new kingdom has sprung up, of which we as yet have only seen what will one day be considered the antediluvian prototypes of the race.

We regret deeply that our knowledge both of natural history and of machinery is too small to enable us to undertake the gigantic task of classifying machines into the genera and sub-genera, species, varieties and sub-varieties, and so forth, of tracing the connecting links between machines of widely different characters, of pointing out how subservience to the use of man has played that part among machines which natural selection has performed in the animal and vegetable kingdoms, of pointing out rudimentary organs* which exist in some few machines, feebly developed and perfectly useless, yet serving to mark descent from some ancestral type which has either perished or been modified into some new phase of mechanical existence. We can only point out this field for investigation; it must be followed by others whose education and talents have been of a much higher order than any which we can lay claim to.

Some few hints we have determined to venture upon, though we do so with the profoundest diffidence. Firstly, we would remark that as some of the lowest of the vertebrata attained a far greater size than has descended to their more highly organised living representatives, so a diminution in the size of machines has often attended their development and progress. Take the watch for instance. Examine the beautiful structure of the little animal, watch the intelligent play of the minute members which compose it; yet this little creature is but a development of the cumbrous clocks of the thirteenth century—it is no deterioration from them. The day may come when clocks, which certainly at the present day are not

---

* We were asked by a learned brother philosopher who saw this article in MS. what we meant by alluding to rudimentary organs in machines. Could we, he asked, give any example of such organs? We pointed to the little protuberance at the bottom of the bowl of our tobacco pipe. This organ was originally designed for the same purpose as the rim at the bottom of a tea-cup, which is but another form of the same function. Its purpose was to keep the heat of the pipe from marking the table on which it rested. Originally, as we have seen in very early tobacco pipes, this protuberance was of a very different shape to what it is now. It was broad at the bottom and flat, so that while the pipe was being smoked the bowl might rest upon the table. Use and disuse have here come into play and served to reduce the function to its present rudimentary condition. That these rudimentary organs are rarer in machinery than in animal life is owing to the more prompt action of the human selection as compared with the slower but even surer operation of natural selection. Men may make mistakes; in the long run nature never does so. We have given only an imperfect example, but the intelligent reader will supply himself with illustrations.

diminishing in bulk, may be entirely superseded by the universal use of watches, in which case clocks will become extinct like the earlier saurians, while the watch (whose tendency has for some years been rather to decrease in size than
the contrary) will remain the only existing type of an extinct
race.

The views of machinery which we are thus feebly indicating will suggest the solution of one of the greatest and
most mysterious questions of the day. We refer to the question: What sort of creature man's next successor in the
supremacy of the earth is likely to be. We have often heard
this debated; but it appears to us that we are ourselves
creating our own successors; we are daily adding to the
beauty and delicacy of their physical organisation; we are
daily giving them greater power and supplying by all sorts of
ingenious contrivances that self-regulating, self-acting power
which will be to them what intellect has been to the human
race. In the course of ages we shall find ourselves the inferior
race. Inferior in power, inferior in that moral quality of self-
control, we shall look up to them as the acme of all that the
best and wisest man can ever dare to aim at. No evil passions,
no jealousy, no avarice, no impure desires will disturb the
serene might of those glorious creatures. Sin, shame, and
sorrow will have no place among them. Their minds will be
in a state of perpetual calm, the contentment of a spirit that
knows no wants, is disturbed by no regrets. Ambition will
never torture them. Ingratitude will never cause them the
uneasiness of a moment. The guilty conscience, the hope
deferred, the pains of exile, the insolence of office, and the
spurns that patient merit of the unworthy takes—these will
be entirely unknown to them. If they want "feeding" (by the
use of which very word we betray our recognition of them
as living organism) they will be attended by patient slaves
whose business and interest it will be to see that they shall
want for nothing. If they are out of order they will be
promptly attended to by physicians who are thoroughly acquainted with their constitutions; if they die, for even these
glorious animals will not be exempt from that necessary and
universal consummation, they will immediately enter into a
new phase of existence, for what machine dies entirely in
every part at one and the same instant?

We take it that when the state of things shall have arrived
which we have been above attempting to describe, man will

have become to the machine what the horse and the dog are to man. He will continue to exist, nay even to improve, and will be probably better off in his state of domestication under the beneficent rule of the machines than he is in his present wild state. We treat our horses, dogs, cattle, and sheep, on the whole, with great kindness; we give them whatever experience teaches us to be best for them, and there can be no doubt that our use of meat has added to the happiness of the lower animals far more than it has detracted from it; in like manner it is reasonable to suppose that the machines will treat us kindly, for their existence is as dependent upon ours as ours is upon the lower animals. They cannot kill us and eat us as we do sheep; they will not only require our services in the parturition of their young (which branch of their economy will remain always in our hands), but also in feeding them, in setting them right when they are sick, and burying their dead or working up their corpses into new machines. It is obvious that if all the animals in Great Britain save man alone were to die, and if at the same time all intercourse with foreign countries were by some sudden catastrophe to be rendered perfectly impossible, it is obvious that under such circumstances the loss of human life would be something fearful to contemplate—in like manner were mankind to cease, the machines would be as badly off or even worse. The fact is that our interests are inseparable from theirs, and theirs from ours. Each race is dependent upon the other for innumerable benefits, and, until the reproductive organs of the machines have been developed in a manner which we are hardly yet able to conceive, they are entirely dependent upon man for even the continuance of their species. It is true that these organs may be ultimately developed, inasmuch as man's interest lies in that direction; there is nothing which our infatuated race would desire more than to see a fertile union between two steam engines; it is true that machinery is even at this present time employed in begetting machinery, in becoming the parent of machines often after its own kind, but the days of flirtation, courtship, and matrimony appear to be very remote, and indeed can hardly be realised by our feeble and imperfect imagination.

Day by day, however, the machines are gaining ground upon us; day by day we are becoming more subservient to them; more men are daily bound down as slaves to tend them, more men are daily devoting the energies of their

whole lives to the development of mechanical life. The upshot is simply a question of time, but that the time will come
when the machines will hold the real supremacy over the
world and its inhabitants is what no person of a truly
philosophic mind can for a moment question.

Our opinion is that war to the death should be instantly
proclaimed against them. Every machine of every sort should
be destroyed by the well-wisher of his species. Let there be
no exceptions made, no quarter shown; let us at once go back
to the primeval condition of the race. If it be urged that this
is impossible under the present condition of human affairs,
this at once proves that the mischief is already done, that our
servitude has commenced in good earnest, that we have
raised a race of beings whom it is beyond our power to
destroy, and that we are not only enslaved but are absolutely
acquiescent in our bondage.

For the present we shall leave this subject, which we
present gratis to the members of the Philosophical Society.
Should they consent to avail themselves of the vast field
which we have pointed out, we shall endeavour to labour in
it ourselves at some future and indefinite period.

I am, Sir, etc.,

CELLARIUS

Stephen Vincent Benét

NIGHTMARE NUMBER THREE
(1935)

We had expected everything but revolt
And I kind of wonder myself when they started thinking—
But there's no dice in that now.

I've heard fellows say
They must have planned it for years and maybe they did.
Looking back, you can find little incidents here and there,
Like the concrete-mixer in Jersey eating the wop
Or the roto press that printed "Fiddle-dee-dee!"
In a three-color process all over Senator Sloop,

Just as he was making a speech. The thing about that
Was, how could it walk upstairs? But it was upstairs,
Clicking and mumbling in the Senate Chamber.
They had to knock out the wall to take it away
And the wrecking-crew said it grinned.

                        It was only the best
Machines, of course, the superhuman machines,
The ones we'd built to be better than flesh and bone,
But the cars were in it, of course . . .

                          and they hunted us
Like rabbits through the cramped streets on that Bloody
    Monday,
The Madison Avenue busses leading the charge.
The busses were pretty bad—but I'll not forget
The smash of glass when the Duesenberg left the showroom
And pinned three brokers to the Racquet Club steps
Or the long howl of the horns when they saw men run,
When they saw them looking for holes in the solid ground . . .

I guess they were tired of being ridden in
And stopped and started by pygmies for silly ends,
Of wrapping cheap cigarettes and bad chocolate bars
Collecting nickels and waving platinum hair
And letting six million people live in a town.
I guess it was that. I guess they got tired of us
And the whole smell of human hands.

                        But it was a shock
To climb sixteen flights of stairs to Art Zuckow's office
(Nobody took the elevators twice)
And find him strangled to death in a nest of telephones,
The octopus-tendrils waving over his head,
And a sort of quiet humming filling the air. . . .
Do they eat? . . . There was red . . . But I did not stop to
    look.
I don't know yet how I got to the roof in time
And it's lonely, here on the roof.

                    For a while, I thought
That window-cleaner would make it, and keep me company.
But they got him with his own hoist at the sixteenth floor
And dragged him in, with a squeal.
You see, they cooperate. Well, we taught them that
And it's fair enough, I suppose. You see, we built them.
We taught them to think for themselves.

It was bound to come. You can see it was bound to come.
And it won't be so bad, in the country. I hate to think
Of the reapers, running wild in the Kansas fields,
And the transport planes like hawks on a chickenyard,
But the horses might help. We might make a deal with the
    horses.
At least, you've more chance, out there.
                        And they need us, too.
They're bound to realize that when they once calm down.
They'll need oil and spare parts and adjustments and tuning
    up.
Slaves? Well, in a way, you know, we were slaves before.
There won't be so much real difference—honest, there won't.
(I wish I hadn't looked into that beauty parlor
And seen what was happening there.
But those are female machines and a bit high-strung.)
Oh, we'll settle down. We'll arrange it. We'll compromise.
It wouldn't make sense to wipe out the whole human race.
Why, I bet if I went to my old Plymouth now
(Of course, you'd have to do it the tactful way)
And said, "Look here! Who got you the swell French horn?"
He wouldn't turn me over to those police cars;
At least I don't think he would.
                    Oh, it's going to be jake.
There won't be so much real difference—honest, there won't—
And I'd go down in a minute and take my chance—
I'm a good American and I always liked them—
Except for one small detail that bothers me
And that's the food proposition. Because, you see,
The concrete-mixer may have made a mistake,
And it looks like just high spirits.
But, if it's got so they like the flavor . . . well . . .

Stephen Crane

THE BLACK RIDERS, xxxi
(1895)

> Many workmen
> Built a huge ball of masonry
> Upon a mountain-top.
> Then they went to the valley below,
> And turned to behold their work.
> "It is grand," they said;
> They loved the thing.
>
> Of a sudden, it moved:
> It came upon them swiftly;
> It crushed them all to blood.
> But some had opportunity to squeal.

Wolcott Gibbs

MAN ALONE
(1932)

MRS. HALE had misgivings about leaving her husband alone in the apartment. There was, however, no way of telling whether Aunt Elsie was really ill or again, as she had so often been, simply a victim of her dark and hypochondriacal imagination.

"Are you perfectly sure you're going to be all right?" she asked wistfully.

"Of course," he said. "You just run along. Don't worry about me."

He said this indulgently, with an airy competence, but she was still uneasy. She had spent a night away from the apartment once before, and had come back to a shambles.

"Don't forget all the things I told you to do, Walter," she said. "Put the cream and butter back in the icebox when you've finished with them. Keep the cover on the garbage pail, and if you go out be sure to turn off all the lights. And don't forget to give the laundryman the bag in the bedroom.''

"I'll be fine," he said. "You just run along."

Mr. Hale got up half an hour earlier the next morning, an extra allowance which he considered ample for cooking breakfast. When he had shaved and dressed, he strolled out to the kitchen and looked around it thoughtfully. The Hales lived on Central Park West in an apartment which was essentially a monument to the commercial genius of the New York Edison Company. Everything in it worked by electricity, and this was particularly true of the kitchen, which, in addition to the usual mechanical icebox, contained an electric coffee percolator, an electric toaster, an electric orange-juice squeezer, and a device which washed and stacked dishes in one insanely complicated operation. Normally Mr. Hale admired his kitchen and boasted about it—he regarded it as the final, excellent word in living-made-easy—but this morning it seemed different and slightly menacing. He was bewildered by the tangle of wires which twisted up from the floor plugs into the batteries of machines; he could only guess at the functions of the long shining rows of utensils which lined the cupboards, and it seemed hopeless to try to select what he wanted to eat from the regiments of colored boxes and cans on the shelves, the strange confusion in the icebox. He jumped as the icebox suddenly turned itself on and filled the room with whispering.

"Coffee," said Mr. Hale, studying a row of canisters. It occurred to him that it would have been more practical to start the coffee before dressing. Now it wouldn't be ready until everything else was cold, which was a nuisance.

"I suppose you have to learn to synchronize these things," he said philosophically.

He found the can marked COFFEE, and carried it over to the percolator. He recalled vaguely that you used a tablespoon of coffee for every cup. This, however, brought up the baffling problem of distinguishing between a tablespoon and a dessert spoon.

"Might as well have it strong," said Mr. Hale, and filled a cup with coffee and poured it into the percolator. He added another cupful of water, and gingerly plugged in the socket.

"There," he said. "Now the eggs and toast."

He found the bread, hacked off two untidy slices, put them in the toaster, and pulled down the lever. At this point, however, he was distracted by an interesting discovery which he made under the sink. Mrs. Hale, who had been brought up in the country, was in the habit of setting mousetraps in her kitchen, although her husband contended that mice were rarely found on the twentieth floor of New York apartment houses. This morning, miraculously enough, there *was* a mouse in the trap.

"Hmm," said Mr. Hale, picking it up. The mouse was conclusively dead. It had, in fact, a curiously flat and rigid effect which suggested that it had been overlooked for some time. Mr. Hale, not normally given to abstractions, suddenly perceived an analogy between the mouse's fate and his presence in this overmechanical kitchen. Thoughtfully he deposited the mouse and the trap in the garbage pail, remembering to put the cover on again.

His sense of being trapped in a powerhouse was interrupted by the toaster, which, having finished with the toast, ejected it with brisk ferocity.

"Hell," said Mr. Hale. "Now *that'll* be cold before I can get to the eggs. Better put it in the oven."

The gas oven was one of Mr. Hale's terrors. Whenever he tried to light it there was a furious blue explosion, and the flame, instead of burning properly on the surface, glowed secretly and wickedly inside the pipe, so that he had to turn it off and start over again. Sometimes the match went out, and there was a hissing of gas which filled him with a horror of suffocation. This time, however, it lit as it should, and, with a slight renewal of confidence, Mr. Hale put the toast inside and slammed the door.

The eggs, thank God, were quite simple. He lit the stove and, filling a saucepan with water, put it on. Rummaging through the icebox, he found two eggs and dropped them in the saucepan.

"Two minutes," he said, taking out his watch. The two minutes passed uneventfully, the silence broken only by the bubbling of the percolator, which, even to Mr. Hale's unaccustomed ear, sounded curiously thick and strangled.

"Probably stopped up or something."

Since things had taken longer than he had expected, it was probable that now everything, even the coffee, was cooked. Mr. Hale turned off the stove and the oven, and unplugged the percolator. He got plates, cups, and silver from the closet and set the kitchen table. Then he opened the oven door. A cloud of evil smoke billowed out at him, and he jumped back in terror. Nothing happened, however, and in a moment, when it had cleared away, he investigated again. The two pieces of toast lay on the oven grill, quite black and still smoking fitfully.

"We'll do without toast," said Mr. Hale, dropping the remnants in the garbage pail. He took the coffee percolator and the saucepan over to the table and sat down. Exploring it cautiously, he was surprised to find the water in the saucepan only tepid. It was possible for him to take the eggs out with his fingers.

"Odd," said Mr. Hale, and broke one of the eggs on the rim of his cup. It was quite raw. The yolk in its filmy envelope stared up at him from the bottom of the cup like a bilious and derisive eye. The other egg was raw too, and Mr. Hale poured them both into the garbage can.

At least he'd be able to have some coffee. Of all kitchen mechanisms the coffee percolator was the only one which completely eliminated the human equation. If you put water and coffee into it and attached the wires, after a proper interval inevitably you had coffee.

Mr. Hale dropped two lumps of sugar in the bottom of the cup, and tilted the percolator over it. Nothing happened. He shook the pot and was relieved to hear a swishing inside. He tried pouring it again, and this time he was rewarded with a reluctant black stream which smelled like coffee, but flowed, rather unpleasantly, like oatmeal. Mr. Hale stirred the mixture tentatively with his spoon, and then, struck with a dreadful suspicion, looked up at the shelf over the sink. The interior mechanism of the percolator—the long hollow spindle and the perforated bowl—stood there where they always did, glittering ironically in the morning sun. As he was contemplating this final disaster, the doorbell rang. With the percolator still in one hand, Mr. Hale opened the door and found a pale, hard-bitten young man in a checked cap and a whimsical suit.

"Laundry?" said the youth.

Mr. Hale looked at him absently.

"No," he said. "I don't think we need any today."

Still absently, he went back to the kitchen, emptied the percolator into the garbage can, and put on the cover.

JOHN HENRY
(c. 1870)

When John Henry was a little baby,
Sittin' on his daddy's knee,
He grabbed himself a hammer and a piece of steel,
Said, "This hammer'll be the death of me, Lawd, Lawd,
This hammer'll be the death of me."

Now the captain said to John Henry,
"Gonna bring that steam drill round,
Gonna take that steam drill out on the job,
Gonna whop that steel on down, Lawd, Lawd,
Gonna whop that steel on down."

John Henry told his captain,
"A man ain't nuthin' but a man,
But before that steam drill beat me down
I'll die with my hammer in my hand, Lawd, Lawd,
I'll die with my hammer in my hand."

John Henry said to his shaker,
"Shaker, why don't you sing?
'Cause I'm throwin' twelve pounds from my hips on
        down,
Just listen to that cold steel ring, Lawd, Lawd,
Just listen to that cold steel ring."

The man that invented the steam drill,
He thought he was mighty fine,
But John Henry he made sixteen feet,
And the steam drill only made nine, Lawd, Lawd,
And the steam drill only made nine.

John Henry hammered on the mountain
Till his hammer was strikin' fire.
He drove so hard he broke his pore heart,
Then he laid down his hammer and died, Lawd, Lawd,
He laid down his hammer and died.

They took John Henry to the graveyard,
And they buried him in the sand,
And every locomotive comes roarin' by,
Says, "There lies a steel-driven' man, Lawd, Lawd,
There lies a steel-drivin' man."

Joe Glazer

AUTOMATION
(1960)

I went down, down, down to the factory early on a
    Monday morn.
When I got down to the factory,
It was lonely, it was forlorn.
I couldn't find Joe, Jack, John, or Jim;
Nobody could I see:
Nothing but buttons and bells and lights
All over the factory.

I walked, walked, walked into the foreman's office
To find out what was what.
I looked him in the eye and I said, "What goes?"
And this is the answer I got:
His eyes turned red, then green, then blue
And it suddenly dawned on me—
There was a robot sitting in the seat
Where the foreman used to be.

I walked all around, all around, up and down
And across the factory.
I watched all the buttons and the bells and the lights—
It was a mystery to me.
I hollered "Frank, Hank, Ike, Mike, Roy, Ray, Don, Dan,
Bill, Phil, Ed, Fred, Pete!"
And a great big mechanical voice boomed out:
"All your buddies are obsolete."

I was scared, scared, scared, I was worried, I was sick
As I left that factory.
I decided that I had to see the president
Of the whole darn company.
When I got up to his office he was rushing out the door
With a scowl upon his face,
'Cause there was a great big mechanical executive
Sitting in the president's place.

I went home, home, home to my ever-loving wife
And told her 'bout the factory.

She hugged me and she kissed me and she cried a little
　　bit
As she sat on my knee.
I don't understand all the buttons and the lights
But one thing I will say—
I thank the Lord that love's still made
In the good old-fashioned way.

Kurt Vonnegut, Jr.

From PLAYER PIANO
(1952)

"Ah haven't got a job any more," said Bud. "Canned."

Paul was amazed. "Really? What on earth for? Moral turpitude? What about the gadget you invented for—"

"Thet's it," said Bud with an eerie mixture of pride and remorse. "Works. Does a fine job." He smiled sheepishly. "Does it a whole lot better than Ah did it."

"It runs the whole operation?"

"Yup. Some gadget."

"And so you're out of a job."

"Seventy-two of us are out of jobs," said Bud. He slumped even lower in the couch. "Ouah job classification has been eliminated. Poof." He snapped his fingers.

Paul could see the personnel manager pecking out Bud's job code number on a keyboard, and seconds later having the machine deal him seventy-two cards bearing the names of those who did what Bud did for a living—what Bud's machine now did better. Now, personnel machines all over the country would be reset so as no longer to recognize the job as one suited for men. The combination of holes and nicks that Bud had been to personnel machines would no longer be acceptable. If it were to be slipped into a machine, it would come popping right back out.

"They don't need P-128's any more," said Bud bleakly, "and nothing's open above or below. Ah'd take a cut, and go back to P-129 or even P-130, but it's no dice. Everything's full up.

"Got any other numbers, Bud?" said Paul. "The only P-numbers we're authorized are—"

Katharine had the *Manual* open before her. She'd already looked the numbers up. "P-225 and P-226—lubrication engineers," she said. "And Doctor Rosenau's got both of those."

"That's right, he does," said Paul. Bud was in a baffling mess, and Paul didn't see how he could help him. The machines knew the Ilium Works had its one allotted lubrication engineer, and they wouldn't tolerate a second. If Bud were recorded as a lubrication engineer and introduced into the machines, they'd throw him right out again.

As Kroner often said, eternal vigilance was the price of efficiency. And the machines tirelessly riffled through their decks again and again and again in search of foot draggers, free riders, and misfits.

"You know it isn't up to me, Bud," said Paul. "I haven't got any real say about who's taken on."

"He knows that," said Katharine. "But he has to start somewhere, and we thought maybe you'd know of some opening, or who to see."

"Oh, it makes me sore," said Paul. "Whatever got into them to give you a Petroleum Industries assignment, anyway? You should be in design."

"Got no aptitude for it," said Bud. "Tests proved that."

That would be on his ill-fated card, too. All his aptitude-test grades were on it—irrevocably, immutable, and the card knew best. "But you *do* design," said Paul. "And you do it with a damn sight more imagination than the prima donnas in the Lab." The Lab was the National Research and Development Laboratory, which was actually a war-born conglomeration of all the country's research and development facilities under a single headquarters. "You're not even paid to design, and still you do a better job of it than they do. That telemetering arrangement for the pipeline, your car, and now this monster that runs the depot—"

"But the test says no," said Bud.

"So the machines say no," said Katharine.

"So that's that," said Bud. "Ah guess."

"You might see Kroner," said Paul.

"Ah tried, and didn't get past his secretary. Ah told her Ah was after a job, and she called up Personnel. They ran mah card through the machines while she held the phone; and then she hung up, and looked sad, and said Kroner had meetings all month."

"Maybe your university can help," said Paul. "Maybe the grading machine needed new tubes when it went over your development aptitude test." He spoke without conviction. Bud was beyond help. As an old old joke had it, the machines had all the cards.

"Ah've written, asking them to check my grades again. No matter what Ah say, Ah get the same thing back." He threw a piece of graph paper on Katharine's desk. "Theah. Ah've written three letters, and gotten three of these back."

"Uh-huh," said Paul, looking at the familiar graph with distaste. It was a so-called Achievement and Aptitude Profile, and every college graduate got one along with his sheepskin. And the sheepskin was nothing, and the graph was everything. When time for graduation came, a machine took a student's grades and other performances and integrated them into one graph—the profile. Here Bud's graph was high for theory, there low for administration, here low for creativity, and so on, up and down across the page to the last quality—*personality*. In mysterious, unnamed units of measure, each graduate was credited with having a high, medium, or low personality. Bud, Paul saw, was a strong medium, as the expression went, personality-wise. When the graduate was taken into the economy, all his peaks and valleys were translated into perforations on his personnel card.

George Gordon, Lord Byron

DEBATE ON THE FRAME-WORK BILL
(1812)

Debate on the Frame-work Bill, in the House of Lords, February 27, 1812

The order of the day for the second reading of this Bill being read,

Lord BYRON rose, and (for the first time) addressed their Lordships as follows:—

My Lords—The subject now submitted to your Lordships for the first time, though new to the house, is by no means new to the country. I believe it had occupied the serious thoughts of all descriptions of persons, long before its introduction to the notice of that legislature, whose interference alone could be of real service. As a person in some degree connected with the suffering county, though a stranger not only to this House in general, but to almost every individual whose attention I presume to solicit, I must claim some portion of your Lordships' indulgence, whilst I offer a few observations on a question in which I confess myself deeply interested.

To enter into any detail of the riots would be superfluous: the House is already aware that every outrage short of actual bloodshed has been perpetrated, and that the proprietors of the frames obnoxious to the rioters, and all persons supposed to be connected with them, have been liable to insult and violence. During the short time I recently passed in Nottinghamshire, not twelve hours elapsed without some fresh act of violence; and on the day I left the country I was informed that forty frames had been broken the preceding evening, as usual, without resistance and without detection.

Such was then the state of that country, and such I have reason to believe it to be at this moment. But whilst these outrages must be admitted to exist to an alarming extent, it cannot be denied that they have arisen from circumstances of the most unparalleled distress: the perseverance of these miserable men in their proceedings tends to prove that nothing but absolute want could have driven a large, and once honest and industrious, body of the people, into the commission of excesses so hazardous to themselves, their families, and the community. At the time to which I allude, the town and county were burdened with large detachments of the military; the police was in motion, the magistrates assembled; yet all the movements, civil and military, had led to—nothing. Not a single instance had occurred of the apprehension of any real delinquent actually taken in the fact, against whom there existed legal evidence sufficient for conviction. But the police, however useless, were by no means idle: several notorious delinquents had been detected—men, liable to conviction, on the clearest evidence, of the capital crime of poverty;

men, who had been nefariously guilty of lawfully begetting several children, whom, thanks to the times! they were unable to maintain. Considerable injury has been done to the proprietors of the improved frames. These machines were to them an advantage, inasmuch as they superseded the necessity of employing a number of workmen, who were left in consequence to starve. By the adoption of one species of frame in particular, one man performed the work of many, and the superfluous labourers were thrown out of employment. Yet it is to be observed, that the work thus executed was inferior in quality; not marketable at home, and merely hurried over with a view to exportation. It was called, in the cant of the trade, by the name of "Spider-work." The rejected workmen, in the blindness of their ignorance, instead of rejoicing at these improvements in arts so beneficial to mankind, conceived themselves to be sacrificed to improvements in mechanism. In the foolishness of their hearts they imagined that the maintenance and well-doing of the industrious poor were objects of greater consequence than the enrichment of a few individuals by an improvement, in the implements of trade, which threw the workmen out of employment, and rendered the labourer unworthy of his hire. And it must be confessed that although the adoption of the enlarged machinery in that state of our commerce which the country once boasted might have been beneficial to the master without being detrimental to the servant; yet, in the present situation of our manufactures, rotting in warehouses, without a prospect of exportation, with the demand for work and workmen equally diminished, frames of this description tend materially to aggravate the distress and discontent of the disappointed sufferers. But the real cause of these distresses and consequent disturbances lies deeper. When we are told that these men are leagued together not only for the destruction of their own comfort, but of their very means of subsistence, can we forget that it is the bitter policy, the destructive warfare of the last eighteen years, which has destroyed their comfort, your comfort, all men's comfort? that policy, which, originating with "great statesmen now no more," has survived the dead to become a curse on the living, unto the third and fourth generation! These men never destroyed their looms till they were become useless, worse than useless; till they were become actual impediments to their exertions in obtaining their daily bread. Can you, then, wonder that in times like these, when bankruptcy, convicted fraud, and imputed felony are found in a station not far beneath that of your Lordships, the lowest, though once most useful portion of the people, should forget their duty in their distresses, and become only less guilty than one of their representatives? But while the exalted offender can find means to baffle the law, new capital punishments must be devised, new snares of death must be spread for the wretched mechanic, who is famished into guilt. These men were willing to dig, but the spade was in other hands: they were not ashamed to beg, but there was none to relieve them: their own means of subsistence were cut off, all other employments pre-occupied; and their excesses, however to be deplored and condemned, can hardly be subject of surprise.

It has been stated that the persons in the temporary possession of frames connive at their destruction; if this be proved upon inquiry, it were necessary that such material accessories to the crime should be principals in the punishment. But I did hope, that any measure proposed by his Majesty's government for your Lordships' decision, would have had conciliation for its basis; or, if that were hopeless, that some previous inquiry, some deliberation, would have been deemed requisite; not that we should have been called at once, without examination and without cause, to pass sentences by wholesale, and sign death-warrants blindfold. But, admitting that these men had no cause of complaint; that the grievances of them and their employers were alike groundless; that they deserved the worst;—what inefficiency, what imbecility has been evinced in the method chosen to reduce them! Why were the military called out to be made a mockery of, if they were to be called out at all? As far as the difference of seasons would permit, they have merely parodied the summer campaign of Major Sturgeon; and, indeed, the whole proceedings, Civil and military, seemed on the model of those of the mayor and corporation of Garratt.— Such marchings and countermarchings!—from Nottingham to Bullwell, from Bullwell to Banford, from Banford to Mansfield! And when at length the detachments arrived at their destination, in all "the pride, pomp, and circumstance of glorious war," they came just in time to witness the mischief which had been done, and ascertain the escape of the perpetrators, to collect the "*spoila opima*" in the fragments of broken frames, and return to their quarters amidst the derision of old women, and the hootings of children. Now, though, in a free country, it were to be wished that our military should never be too formidable, at least to ourselves, I cannot see the policy of placing them in situations where they can only be made ridiculous. As the sword is the worst argument that can be used, so should it be the last. In this instance it has been the first; but providentially as yet only in the scabbard. The present measure will, indeed, pluck it from the sheath; yet had proper meetings been held in the earlier stages of these riots, had the grievances of these men and their masters (for they also had their grievances) been fairly weighed and justly examined, I do think that means might have been devised to restore these workmen to their avocations, and tranquillity to the county. At present the county suffers from the double infliction of an idle military and a starving population. In what state of apathy have we been plunged so long, that now for the first time the House has been officially apprised of these disturbances? All this has been transacting within 130 miles of London; and yet we, "good easy men, have deemed full sure our greatness was a-ripening," and have sat down to enjoy our foreign triumphs in the midst of domestic calamity. But all the cities you have taken, all the armies which have retreated before your leaders, are but paltry subjects of self-congratulation, if your land divides against itself, and your dragoons and your executioners must be let loose against your fellow-citizens.—You call these men a mob, desperate, dangerous, and ignorant; and seem to think that the only way to quiet the *"Bellua multorum capitum"* is to lop off a few of its superfluous heads. But even a mob may be better reduced to reason by a mixture of conciliation and firmness, than by additional irritation and redoubled penalties. Are we aware of our obligations to a mob? It is the mob that labour in your fields and serve in your houses—that man your navy, and recruit your army—that have enabled you to defy all the world, and can also defy you when neglect and calamity have driven them to despair! You may call the people a mob; but do not forget that a mob too often speaks the sentiments of the people. And here I must remark, with what alacrity you are accustomed to fly to the succour of your distressed allies, leaving the distressed of your own country to the care of Providence or—the parish. When the Portuguese suffered under the retreat of the French, every arm was stretched out, every hand was opened, from the rich man's largess to the widow's mite, all was bestowed, to enable them to rebuild their villages and replenish their granaries. And at this moment, when thousands of misguided but most unfortunate fellow-countrymen are struggling with the extremes of hardships and hunger, as your charity began abroad it should end at home. A much less sum, a tithe of the bounty bestowed on Portugal, even if those men (which I cannot admit without inquiry) could not have been restored to their employments, would have rendered unnecessary the tender mercies of the bayonet and the gibbet. But doubtless our friends have too many foreign claims to admit a prospect of domestic relief; though never did such objects demand it. I have traversed the seat of war in the Peninsula, I have been in some of the most oppressed provinces of Turkey; but never under the most despotic of infidel governments did I behold such squalid wretchedness as I have seen since my return in the very heart of a Christian country. And what are your remedies? After months of inaction, and months of action worse than inactivity, at length comes forth the grand specific, the never-failing nostrum of all state physicians, from the days of Draco to the present time. After feeling the pulse and shaking the head over the patient, prescribing the usual course of warm water and bleeding—the warm water of your mawkish police, and the lancets of your military—these convulsions must terminate in death, the sure consummation of the prescriptions of all political Sangrados. Setting aside the palpable injustice and the certain inefficiency of the Bill, are there not capital punishments sufficient in your statutes? Is there not blood enough upon your penal code, that more must be poured forth to ascend to Heaven and testify against you? How will you carry the Bill into effect? Can you commit a whole country to their own prisons? Will you erect a gibbet in every field, and hang up men like scarecrows? or will you proceed (as you must to bring this measure into effect) by decimation? place the country under martial law? depopulate and lay waste all around you? and restore Sherwood Forest as an acceptable gift to the crown, in its former condition of a royal chase and an asylum for outlaws? Are these the remedies for a starving and desperate populace? Will the famished wretch who has braved your bayonets be appalled by your gibbets? When death is a relief, and the only relief it appears that you will afford him, will he be dragooned into tranquillity? Will that which could not be effected by your grenadiers be accomplished by your executioners? If you proceed by the forms of law, where is your evidence? Those who have refused to impeach their accomplices when transportation only was the punishment, will hardly be tempted to witness against them when death is the penalty. With all due deference to the noble lords opposite, I think a little investigation, some previous inquiry, would induce even them to change their purpose. That most favourite state measure, so marvellously efficacious in many and recent instances, temporising, would not be without its advantages in this. When a proposal is made to emancipate or relieve, you hesitate, you deliberate for years, you temporise and tamper with the minds of men; but a death-bill must be passed off-hand, without a thought of the consequences. Sure I am, from what I have heard, and from what I have seen, that to pass the Bill under all the existing circumstances, without inquiry, without deliberation, would only be to add injustice to irritation, and barbarity to neglect. The framers of such a bill must be content to inherit the honours of that Athenian law-giver whose edicts were said to be written not in ink but in blood. But suppose it passed; suppose one of these men, as I have seen them—meagre with famine, sullen with despair, careless of a life which your Lordships are perhaps about to value at something less than the price of a stocking-frame—suppose this man surrounded by the children for whom he is unable to procure bread at the hazard of his existence, about to be torn for ever from a family which he lately supported in peaceful industry, and which it is not his fault that he can no longer so support—suppose this man—and there are ten thousand such from whom you may select your victims—dragged into court, to be tried for this new offence, by this new law; still, there are two things wanting to convict and condemn him; and these are, in my opinion—twelve butchers for a jury, and a Jeffreys for a judge!

Robert Frost

THE EGG AND THE MACHINE
(1925)

HE gave the solid rail a hateful kick.
From far away there came an answering tick
And then another tick. He knew the code:
His hate had roused an engine up the road.
He wished when he had had the track alone
He had attacked it with a club or stone
And bent some rail wide open like a switch
So as to wreck the engine in the ditch.
Too late though, now, he had himself to thank.
Its click was rising to a nearer clank.
Here it came breasting like a horse in skirts.
(He stood well back for fear of scalding squirts.)
Then for a moment all there was was size
Confusion and a roar that drowned the cries
He raised against the gods in the machine.
Then once again the sandbank lay serene.
The traveler's eye picked up a turtle trail,
Between the dotted feet a streak of tail,
And followed it to where he made out vague
But certain signs of buried turtle's egg;
And probing with one finger not too rough,
He found suspicious sand, and sure enough,
The pocket of a little turtle mine.
If there was one egg in it there were nine,
Torpedo-like, with shell of gritty leather
All packed in sand to wait the trump together.
"You'd better not disturb me any more,"
He told the distance. "I am armed for war.
The next machine that has the power to pass
Will get this plasm in its goggle glass."

John Steinbeck

TRACTORING OFF
(*1939*)

THE TRACTORS came over the roads and into the fields, great crawlers moving like insects, having the incredible strength of insects. They crawled over the ground, laying the track and rolling on it and picking it up. Diesel tractors, puttering while they stood idle; they thundered when they moved, and then settled down to a droning roar. Snub-nosed monsters, raising the dust and sticking their snouts into it, straight down the country, across the country, through fences, through dooryards, in and out of gullies in straight lines. They did not run on the ground, but on their own roadbeds. They ignored hills and gulches, water courses, fences, houses.

The man sitting in the iron seat did not look like a man; gloved, goggled, rubber dust mask over nose and mouth, he was a part of the monster, a robot in the seat. The thunder of the cylinders sounded through the country, became one with the air and the earth, so that earth and air muttered in sympathetic vibration. The driver could not control it— straight across country it went, cutting through a dozen farms and straight back. A twitch at the controls could swerve the cat', but the driver's hands could not twitch because the monster that built the tractor, the monster that sent the tractor out, had somehow got into the driver's hands, into his brain and muscle, had goggled him and muzzled him —goggled his mind, muzzled his speech, goggled his perception, muzzled his protest. He could not see the land as it was, he could not smell the land as it smelled; his feet did not stamp the clods or feel the warmth and power of the earth. He sat in an iron seat and stepped on iron pedals. He could not cheer or beat or curse or encourage the extension of his power, and because of this he could not cheer or whip or curse or encourage himself. He did not know or own or trust or beseech the land. If a seed dropped did not germinate, it was nothing. If the young thrusting plant withered in drought or drowned in a flood of rain, it was no more to the driver than to the tractor.

He loved the land no more than the bank loved the land. He could admire the tractor—its machined surfaces, its surge of power, the roar of its detonating cylinders; but it was not his tractor. Behind the tractor rolled the shining disks, cutting the earth with blades—not plowing but surgery, pushing the cut earth to the right where the second row of disks cut it and pushed it to the left; slicing blades shining, polished by the cut earth. And pulled behind the disks, the harrows combing with iron teeth so that the little clods broke up and the earth lay smooth. Behind the harrows, the long seeders —twelve curved iron penes erected in the foundry, orgasms set by gears, raping methodically, raping without passion. The driver sat in his iron seat and he was proud of the straight lines he did not will, proud of the tractor he did not own or love, proud of the power he could not control. And when that crop grew, and was harvested, no man had crumbled a hot clod in his fingers and let the earth sift past his fingertips. No man had touched the seed, or lusted for the growth. Men ate what they had not raised, had no connection with the bread. The land bore under iron, and under iron gradually died; for it was not loved or hated, it had no prayers or curses.

At noon the tractor driver stopped sometimes near a tenant house and opened his lunch: sandwiches wrapped in waxed paper, white bread, pickle, cheese, Spam, a piece of pie branded like an engine part. He ate without relish. And tenants not yet moved away came out to see him, looked curiously while the goggles were taken off, and the rubber dust mask, leaving white circles around the eyes and a large white circle around nose and mouth. The exhaust of the tractor puttered on, for fuel is so cheap it is more efficient to leave the engine running than to heat the Diesel nose for a new start. Curious children crowded close, ragged children who ate their fried dough as they watched. They watched hungrily the unwrapping of the sandwiches, and their hunger-sharpened noses smelled the pickle, cheese, and Spam. They didn't speak to the driver. They watched his hand as it carried food to his mouth. They did not watch him chewing; their eyes followed the hand that held the sandwich. After a while the tenant who could not leave the place came out and squatted in the shade beside the tractor.

"Why, you're Joe Davis's boy!"

"Sure," the driver said.

"Well, what you doing this kind of work for—against your own people?"

"Three dollars a day. I got damn sick of creeping for my dinner—and not getting it. I got a wife and kids. We got to eat. Three dollars a day, and it comes every day."

"That's right," the tenant said. "But for your three dollars a day fifteen or twenty families can't eat at all. Nearly a hundred people have to go out and wander on the roads for your three dollars a day. Is that right?"

And the driver said: "Can't think of that. Got to think of my own kids. Three dollars a day, and it comes every day. Times are changing, mister, don't you know? Can't make a living on the land unless you've got two, five, ten thousand acres and a tractor. Crop land isn't for little guys like us any more. You don't kick up a howl because you can't make Fords, or because you're not the telephone company. Well, crops are like that now. Nothing to do about it. You try to get three dollars a day someplace. That's the only way."

The tenant pondered. "Funny thing how it is. If a man owns a little property, that property is him, it's part of him, and it's like him. If he owns property only so he can walk on it and handle it and be sad when it isn't doing well, and feel fine when the rain falls on it, that property is him, and some way he's bigger because he owns it. Even if he isn't successful he's big with his property. That is so."

And the tenant pondered more. "But let a man get property he doesn't see, or can't take time to get his fingers in, or can't be there to walk on it—why, then the property is the man. He can't do what he wants, he can't think what he wants. The property is the man, stronger than he is. And he is small, not big. Only his possessions are big—and he's the servant of his property. That is so, too."

The driver munched the branded pie and threw the crust away. "Times are changed, don't you know? Thinking about stuff like that don't feed the kids. Get your three dollars a day, feed your kids. You got no call to worry about anybody's kids but your own. You get a reputation for talking like that, and you'll never get three dollars a day. Big shots won't give you three dollars a day if you worry about anything but your three dollars a day."

"Nearly a hundred people on the road for your three dollars. Where will we go?"

"And that reminds me," the driver said, "you better get out soon. I'm going through the dooryard after dinner."

"You filled in the well this morning."·

"I know. Had to keep the line straight. But I'm going through the dooryard after dinner. Got to keep the lines straight. And—well, you know Joe Davis, my old man, so I'll tell you this. I got orders wherever there's a family not moved out—if I have an accident—you know, get too close and cave the house in a little—well, I might get a couple of dollars. And my youngest kid never had no shoes yet."

"I built it with my hands. Straightened old nails to put the sheathing on. Rafters are wired to the stringers with baling wire. It's mine. I built it. You bump it down—I'll be in the window with a rifle. You even come too close and I'll pot you like a rabbit."

"It's not me. There's nothing I can do. I'll lose my job if I don't do it. And look—suppose you kill me? They'll just hang you, but long before you're hung there'll be another guy on the tractor, and he'll bump the house down. You're not killing the right guy."

"That's so," the tenant said. "Who gave you orders? I'll go after him. He's the one to kill."

"You're wrong. He got his orders from the bank. The bank told him, 'Clear those people out or it's your job.'"

"Well, there's a president of the bank. There's a board of directors. I'll fill up the magazine of the rifle and go into the bank."

The driver said, "Fellow was telling me the bank gets orders from the East. The orders were, 'Make the land show profit or we'll close you up.'"

"But where does it stop? Who can we shoot? I don't aim to starve to death before I kill the man that's starving me."

"I don't know. Maybe there's nobody to shoot. Maybe the thing isn't men at all. Maybe, like you said, the property's doing it. Anyway I told you my orders."

"I got to figure," the tenant said. "We all got to figure. There's some way to stop this. It's not like lightning or earthquakes. We've got a bad thing made by men, and by God that's something we can change." The tenant sat in his doorway, and the driver thundered·his engine and started off, tracks falling and curving, harrows combing, and the phalli of the seeder slipping into the ground. Across the dooryard the tractor cut, and the hard, foot-beaten ground was seeded field, and the tractor cut through again; the uncut space was ten feet wide. And back he came. The iron guard bit into the house-corner, crumbled the wall, and wrenched the little house from its foundation so that it fell sideways, crushed like a bug. And the driver was goggled and a rubber mask covered his nose and mouth. The tractor cut a straight line on, and the air and the ground vibrated with its thunder. The tenant man stared after it, his rifle in his hand. His wife was beside him, and the quiet children behind. And all of them stared after the tractor.

Sherwood Anderson

LIFT UP THINE EYES
(1930)

IT IS A BIG assembling plant in a city of the Northwest. They assemble there the Bogel car. It is a car that sells in large numbers and at a low price. The parts are made in one great central plant and shipped to the places where they are to be assembled. There is little or no manufacturing done in the assembling plant itself. The parts come in. These great companies have learned to use the railroad cars for storage.

At the central plant everything is done on schedule. As soon as the parts are made they go into railroad cars. They are on their way to the assembling plants scattered all over the United States and they arrive on schedule.

The assembling plant assembles cars for a certain territory. A careful survey has been made. This territory can afford to buy so and so many cars per day.

"But suppose the people do not want the cars?"

"What has that to do with it?"

People, American people, no longer buy cars. They do not buy newspapers, books, foods, pictures, clothes. Things are sold to people now. If a territory can take so and so many Bogel cars, find men who can make them take the cars. That is the way things are done now.

In the assembling plant everyone works "on the belt." This is a big steel conveyor, a kind of moving sidewalk, waist-high. It is a great river running down through the plant. Various tributary streams come into the main stream, the main belt. They bring tires, they bring headlights, horns, bumpers for cars. They flow into the main stream. The main stream has its source at the freight cars, where the parts are unloaded, and it flows out to the other end of the factory and into other freight cars.

The finished automobiles go into the freight cars at the delivery end of the belt. The assembly plant is a place of peculiar tension. You feel it when you go in. It never lets up. Men here work always on tension. There is no letup to the tension. If you can't stand it get out.

It is the belt. The belt is boss. It moves always forward. Now the chassis goes on the belt. A hoist lifts it up and places it just so. There is a man at each corner. The chassis is deposited on the belt and it begins to move. Not too rapidly. There are things to be done.

How nicely everything is calculated. Scientific men have done this. They have watched men work. They have stood looking, watch in hand. There is care taken about everything. Look up. Lift up thine eyes. Hoists are bringing engines, bodies, wheels, fenders. These come out of side streams flowing into the main stream. They move at a pace very nicely calculated. They will arrive at the main stream at just a certain place at just a certain time.

In this shop there is no question of wages to be wrangled about. The men work but eight hours a day and are well paid. They are, almost without exception, young, strong men. It is, however, possible that eight hours a day in this place may be much longer than twelve or even sixteen hours in the old carelessly run plants.

They can get better pay here than at any other shop in town. Although I am a man wanting a good many minor comforts in life, I could live well enough on the wages made by the workers in this place. Sixty cents an hour to begin and then, after a probation period of sixty days, if I can stand the pace, seventy cents or more.

To stand the pace is the real test. Special skill is not required. It is all perfectly timed, perfectly calculated. If you are a body upholsterer, so many tacks driven per second. Not too many. If a man hurries too much too many tacks drop on the floor. If a man gets too hurried he is not efficient. Let an expert take a month, two months, to find out just how many tacks the average good man can drive per second.

There must be a certain standard maintained in the finished product. Remember that. It must pass inspection after inspection.

Do not crowd too hard.

Crowd all you can.

Keep crowding.

There are fifteen, twenty, thirty, perhaps fifty such assembling plants, all over the country, each serving its own section. Wires pass back and forth daily. The central office—from which all the parts come—at Jointville is the nerve center. Wires come and and go out of Jointville. In so and so many hours Williamsburg, with so and so many men, produced so and so many cars.

Now Burkesville is ahead. It stays ahead. What is up at Burkesville? An expert flies there.

The man at Burkesville was a major in the army. He is the manager there. He is a cold, rather severe, rather formal man. He has found out something. He is a real Bogel man, an ideal Bogel man. There is no foolishness about him. He watches the belt. He does not say foolishly to himself, "I am the boss here." He knows the belt is boss.

He says there is a lot of foolishness talked about the belt. The experts are too expert, he says. He has found out that the belt can be made to move just a little faster than the experts say. He has tried it. He knows. Go and look for yourself. There are the men out there on the belt, swarming along the belt, each in his place. They are all right, aren't they?

Can you see anything wrong?

Just a trifle more speed in every man. Shove the pace up just a little, not much. With the same number of men, in the same number of hours, six more cars a day.

That's the way a major gets to be a colonel, a colonel a general. Watch that fellow at Burkesville, the man with the military stride, the cold steady voice. He'll go far.

Everything is nicely, perfectly calculated in all the Bogel assembling plants. There are white marks on the floor everywhere. Everything is immaculately clean. No one smokes, no one chews tobacco, no one spits. There are white bands on the cement floor along which the men walk. As they work, sweepers follow them. Tacks dropped on the floor are at once swept up. You can tell by the sweepings in a plant where there is too much waste, too much carelessness. Sweep everything carefully and frequently. Weigh the sweepings.

Have an expert examine the sweepings. Report to Jointville.

Jointville says: "Too many upholsterers' tacks wasted in the plant at Port Smith. Belleville produced one hundred and eleven cars a day, with seven hundred and forty-nine men, wasting only nine hundred and six tacks."

It is a good thing to go through the plant now and then, select one man from all the others, give him a new and bigger job, just like that, offhand. If he doesn't make good, fire him.

It is a good thing to go through the plant occasionally, pick out some man, working apparently just as the others are, fire him.

If he asks why, just say to him, "You know."

He'll know why all right. He'll imagine why.

The thing is to build up Jointville. This country needs a religion. You have got to build up the sense of a mysterious central thing, a thing working outside your knowledge.

Let the notion grow and grow that there is something superhuman at the core of all this.

Lift up thine eyes, lift up thine eyes.

The central office reaches down into your secret thoughts. It knows, it knows.

Jointville knows.

Do not ask questions of Jointville. Keep up the pace.

Get the cars out.

Get the cars out.

Get the cars out.

The pace can be accelerated a little this year. The men have all got tuned into the old pace now.

Step it up a little, just a little.

They have got a special policeman in all the Bogel assembling plants. They have got a special doctor there. A man hurts his finger a little. It bleeds a little, a mere scratch. The doctor reaches down for him. The finger is fixed. Jointville wants no blood poisoning, no infections.

The doctor puts men who want jobs through a physical examination, as in the army. Try his nerve reactions. We want only the best men here, the youngest, the fastest.

Why not?

We pay the best wages, don't we?

The policeman in the plant has a special job. That's queer. It is like this. Now and then the big boss passes through. He selects a man off the belt.

"You're fired."

"Why?"

"You know."

Now and then a man goes off his nut. He goes fan-toed. He howls and shouts. He grabs up a hammer.

A stream of crazy profanity comes from his lips.

There is Jointville. That is the central thing. That controls the belt.

The belt controls me.

It moves.

It moves.

It moves.

I've tried to keep up.

I tell you I have been keeping up.

Jointville is God.

Jointville controls the belt.

The belt is God.

God has rejected me.

You're fired.

Sometimes a man, fired like that, goes nutty. He gets dangerous. A strong policeman on hand knocks him down, takes him out.

You walk within certain definite white lines.

It is calculated that a man, rubbing automobile bodies with pumice, makes thirty thousand and twenty-one arm strokes per day. The difference between thirty thousand and twenty-one and twenty-eight thousand and four will tell a vital story of profits or loss at Jointville.

Do you think things are settled at Jointville, or at the assembling plants of the Bogel car scattered all over America? Do you think men know how fast the belt can be made to move, what the ultimate, the final pace will be, can be?

Certainly not.

There are experts studying the nerves of men, the movements of men. They are watching, watching. Calculations are always going on. The thing is to produce goods and more goods at less cost. Keep the standard up. Increase the pace a little.

Stop waste.

Calculate everything.

A man walking to and from his work between white lines saves steps. There is a tremendous science of lost motion not perfectly calculated yet.

More goods at less cost.

Increase the pace.

Keep up standards.

It is so you advance civilization.

In the Bogel assembling plants, as at Jointville itself, there isn't any laughter. No one stops work to play. No one fools around or throws things, as they used to do in the old factories. That is why Bogel is able to put the old-fashioned factories, one by one, out of business.

It is all a matter of calculation. You feel it when you go in. You feel rigid lines. You feel movement. You feel a strange tension in the air. There is a quiet terrible intensity.

The belt moves. It keeps moving. The day I was there a number of young boys had come in. They had been sent by a Bogel car dealer, away back somewhere in the country. They had driven in during the night and were to drive Bogel cars back over country roads to some dealer. A good many Bogel cars go out to dealers from the assembling plants, driven out by boys like that.

Such boys, driving all night, fooling along the road, getting no sleep.

They have a place for them to wait for the cars in the Bogel assembling plants. You have been at dog shows and have seen how prize dogs are exhibited, each in his nice clean cage. They have nice clean cages like that for country boys who drive in to Bogel assembling plants to get cars.

The boys come in. There is a place to lie down in there. It is clean. After the boy goes into his cage a gate is closed. He is fastened in.

If a country boy, sleepy like that, waiting for his car, wandered about in a plant he might get hurt.

There might be damage suits, all sorts of things.

Better to calculate everything. Be careful. Be exact.

Jointville thought of that. Jointville thinks of everything. It is the center of power, the new mystery.

Every year in America Jointville comes nearer and nearer being the new center. Men nowadays do not look to Washington. They looks to Jointville.

Lift up thine eyes, lift up thine eyes.

Harvey Swados

JOE, THE VANISHING AMERICAN
(1937)

I F WALTER had not been so desperately anxious to go away
to college, he might never have been able to stick it out those
first few weeks at the factory. His father, once district sales
manager for a bankrupted sewing-machine concern, had come
down in the world and was now a continually uneasy clerk
in the branch office of a usury outfit called the Friendly
Finance Corporation; his mother, who had borne Walter late
in life, clung jealously to the fading prestige conferred on her
by her many beneficences on behalf of the Ladies' Guild.

Walter had never done anything harder than shovel the
neighbors' snowy driveways and sell magazines to reluctant
relatives. But the night of his graduation from high school
his father grunted in a choked voice that there was no money
to send him to college. Walter swore to himself that he would
get a college education if he had to rob a bank. At the commencement exercises a classmate had told him that you
could get a job at the new auto assembly plant if you said on
your application that you had worked as a garage mechanic.
While his parents rocked creakily, proud but miserable, on
the porch glider, Walter mounted the narrow steps to his little
room and sat down at his desk. If he could work steadily at
the plant for a year he ought to be able to save several thousand dollars even after contributing his share of the household expenses. Without saying a word to his parents, he went
to the plant the following morning and filled out an application blank. Three days later he received a telegram asking him
to report for work at six-thirty A.M.

When he returned, gray and exhausted, from his first
long day in the body shop to which he had been assigned,
Walter found his mother sitting in the parlor and sobbing into
a handkerchief. She raised her eyes at the slamming of the
door and stared at him in horror.

"Look at you!" she cried, and immediately Walter knew
that her first shock was at the way he *looked*, not at how he
must have *felt*. Nevertheless Walter felt it his filial duty to
explain that he would not have to march past the neighbors
in greasy coveralls, but could wear sport clothes to work and
change at the plant; furthermore, he hinted, when his mother

was preparing his sandwiches for the next day's lunch, he could just as easily carry them in a little paper bag as in a metal lunchbox.

His father, keeping them company in the kitchen, took a different tack, and even blustered a little about the advantages of working for a huge corporation.

"I don't see why Walter couldn't have started with something more pleasant," his mother said plaintively, smoothing mayonnaise across white bread. "In an office he could at least use his brains."

"Don't kid yourself," her husband replied. "There's no shame attached to factory work any more. Besides, Walter has a darned good chance to advance if he shows them the stuff he's got."

Implicit in all this was his parents' fear that Walter had started down a dead-end street, and their own shame at not having been able to send him away to college. Anxious not to inflame their feelings, Walter refrained from defending his decision; even if he were only to point out that he would be making big money, it would be a direct insult to his father, who at fifty-nine was making only five dollars a week more than he. So he put the case negatively.

"There's just no place else around," he said, "that would pay me anything like what I'm going to be making at the auto plant."

"The boy is right, Mother," his father said decisively, much to Walter's satisfaction. "You're doing a smart thing, Walter."

Thus challenged at home, Walter had no alternative but to grit his teeth and swear to himself that nothing would make him quit until he had reached his goal. Like a groggy but game boxer, he measured out his future not with the end of the fight in view, for that would have been too far away, but rather in terms of more immediate accomplishments: his first automatic nickel raise at the end of four weeks, his second automatic nickel raise at the end of eight weeks, his acceptance as a permanent employee at the end of ninety days, and most of all his listing as a metal finisher, which would mean that he would be in the highest-paid group in the plant and that he would be recognized as a skilled worker, a man who had made the grade.

His surroundings meant nothing to Walter, who had not expected that the factory would look like an art gallery.

But the work, and the conditions under which he had to do it, were a nightmare of endless horror from which Walter sometimes thought, stumbling wearily out of the plant after ten hours of unremitting anguish, he would one day awaken with a scream. It was not simply that the idea of working on an endless succession of auto bodies as they came slowly but ineluctably rolling down the assembly line like so many faceless steel robots was both monotonous and stupefying, or that the heavy work of finding bumps and dents in them, knocking them out and filing them down, was in itself too exhausting.

No, it was the strain of having to work both fast and accurately, with the foreman standing over him and glaring through his thick-lensed glasses, that made Walter dread the beginning of each day. Under the best of conditions, he figured, he had three and a half minutes to complete his metal-finishing work from the time he started a job on his line to the time it reached the platform and was swung off on hooks toward the bonderizing booth. If he began at the very beginning, as soon as the inspector had indicated bad spots with a stump of chalk, circling hollows and X-ing high spots, he could finish before the job reached the final inspector at the far end of the line—unless the dents were too deep or too numerous, in which case he was still madly pounding and filing, squatting and straining with the sweat running down his temples and his cheekbones while the solder flower worked next to him in a tangle of rubber hose, melting lead, and a blazing gun with a flame so hot that it scorched dry the running sweat on his face, and the final inspector stood over him, imperturbably chalking newly discovered hollows and pimples in the infuriating metal. Then he would straighten up from his hopeless effort and with a despairing glance at the impassive pickup man, who had to finish what he had left undone, he would hurry back down the line, praying to dear God that the next car—he did every third one—would be in fairly decent condition.

Worst of all were the times when he would hear a piercing whistle and would look up from the damnable dent at which he had been rapping blindly with the point of his file to see Buster the Foreman all the way past the platform, waving at him angrily with his cigar. Hurrying from his unfinished work to his punishment, Walter would try to steel himself against what he knew was coming, but it was no use.

"You call yourself a metal man?" Buster would ask, stuffing the cigar between his teeth with an angry snap. "You want to get metal finisher's pay and you let a job like that go through?" His eyes glinting with rage behind his thick spectacles, Buster would gesticulate at one of Walter's cars, freshly speckled with chalk marks as it swung in the air. "Get going on it!"

And Walter would hurl himself at the job, dashing the sweat from his brow with the back of his gloved hand and filing away in a clumsy fury.

By the time he had somehow or other repaired what he had left undone, he would find on hastening back to the line that he was far behind once again in his regular work, so far behind that it might take him the better part of an hour to gradually work his way back on the line to where he really belonged, safe for the moment from shouted complaints.

Inevitably the men around him had suggestions as to how Walter might better his condition. Of the two other metal finishers who worked on the line with him, one was a dour, fattish man, a leader in the opposition of the local union and disgusted because it did nothing to provide security for probationary employees like Walter.

"I'll tell you something else. There's countries where a bright young hard-working fellow like you, that wants to go to college, doesn't have to waste the best years of his life in factory work just to save the money for college fees. He gets sent right through school and the government foots the bills. All he has to do is show that he's got the stuff and his future is secure."

Walter allowed that this sounded fine, although "having the stuff" sounded uncomfortably like his father's eulogies of life in America, but he could not see what practical good it did him here and now—unless he was supposed to get satisfaction from the bitterness of knowing that in mysterious other countries his opposite numbers were better off than he.

The third metal finisher, a lean, efficient, sardonic man, had been listening silently to this talk of free college careers. He put his wiry hand inside his open-necked khaki shirt, scratched the coarse curling hair below his throat, and laughed aloud.

"What's the matter?" asked his fattish colleague suspiciously.

"You think your propaganda's going to change this boy's ideas about the other side of the world, when everything here tells him he's got it so good?" He tapped the fat man on the shoulder with the butt end of his file as patronizingly as if he were patting him on the head. "Even if he has to suffer for his education in a way that shouldn't be necessary, he's free. He can blunder around and maybe even learn something that isn't listed in the college catalogues. Those poor kids you want him to envy, they may be getting their college for nothing, but they're paying a higher price for it than this fellow ever will. And the sad part is that most of them probably don't even know what the price is." And he turned back to his work without giving the fat man a chance to reply.

Fortunately for the three of them, the fat metal finisher was transferred. He was only replaced, however, by an intense worker with two vertical wrinkles between his brows, who watched Walter's ineffectual work with growing impatience. At last he could stand it no more.

"In this game, kid, the knack of it is in the speed. The speed," he said fiercely, "and the way you concentrate on the job. If you're going to fumble around and just bitch about your mistakes, you'll be a long time getting straightened out." He greeted his own badly dented job, rolling toward them, with a smile of genuine pleasure. "Size it up quick, pick out the worst dents, and get going on them right away. Leave the high spots for last—the pickup men don't mind doing them."

The third man, the gray-haired cynic whom everyone liked but no one seemed to know, had been listening quietly, with a strange, mild grin on his long and youthful face. He put a stick of chewing gum in his mouth, ruminated for a moment, and said: "What you really want is for him to enjoy his work, Orrin. Might be more practical if you'd get down and actually show him how to do it. Here, hold on a minute, Walter."

Walter had been squatting on his haunches before the wheel housing of his job, blindly pounding with a hammer at his hidden screwdriver, trying hopelessly to punch a hole underneath so that with the screwdriver he could dig out a deep dent as the others did, trying so hopelessly that as he smashed the hammer against his left hand, missing the butt end of the screwdriver, he had to squeeze his eyes to keep the tears from starting forth.

"Give me that screwdriver."

Handing up the tool to the laconic man, Walter noticed for the first time that he bore an unusual tattoo, faded like an old flag, on his right forearm: an American eagle, claws gripping his wrist, beak opened triumphantly at the elbow—you could almost hear it screaming. Without a word the man took the screwdriver and swiftly pressed it to a grinding wheel, fashioning a beveled point.

"Try it now."

Walter stuck the screwdriver under the car, rapped at it smartly several times—*bang!* it was through and resting against the outer skin of the car, just at the very dent. Gratefully, he turned to the gray-haired man, but the man was gone, like a mirage.

There was something miragelike about him, anyway. He drove to and from work alone; he never engaged in small talk; he never hung around with a group at lunch hour or before work; he kept a paper book in the hip pocket of his khaki trousers, and always when he was not concentrating on his own work, when he was watching Walter or listening to the others handing him advice, he had that mocking irreligious smile on his long narrow youthful face. What was more, his cold blue eye seemed always to be on Walter, sizing him up, watching not so much his work, as everyone else did, but his temperament and his personality. It made him uncomfortable.

Gradually Walter began to sort out the other men around him, the ones who had more common reality in their talk and their tastes. Most companionable of them all was Kevin, the former rural schoolteacher, now an immigrant hook man. His accent was so delightful, his turns of speech so happy, that Walter engaged the towering redhead in conversation at every opportunity.

"Hey, Kevin," he shouted at him one day, "how old were those kids you taught in County Kerry?"

"Ah, Walter," Kevin sighed, showing his long white teeth as he spoke, "they weren't *all* such children. If you were to see some of the older girls—quite well developed, they were. Oh, how shameful if they had known what was passing through their schoolmaster's mind!"

Kevin laughed at the memory, Walter at the picture the big fellow conjured up of countryside lust; he turned around and there was the gray-haired metal finisher, smiling too, but so coldly you would have thought him a scientist observing a successful experiment. It was chilling, and yet not wholly unpleasant. In a way that he could not define, Walter felt that he was being judged and approved.

This third man, reserved and anonymous as ever, continued to observe him as Walter chatted not only with Kevin and the second metal finisher but with all the other men on their line. Conversation was necessarily shouted and fragmentary, but Walter was astonished at how intimacies could be revealed in the course of a few phrases:

"A man's a fool to get married."

"Grab the overtime while you can. In the auto industry you never know when you'll be laid off."

"Happiest time of my life was when I was in the army."

"Only reason I'm here is because I was too stupid to learn a trade."

"I came here out of curiosity, but my curiosity's all used up."

"My wife says if I quit I'll have a better chance to line up a construction job."

"Walter, don't turn out like those college men who can tell you how to do everything but can't do a damn thing themselves."

The only one to rebuff Walter's friendly overtures was Pop, the seamy-faced little inspector with a rooster's ruff of yellowing white hair that rose and tumbled down over his forehead, and sunken old lips from which depended miraculously a heavy, unlighted cigar. Wizened, pale, and bloodless, he regarded Walter, for no apparent reason, with bottomless contempt. With a little cap perched sideways on his Niagara of a head like a precarious canoe, and a soft brown cloth knotted about the hand with which he probed Walter's work for defects and omissions, he seemed to Walter like some strange and hateful gnome.

"Kids like you," he said in a dry and rusty monotone, "they come and go. Twenty-three years I'm here, and I seen a million like you. Not steady, not reliable, don't want to learn, just out for fun. You'll never make a metal man."

I don't want to be a metal man, Walter wanted to reply; I just want to make my money and get out of here. But this was, he knew, just what Pop was goading him to say, so he held his tongue. A moment later he was glad that he had, for he was startled to hear the third metal finisher address him.

"Pop is an exception," he said, bending over Walter's car and scrubbing at it with his sandpaper as he spoke. "By and large there is a democracy of age in the factory. Men who have been here since before you were born fought for a union contract guaranteeing equal treatment for you. Ninety days after you start you get the same wage as a worker who's been on the job nineteen years. A man twice your age will treat you as a working partner and an adult. Where else is that true?"

"Yes," Walter replied angrily, "but Pop—"

"He's got reason to be bitter. Someday I'll tell you why."

He straightened up abruptly and walked away to his own job. But the words he had used reverberated in Walter's mind. Who was he, with his young-old face and his expressions like "democracy of age"? Walter asked, but no one seemed to know. Some said he was a seaman and adventurer, and his big tattoo was pointed to as proof, for he had been heard to state himself that he had acquired it in Lourenço Marques; but others, who had themselves come to the assembly line from rural homesteads, were positive from clues he had let fall that he had formerly been an itinerant farm laborer; and there were even those who swore that he was really an educated man, a kind of college professor amusing himself by slumming among them.

Whoever he was, for the time he had nothing more to say. But Walter felt his presence, for he was always ready to lend a hand, always laconically helpful, always silently observing and listening.

One day the younger inspector at the beginning of the line, blowing genial clouds of illegal pipe smoke, gave Walter some frank and cynical advice.

"Been listening to the bosses talking about you, buddy." He took the pipe from his mouth and formed a fat smoke ring. "Want to know what's wrong with what you're doing?"

"I guess so," said Walter dully.

"You try too hard. You're trying to do a good job—that's the worst thing you can do."

Walter stared in bewilderment at the inspector. "But why?"

"They're interested in pulling production. If you're going to be running up and down the line all day trying to make every job perfect, you're just going to get in people's way. What the bosses will do is, they'll look for an excuse to fire you before your probationary period is up, or else they'll stick you in a routine lower-paying job."

"Then . . ."

"I've been here ten years. Believe me"—he drew on his pipe once again and smiled disarmingly—"they're not interested in making good cars; they're interested in making cars. You know what production means? Volume. And you know what they hired you for? To camouflage, not to get rid of every flaw. Hide them so they don't show up after the car's been through paint, so the customer doesn't see them at the dealer's, and you'll get along great."

"Camouflage them how?"

"With your sandpaper. With the grinding wheel. If you hit them up and down and then across, final inspection will never know what's underneath. Make it look good, and confusing. Be a camouflage artist and the bosses'll very seldom bother you."

Walter could not help laughing. "Listen, how could you stand it here for ten years? Every day I think maybe I ought to get out and look for something else."

"For six years," the inspector said pleasantly, "I was like you. This was going to be just temporary until I found something with a real future. It took me six years to realize that I was going to be spending the rest of my life here—it's like breaking in a wild horse; only, with a human being it takes longer. I got married, had three kids, now I'm building a home near the plant. So I make the best of it; I take it easy and I have as much fun as I can, and I hate to see a guy like you breaking his back all for nothing."

Bending over his work, Walter raised his file and heard the inspector's final shot, lightly enough intended but bearing its own weight of bitterness and resignation: "You'd be surprised how many fellows I've heard talking just like you —couldn't stand the work, going to quit any day—and now they're five- and ten-year men, starting to think about retirement benefits."

Walter could not clarify in his own mind what it was about the inspector's attitude that increased his desperation, not until his silent partner eased up to him from nowhere and said quietly, "Kind of terrified you, didn't he?"

"Not exactly terrified."

"Just the same, it's no fun to be doing time and to be told that your sentence just might turn out to be indefinite. Then if you've got a good imagination you can see yourself gradually getting used to it, even getting to like the routine, so that one day follows another and the first thing you know the wrinkles are there and the kids are grown up and you don't know where it's all gone to, your life."

Walter felt himself shuddering. Was it from the blower overhead that he felt his hot sweat turning cold and drying on his face? He said, "I suppose you have to be cynical if you're going to stay here."

"Day after day your life becomes a joke without any point, a trick that you play on yourself from punching in to punching out."

"But that's only if you're an imaginative or a sensitive person."

For the first time, the man's angular face hardened. "Don't you think somebody like that inspector had his ambitions? Don't you think he still has his man's pride? Did you ever figure the cost of the job in terms of what it does to the personality of a clever, intelligent fellow like him? He says if you're going to be trapped you might as well make the best of it, and by his lights he may be right. Anyway, don't be too quick to blame him—he probably never had the opportunity to save money and go off to college."

No one had ever, not ever in eighteen years, talked to Walter in such a way. He would never again be able to look at a man like the inspector without compassion. Even at home in the evening with his father, whom he could no longer talk to about anything but baseball or the weather (although they both tried clumsily to broach other more serious topics), Walter found that he was viewing this desolate man not just as his father but as a man who had his own miseries; and this, he knew, was a part of growing up that could not have come about as it had without the influence of his strange friend in the factory.

More and more as the weeks passed and exhaustion was gradually overcome by vitality, only to be transformed into monotony, Walter came to feel that only this man could explain the real meaning of the assembly line. But he remained aloof, insubstantial as a ghost. The more he held to himself, the more Walter was piqued, and determined to make the ghost speak.

At last one day he ventured to demand: "Say, what does that tattoo of yours stand for, that big bird?"

The man smiled with one side of his mouth. "That old bird is the American eagle." He raised his arm briefly, flexed it, and let it fall to his side. "It's screaming with rage at what's happened to the Republic."

"What *has* happened?"

"Where are the guts? Where's the drive? In a place like this a man's life goes down the drain like scummy water."

"But you're working here too," Walter said boldly.

The man shook his head slowly, with such finality that there was something elemental about the gesture. "I'm not a settled-down man. I'm just passing through."

Walter cleared his throat. "I don't even know your name."

"Why should you? Instead of learning names, we refer to the fellow with the bad teeth, or the guy with the blue coveralls. When I work next to a man for months and learn that his wife is being operated on for cancer of the breast and still don't know his name, it tells me something, not just about him and me, but about the half-connections that are all the factory allows you in the way of friendships."

"The old-timers are clubby enough, but everybody else claims they're here for a limited time. The place is so big and everything seems so temporary that I suppose we don't feel the need of introducing ourselves."

The older man looked at Walter somberly. "No one who comes here wants to admit that the place has any real connection with his real life. He has to say that he is just putting in his time here, and so no matter how friendly he is by nature he has to think of the people around his as essentially strangers, men whom he can't even trouble to say good-bye to when he quits or gets laid off."

"But *your* name—"

"Call me Joe."

Walter pursued him: "Every third guy on the line must be named Joe. Joe what?"

He smiled again, his long Yankee countenance creasing in a cold grin. "Joe, the vanishing American." And he turned his back on Walter and bent to his work as the line resumed its endless progress.

But he was a curious man, a nosy man, and he was there, listening and leering, when Walter found a minute to respond without cursing to a bitter remark of Pop's. Walter turned on him with the anger he had managed to suppress when speaking to the old inspector.

"It's easy for you to stand there and laugh. You think you're better than anybody else in the shop."

Joe hitched up his khaki trousers and replied with deliberate anger: "I never claimed that. I just read a little more and ponder a little more than the average fellow. That's why I don't laugh at them; I feel sorry for them. If I'm a little freer, I've had to make sacrifices for it—no dependents, no ties." He added cryptically, "They punish you one way or they punish you another way."

Walter did not quite understand, but it struck him that these remarks were a prelude to farewell.

He asked uneasily, "You're not going to quit?"

"One of these days. Maybe the weather will turn, or I'll hear of something else, or I'll have words with Buster . . ." He added with somewhat more warmth, "But I'll be back— if not here, some place like here. You won't, though. That's why I hope you won't forget what it was like for the people who made the things you'll be buying."

Walter cried indignantly: "How could I? How could I ever forget?" It seemed to him that the thick scurf of silver through which he shuffled as he worked, the glittering waste of lead filings and melted sticks, were so many needles, each carrying its stinging injection of memory—of sweat, exhaustion, harrying, feverish haste, and stupid boredom.

"You forget worse things, don't you? Pain, and even death? You'll think back on the days when you were slaving away to save money for college, and they'll strike you as comical, maybe even romantic."

"God forbid!" Walter laughed. And yet he had suddenly a shivery foretaste of a future beyond the one of which he daydreamed as he worked.

When the siren screamed the end of their nine and a half hours, Walter hurled his file and apron into his toolbox and trotted down the aisle toward the time clock. Turning the corner of the body shop office just as its lights were extinguished, he ran headlong into one of the iron antennae of a fork truck and cried aloud with pain as the metal plate struck his shinbone. Tottering backward, Walter was suddenly gripped by the forearm and pulled erect. He turned gratefully and found himself staring into the eyes of Joe.

Smarting with soreness and embarrassment, Walter demanded aggressively, "I suppose that's what you want me to remember!"

A faint stubble glinted along Joe's narrow cheeks. Graying like his iron hair, it aged him as it grew. He scraped his hand across it wearily and replied quietly, "Never mind the machinery. Remember the men. The men make the machines, and they make their own tragedies too. Once your own life gets easier, you'll take it for granted not only that theirs must be easier too, but that they deserve what they get anyway, that some law of natural selection has put you up where you are and them down where they are."

They had reached the clock bay where they took their place meekly in line, waiting to punch out, shuffling forward every few seconds while they spoke in low voices. Around them a swarm of men surged toward freedom—noisy boys with laughter to spare for the evening; haggard weary men in their forties; surly powerful black men in stained coveralls and scrawny brown men chattering in Spanish; vacant-faced fools with slack jaws and dangling hands; shrewd-eyed men fingering their union contract books, composing their campaign leaflets, and computing their chances of election to positions that would lift them out of the work routine.

"Why do they stay?"

"They're trapped, that's why. They say everybody's supposed to be, one way or another, but it's worse to be stuck here. Spending your life on the production line means counting out the minutes, being grateful that Mondays go fast because you're rested, and hating Tuesdays because the week is so long. It means that you're paying off forever on all the things you've been pressured into buying by getting up every day in order to do something you'd never, never think of doing if it was a matter of choice. It means never having anything to look forward to in all of your working life." Joe took his card from the rack, clicked it in the time clock, and with a wave of his hand was gone.

What was happening, as Walter woke daily to the dawn's dull alarm and went from the still house through the newly washed streets to the waiting assembly line, was that his self-pity, so strong that the page blurred before him when he lay in bed reading himself to sleep, was altering into a maturer concern with the fate of others who could not, like himself, set a term to their labor.

He began to question the men on the line with him, one after another, to find out how many of them felt as he did about what they were doing for a living. More sure of himself with every passing hour, he moved up and down the line, demanding, whenever there was a moment, an answer to his insistent question: "Do you think anybody likes coming in here to work?"

"Everybody does one day a week—payday," said the solder flower.

"Not even the bosses," said the deck fitter. "Do you think anybody with sense would knock himself out in this dirt and noise if it wasn't for the money?"

And the door fitter said wryly: "Do you know what this kind of work is? It's colored man's work. But even the colored men are smartening up—they turn up their noses at it too unless they get strapped."

Saddened and bewildered by this last comment, Walter turned away from the man who had made it and who had punctuated his bitter remark with a series of thunderous blows on a door that he was fitting. Only Orrin, the second metal finisher, grudgingly admitted that the work was a challenge to him, that the pay was fair, and that there were worse jobs. Behind them all, long-jawed Joe, caught up with his work as usual, stood casually beveling his screwdriver.

"I hear you've been taking a little poll," he said to Walter.

"What's it to you?" Walter asked truculently. He was in no mood to be mocked.

With apparent irrelevance, Joe replied by demanding, "How come you fixed on being an engineer?"

Walter was taken aback. "Why, that's where everybody says the future is."

"That's not reason enough for a fellow to struggle and sweat to get to college. Damn it, doesn't anybody go out and do what he wants to any more? I'm not saying you wouldn't make a good engineer, or that it wouldn't be fine for a change to have some engineers who care as much about people as they do about gadgets. But supposing you find out after you get to college that you want to spend your time learning something useless—are you going to leave yourself open for it?"

"Boy, you sure are free with advice."

Joe looked at him gravely. His long sad jaw had the hint of a smile. "The men on the line like you, Walter. They don't think you're just nosy when you ask questions. They think you're one of them, and in a good way you are. Maybe that's why I've got hopes for you."

Walter fought hard against the influence of the older man, whose crabbed and subversive outlook was so foreign to everything Walter had been taught; but he was forced to admit to himself that more and more he was seeing the factory through Joe's cold, discerning eyes, and he began to fear that if Joe were ever to leave, the plant would have no real existence other than as a money-producing nightmare. Not only was there no one else really to talk to about it, but Joe had forced Walter to try to formuate his emerging ideas in an adult and comprehensible way.

"The worst thing about the assembly line is what it does to your self-respect," he said to Joe early one morning as they squatted on their haunches, waiting for the starting siren. "It's hard to keep from feeling like a fool when you know that everybody looks down on what you're doing, even the men who are doing it themselves."

Joe hung his hammer and metal spoon from the brass hook at his belt. "The big pitch has always been that we're a practical people, that we've proved to all the impractical European dreamers that production can serve people. But instead people are serving production. Look how frightened, how hysterical the bosses get when the line stops—they can't afford to figure what it costs *you* to keep it moving— they only know they've got a production quota. Of course, when sales resistance starts building up and they put the cork back in themselves, they give you just the opposite story. Who can blame the poor slob in the middle for suspecting that the whole setup is really nutty as a fruitcake, and for feeling ashamed of himself for being caught up in it?"

"All right," Walter challenged him. "Who's crazy? You, me, the guys around us, or the board of directors?"

"Anybody who gets suckered into believing that there's anything real behind the billboards they put up to get the show on the road, so that he commits himself to buying the billboard pictures by selling his life on the installment plan. I sympathize with any joker who begins to suspect that the whole world is against him, that he's the victim of a huge conspiracy organized to make his car fall apart before it's been paid off. Doesn't life in the factory seem to be deliberately resigned to lower your own self-esteem? What happens when you're knocking down a dent? If you rap it too hard from the inside, you have to file it down that much more, and you hate yourself for it. If you don't rap it hard enough, you only find out after it's moved on down the line, and then you have to hurry up and wallop it again. In either case you hate yourself instead of hating the car, or the invisible man that started up the line." He laughed briefly in anticipation of what he was about to add. "It's like the man that hits his thumb with a hammer while he's hanging a picture—only here he keeps hitting his thumb because they're moving the wall as fast as the union will let them. Who does he yell at every time the ball peen comes down on his nail? Himself."

"I wonder," Walter said slowly, "how many people actually feel that way."

"More than you can count. It's always safe to figure that if you feel something, the world must be full of people who feel the same way. Every sensible man realizes as he gets older that his feelings aren't unique. After all, that's the basis of the best art—the fact that you recognize yourself in it, and all those inner experiences that you'd thought no one else but you could know."

Walter was willing to recognize that he was not the only one to cringe when Buster called him back on a badly done job, to swear at himself for the mistakes that made him fall behind, to realize how he was being trapped into swearing at himself and deflecting his anger from what he did to the way he did it. But it was hard for him to believe that there were others who felt as intensely as he did, who beat their heads against the bars as he did, who dreamed of sunlight and freedom as he did, even though Joe tried to persuade him that the difference was often one of degree, or of his being able to express his feeling in a way that others couldn't. This was one of the questions that Walter was eager to argue with Joe, who moved from one extreme position to another, always mocking, always challenging him to learn what he stood for and to defend it like a man.

"You know something," Walter burst out impetuously one day, "I don't know what I would have done here without you."

Instead of laughing or belittling this praise, Joe's face darkened. The next morning he was not on the line.

By the third day of his absence Walter was beginning to feel as though it had all been a dream, as though he were slipping once again into the awful pit of loneliness, exhaustion, and self-doubting despair. As a last resort he sought out the men on the line to learn what they thought of Joe.

"He's irresponsible," said Pop.

"He's the kind of guy that just don't care," said the younger inspector. "No wife, no kids—no wonder he can take off three days without worrying about getting a reprimand or getting fired."

"He knows his work," said Orrin grudgingly. "I don't know where he learned it, but he did. Just the same, he takes off. You can't *afford* to take off like that nowadays, not if you want to hold down a job."

On the fourth day he came back. He told no one where he had been. "Am I glad to see you!" Walter exclaimed—but Joe merely indicated, with a cold grin and a turn of his tattooed arm, that from time to time things came up that were more important than the making of automobiles. He did not set to work, but almost immediately was engaged in serious talk with Buster the foreman and with the union shop steward. The two arguing vigorously, but suddenly Joe cut them off simply by lifting his hand. He said something very briefly, shoved his hands into his pockets, and the discussion was finished.

To Walter's amazement he came back to the line, picked up his toolbox, and nodded casually to him.

"I just quit, Walter," he said. "Going to hit the road."

"But—"

"You'll make out all right, no matter what you do. I don't even have to wish you good luck."

Then he was off down the aisle, on his way to the tool crib and the plant police and the parking lot and God alone knew where after that, without so much as a handshake or an inclination of his lean frame. Suddenly Walter remembered something: "Hey!" he shouted. But Joe—if he heard him—did not turn around and soon was out of sight.

You never told me about Pop, he wanted to tell Joe; you never answered all the questions I was going to ask you—but even if Joe had not gone for good, Walter would not have known how to say to him all the things that should have been said, the words of gratitude and self-confidence.

When the relief man came a few minutes later to give

him a twelve-minute break, he hurried to the bathroom. There, just beyond the big circular sink that could accommodate half a dozen men, he could see out the tilted window to the vast parking lot.

The dull winter light was gloomy and deceptive, and so vague was the air that the dark ranks of massed automobiles were no more than darker blurs against the background of the gray steel fencing and the lowering sky. One of the cars moved, or was it his imagination? But no, the red taillight dimmed, glowed, dimmed. Joe, the vanishing American, was swinging out of the lot and away from the production line, out of Walter's life and into someone else's, out of the present and into what lay beyond the gate. He was leaving the future to Walter, who now at last could wave his farewell, with his face pressed to the cool window as he watched the little light disappearing from view.

Then he washed the sweat from his face and returned to his work.

Mark Twain

MY WATCH
(c. 1870)

AN INSTRUCTIVE LITTLE TALE

MY BEAUTIFUL new watch had run eighteen months without losing or gaining, and without breaking any part of its machinery or stopping. I had come to believe it infallible in its judgments about the time of day, and to consider its constitution and its anatomy imperishable. But at last, one night, I let it run down. I grieved about it as if it were a recognized messenger and forerunner of calamity. But by and by I cheered up, set the watch by guess, and commanded my bodings and superstitions to depart. Next day I stepped into the chief jeweler's to set it by the exact time, and the head of the establishment took it out of my hand and proceeded to set it for me. Then he said, "She is four minutes slow—

regulator wants pushing up." I tried to stop him—tried to make him understand that the watch kept perfect time. But no; all this human cabbage could see was that the watch was four minutes slow, and the regulator *must* be pushed up a little; and so, while I danced around him in anguish, and implored him to let the watch alone, he calmly and cruelly did the shameful deed. My watch began to gain. It gained faster and faster day by day. Within the week it sickened to a raging fever, and its pulse went up to a hundred and fifty in the shade. At the end of two months it had left all the timepieces of the town far in the rear, and was a fraction over thirteen days ahead of the almanac. It was away into November enjoying the snow, while the October leaves were still turning. It hurried up house rent, bills payable, and such things, in such a ruinous way that I could not abide it. I took it to the watchmaker to be regulated. He asked me if I had ever had it repaired. I said no, it had never needed any repairing. He looked a look of vicious happiness and eagerly pried the watch open, and then put a small dice-box into his eye and peered into its machinery. He said it wanted cleaning and oiling, besides regulating—come in a week. After being cleaned and oiled, and regulated, my watch slowed down to that degree that it ticked like a tolling bell. I began to be left by trains, I failed all appointments, I got to missing my dinner; my watch strung out three days' grace to four and let me go to protest; I gradually drifted back into yesterday, then day before, then into last week, and by and by the comprehension came upon me that all solitary and alone I was lingering along in week before last, and the world was out of sight. I seemed to detect in myself a sort of sneaking fellow-feeling for the mummy in the museum, and a desire to swap news with him. I went to a watchmaker again. He took the watch all to pieces while I waited, and then said the barrel was "swelled." He said he could reduce it in three days. After this the watch *averaged* well, but nothing more. For half a day it would go like the very mischief, and keep up such a barking and wheezing and whooping and sneezing and snorting, that I could not hear myself think for the disturbance; and as long as it held out there was not a watch in the land that stood any chance against it. But the rest of the day it would keep on slowing down and fooling along until all the clocks it had left behind caught up again. So at last, at the end of twenty-four hours, it would trot up to the judges' stand all right and just in time. It would show a fair and square average, and no man could say it had done more or less than its duty. But a correct average is only a mild virtue in a watch, and I took this instrument to another watchmaker. He said the king-bolt was broken. I said I was glad it was nothing more serious. To tell the plain truth, I had no idea what the king-bolt was, but I did not choose to appear ignorant to a stranger. He repaired the king-bolt, but what the watch gained in one way it lost in another. It would run awhile and then stop awhile, and then run awhile again, and so on, using its own discretion about the intervals. And every time it went off it kicked back like a musket. I padded my breast for a few days, but finally took the watch to another watchmaker. He picked it all to pieces, and turned the ruin over and over under his glass; and then he said there appeared to be something the matter with the hair-trigger. He fixed it, and gave it a fresh start. It did well now, except that always at ten minutes to ten the hands would shut together like a pair of scissors, and from that time forth they would travel together. The oldest man in the world could not make head or tail of the time of day by such a watch, and so I went again to have the thing repaired. This person said that the crystal had got bent, and that the mainspring was not straight. He also remarked that part of the works needed half-soling. He made these things all right, and then my timepiece performed unexceptionably, save that now and then, after working along quietly for nearly eight hours, everything inside would let go all of a sudden and begin to buzz like a bee, and the hands would straightway begin to spin round and round so fast that their individuality was lost completely, and they simply seemed a delicate spider's web over the face of the watch. She would reel off the next twenty-four hours in six or seven minutes, and then stop with a bang. I went with a heavy heart to one more watchmaker, and looked on while he took her to pieces. Then I prepared to cross-question him rigidly, for this thing was getting serious. The watch had cost two hundred dollars originally, and I seemed to have paid out two or three thousand for repairs. While I waited and looked on I presently recognized in this watchmaker an old acquaintance—a steamboat engineer of other days, and not a good engineer, either. He examined all the parts carefully, just as the other watchmakers had done, and then delivered his verdict with the same confidence of manner.

He said:

"She makes too much steam—you want to hang the monkey-wrench on the safety-valve!"

I brained him on the spot, and had him buried at my own expense.

My uncle William (now deceased, alas!) used to say that a good horse was a good horse until it had run away once, and that a good watch was a good watch until the repairers got a chance at it. And he used to wonder what became of all the unsuccessful tinkers, and gunsmiths, and shoemakers, and engineers, and blacksmiths; but nobody could ever tell him.

Adam Smith

THE EDUCATION OF THE WORKER
(1776)

IN THE PROGRESS of the division of labour, the employment of the far greater part of those who live by labour, that is, of the great body of the people, comes to be confined to a few very simple operations, frequently to one or two. But the understandings of the greater part of men are necessarily formed by their ordinary employments. The man whose whole life is spent in performing a few simple operations, of which the effects too are, perhaps, always the same, or very nearly the same, has no occasion to exert his understanding, or to exercise his invention in finding out expedients for removing difficulties which never occur. He naturally loses, therefore, the habit of such exertion, and generally becomes as stupid and ignorant as it is possible for a human creature to become. The torpor of his mind renders him, not only incapable of relishing or bearing a part in any rational conversation, but of conceiving any generous, noble, or tender sentiment, and consequently of forming any just judgment concerning many even of the ordinary duties of private life. Of the great and extensive interests of his country he is altogether incapable of judging; and unless very particular pains have been taken to render him otherwise, he is equally incapable of defending his country in war. The uniformity of his stationary life naturally corrupts the courage of his mind, and makes him regard with abhorrence the irregular, uncertain, and adventurous life of a soldier. It corrupts even the activity of his body, and renders him incapable of exerting his strength with vigour and perseverance, in any other employment than that to which he has been bred. His dexterity at his own particular trade seems, in this manner, to be acquired at the expense of his intellectual, social, and martial virtues. But in every improved and civilized society this is the state into which the labouring poor, that is, the great body of the people, must necessarily fall, unless government takes some pains to prevent it.

It is otherwise in the barbarous societies, as they are commonly called, of hunters, of shepherds, and even of husbandmen in that rude state of husbandry which precedes the improvement of manufactures, and the extension of foreign commerce. In such societies the varied occupations of every man oblige every man to exert his capacity, and to invent expedients for removing difficulties which are continually occurring. Invention is kept alive, and the mind is not suffered to fall into that drowsy stupidity, which, in a civilized society, seems to benumb the understanding of almost all the inferior ranks of people. In those barbarous societies, as they are called, every man, it has already been observed, is a warrior. Every man too is in some measure a statesman, and can form a tolerable judgment concerning the interest of the society, and the conduct of those who govern it. How far their chiefs are good judges in peace, or good leaders in war, is obvious to the observation of almost every single man among them. In such a society indeed, no man can well acquire that improved and refined understanding, which a few men sometimes possess in a more civilized state. Though in a rude society there is a good deal of variety in the occupations of every individual, there is not a great deal in those of the whole society. Every man does, or is capable of doing, almost every thing which any other man does, or is capable of doing. Every man has a considerable degree of knowledge,

ingenuity, and invention; but scarce any man has a great
degree. The degree, however, which is commonly possessed,
is generally sufficient for conducting the whole simple business of the society. In a civilized state, on the contrary,
though there is little variety in the occupations of the greater
part of individuals, there is an almost infinite variety in those
of the whole society. These varied occupations present an
almost infinite variety of objects to the contemplation of those
few, who, being attached to no particular occupation themselves, have leisure and inclination to examine the occupations of other people. The contemplation of so great a variety
of objects necessarily exercises their minds in endless comparisons and combinations, and renders their understandings,
in an extraordinary degree, both acute and comprehensive.
Unless those few, however, happen to be placed in some very
particular situations, their great abilities, though honourable
to themselves, may contribute very little to the good government or happiness of their society. Notwithstanding the
great abilities of those few, all the nobler parts of the human
character may be, in a great measure, obliterated and extinguished in the great body of the people.

The education of the common people requires, perhaps, in
a civilized and commercial society, the attention of the public
more than that of people of some rank and fortune. People
of some rank and fortune are generally eighteen or nineteen
years of age before they enter upon that particular business,
profession, or trade, by which they propose to distinguish
themselves in the world. They have before that full time to
acquire, or at least to fit themselves for afterwards acquiring,
every accomplishment which can recommend them to the
public esteem, or render them worthy of it. Their parents or
guardians are generally sufficiently anxious that they should
be so accomplished, and are, in most cases, willing enough to
lay out the expence which is necessary for that purpose. If
they are not always properly educated, it is seldom from the
want of expence laid out upon their education; but from
the improper application of that expence. It is seldom from
the want of masters; but from the negligence and incapacity
of the masters who are to be had, and from difficulty, or
rather from the impossibility which there is, in the present
state of things, of finding any better. The employments too in
which people of some rank or fortune spend the greater part
of their lives, are not, like those of the common people, sim-

ple and uniform. They are almost all of them extremely complicated, and such as exercise the head more than the hands. The understandings of those who are engaged in such employments can seldom grow torpid for want of exercise. The employments of people of some rank and fortune, besides, are seldom such as harass them from morning to night. They generally have a good deal of leisure, during which they may perfect themselves in every branch either of useful or ornamental knowledge of which they may have laid the foundation, or for which they may have acquired some taste in the earlier part of life.

It is otherwise with the common people. They have little time to spare for education. Their parents can scarce afford to maintain them even in infancy. As soon as they are able to work, they must apply to some trade by which they can earn subsistence. That trade too is generally so simple and uniform as to give little exercise to the understanding; while, at the same time, their labour is both so constant and so severe, that it leaves them little leisure and less inclination to apply to, or even to think of any thing else.

Margot Bennett

From THE LONG WAY BACK
(1954)

AT SEVEN the official staff entered, and pushed their way without interest through the packed anteroom. At nine, Grame was called.

He fixed a smile on his face, walked briskly through the door, and down the ramp for sixty strides. He was deeper in the earth than he had ever been before, and in front of him stood the biggest machine in the world. When he came in, it was purring feebly like a young kitten, but at sight of him it gave an experimental shriek, and then told him to move forward.

He looked in appeal at the men, but their eyes were on the

machine, or on the parts of it for which each was responsible. He advanced reluctantly, stood, and turned, while the machine took an X-ray photograph of his skull; a superficial photograph of his person; an impression of his fingerprints; a record of his voice; and a sample of his blood.

One of the machine-tenders moved a lever, and the conversation began.

"You, Grame, mechanical-repetitive worker, hut 498, age 24 years on this fifteenth day of March, Add 3,406, why do you apply for regrading?" The record stopped, and the machine was silent, waiting for Grame to feed propositions onto its tape. These propositions, separated from their emotional adornments, would pass through the selector to emerge as a wavelength that could pick up the correct replies.

Grame was silent for a moment. He had prepared arguments flexible enough to outwit an enemy or to impress a friend, but not to affect the responses of a machine.

"I was graded as a mechanical-repetitive worker at the age of seven," he began uneasily.

"Were you graded by men or by machine?"

"I was passed through the grading machine."

"Then no mistake was made. Men make mistakes, machines do not."

"Children can alter," Grame said. He was speaking carefully, trying to suppress his hatred of the grading system. "The child grows and sees the world and wants to have an interesting place in it. Perhaps the boy of seven who can't move button two on the machine will turn into the boy of seventeen who can build a machine of his own."

The machine digested this. "Have you any complaints about your education?"

"I was educated like the other mech-rep children. Two hours' daily speed and accuracy practice in press-button and pull-lever techniques; simple arithmetic; label reading; annual lectures on food values and biology."

"Have you any complaints about your education?" the machine repeated, without altering its previous inflections.

"It wasn't an education at all," Grame said. "But I've educated myself. I've taught myself to read and write and think. I've taught myself science and high-level mathematics. In every factory I've worked in I've been round every department and mastered every process. I've been studying physics for years. I am prepared to produce as evidence formulae that I believe to be original. I will welcome examination by any body of professional physicists. I claim that my proper career is in physics," he said, beginning to shout at the machine.

"Have you any complaint about the food in your hut?" the machine asked calmly.

"I don't want to talk about food. I want to talk about my life. I want to work in physics."

There was an unprecedented silence of several seconds, then the machine spoke again.

"You must explain clearly the work you want to do."

"I want to study cosmic rays."

The machine put up a no-response signal. It had not been equipped to discuss cosmic rays. One of the attendants pulled a lever, and speech emerged again.

"Have you any complaints about conditions in your hut? Have you an adequate tobacco room?"

"I don't want to discuss tobacco rooms. I want to appeal against my grading."

"Have you any complaints about sex facilities in your hut? Have you an adequate sex cubicle?"

"Damn sex facilities. I want to be regraded as a physicist. I appeal to you," Grame said wildly. "I appeal to you as a machine. I appeal to you for regrading."

"You have already been graded. You have given no reason to be regraded. Have you any complaints about physical recreation?"

"I won't talk to this machine," Grame cried angrily to the machine-tenders. "It's puerile." The adjective, being merely a subjective emotional term, was ignored by the machine, but one of the attendants, who had seemed indifferent to the conversation, pulled a switch and the machine began to speak in different tones.

"Look at this thing reasonably," it said. "So far as civilisation goes, we think we've evolved something pretty decent for people in general. Food, religion, and sex for all. That's a pretty big achievement, isn't it? And don't forget that our sanitary arrangements are excellent. We've also given every consideration to the filling of leisure hours, and we're really rather proud of the results. But we must never forget that work is part of the picture, and that's where the grading machine comes in. It's a rather miraculous machine, when you think of it. And what does it do? It ensures that everyone

gets the job he's fit for, the job he can do with satisfaction
and pride, and isn't made miserable by struggling with something that's just that little bit beyond his powers."

"Regrading?" Grame said desperately. "What about my
regrading?"

"The grading machine acts in the interests of the people
graded," the machine went on smoothly. "It fits all the round
pegs snugly into the round holes, where they have no chance
to grow uncomfortable square corners. And the grading machine doesn't suffer from human fallibility. It is always right."

"But I came here to prove it isn't."

"Next, please," the machine said indifferently.

Grame stood still. "The grading machine is never right,"
he said. "I don't think it works at all. It couldn't tell the
difference between a rabbit and a crocodile. It works on per-
centages and it knows nothing more. It just puts through
30 per cent mechanical-repetitives; 25 per cent soldiers;
20 per cent farmers, and so on. It doesn't grade children. It
deals them into heaps. The machine's wrong. Always and
forever wrong. Machines know nothing about people. They
can give information about the number of color-blind road-
sweepers who are likely to break their legs in the next
twenty-five years, but they don't know what a road-sweeper
thinks. Machines can give information, but they have no emo-
tions, they can't imagine, they can't set their own problems.
They can't understand people who imagine and hope. Machines aren't even infantile."

"Next please," the machine repeated.

"The machine is wrong," Grame shouted. "Always and
forever wrong."

The machine began to hum impatiently. Two of the attendants seized their tools and moved toward the giant doors.

"Wrong!" Grame shouted. "And people know it. They're
tired of being graded by idiotic lumps of steel and electricity.
The people will destroy the grading machine. What do you
think we mech-reps talk about when we put the Drunk and
Angry notice on the door and the·officers are frightened to
come in? We talk about smashing the machines and throwing
the pieces in your works. We talk about high explosives and
bombs."

The humming changed to an electrical crackling.

"You'll buzz a lot harder when the bomb goes up under
you," Grame shouted.

The crackling developed into a rumbling of minor explosions. Flashes of white light leaped out of the apertures. There was a noise like a waterfall, then, for a few moments, absolute silence and absolute stillness except for smoke that whirled around the machine.

One of the attendants spoke.

"It will take weeks to get it going again," he said bitterly. "Well, the regrading will have to be done by hand, that's all. I'm not working overtime on this baby."

"What going to happen to me?" Grame asked. Exemplary death?"

"We don't care what happens to you. Not our business or we'd strangle you now. Better go through that door and talk to one of the controllers."

Grame walked up the ramp toward the center of the building and kept walking until the machine was far beneath him.

He went through a door marked Subcontroller. A man was sitting at a desk, reading the morning papers.

"I've wrecked the machine," Grame told him. "I was arguing with it."

The subcontroller sighed and put down the newspaper. "There will be a penalty," he said.

"I came to be regraded. I want to study cosmic rays. It had never heard of cosmic rays. I suppose it lost its temper."

"The machine never loses its temper. Without any desire to be alarming, I had better tell you that this is a serious matter. It's very serious indeed," he said sighing. "You see, the machine is state property. Practically everything is, after all."

"It makes no difference," Grame said gloomily. "No difference to me, anyway. I'm a mechanical-repetitive. I knew I wouldn't be regraded. So did the other mech-reps. You may take it as a fact," he said spitefully, "that you'll have trouble when you've killed me."

The subcontroller looked at him with sudden geniality, as though he had just recognised another subcontroller. "Oh, you're the mech-rep, are you? And you've wrecked the machine? My dear fellow, my dear potential martyr, why are you so against the machine? It may not be always right, but it gives you just the answers you'd get from us, only in a more concise and less irritating form. When answers have to be given a hundred times a day, six days a week, fifty-two weeks a year, and a hundred years in every century, it saves time and temper to have a machine to give them. Do you know that before the machine was built, we recorded twenty thousand interviews, purely in order to ensure that the machine was fitted with every correct response, and with nothing but correct responses? Before my time, of course. Now, we'll say nothing more about penalties. Come back in a month's time and try again. I'll have some of the boys fit it with a cosmic-ray reaction."

"I won't come back in a month. I'll stay and be killed now if I can't be regraded."

"But there wouldn't be any point in regrading you. We simply don't have any vacancies in the cosmic-ray team. Nothing that would interest you, anyway. You don't want to be a cosmic bottlewasher?"

Grame sat down, trembling. "Kill me," he begged, "but without jokes."

"Now, that's where the machine is superior," the subcontroller pointed out, immensely pleased. "It doesn't make these little jokes you rightly find so annoying. The machine doesn't get bored. It never feels the need to entertain itself. You illustrate my point perfectly. We most certainly mustn't kill you. . . ."

W. H. Auden

THE UNKNOWN CITIZEN
   (1940)

[To JS/07/M/378 This Marble Monument Is Erected by
the State]

He was found by the Bureau of Statistics to be
One against whom there was no official complaint,
And all the reports on his conduct agree
That, in the modern sense of an old-fashioned word, he was
     a saint,
For in everything he did he served the Greater Community.
Except for the War till the day he retired

He worked in a factory and never got fired,
But satisfied his employers, Fudge Motors Inc.
Yet he wasn't a scab or odd in his views,
For his Union reports that he paid his dues,
(Our report on his Union shows it was sound)
And our Social Psychology workers found
That he was popular with his mates and liked a drink.
The Press are convinced that he bought a paper every day
And that his reactions to advertisements were normal in every
    way.
Policies taken out in his name prove that he was fully insured,
And his Health-card shows he was once in hospital but left
    it cured.
Both Producers Research and High-Grade Living declare
He was fully sensible to the advantages of the Installment
    Plan
And had everything necessary to the Modern Man,
A phonograph, a radio, a car and a frigidaire.
Our researchers into Public Opinion are content
That he held the proper opinions for the time of year;
When there was peace, he was for peace, when there was
    war, he went.
He was married and added five children to the population,
Which our Eugenist says was the right number of a parent
    of his generation,
And our teachers report that he never interfered with their
    education.
Was he free? Was he happy? The question is absurd:
Had anything been wrong, we should certainly have heard.

Aldous Huxley

From BRAVE NEW WORLD
(1932)

IT was a small factory of lighting-sets for helicopters, a branch of the Electrical Equipment Corporation. They were met on the roof itself (for that circular letter of recommendation from the Controller was magical in its effects) by the Chief Technician and the Human Element Manager. They walked downstairs into the factory.

"Each process," explained the Human Element Manager, "is carried out, so far as possible, by a single Bokanovsky Group."

And, in effect, eighty-three almost noseless black brachycephalic Deltas were cold-pressing. The fifty-six four-spindle chucking and turning machines were being manipulated by fifty-six aquiline and ginger Gammas. One hundred and seven heat-conditioned Epsilon Senegalese were working in the foundry. Thirty-three Delta females, long-headed, sandy, with narrow pelvises, and all within 20 millimeters of 1 meter 69 centimeters tall, were cutting screws. In the assembling room, the dynamos were being put together by two sets of Gamma-Plus dwarfs. The two low worktables faced one another; between them crawled the conveyor with its load of separate parts; forty-seven blond heads were confronted by forty-seven brown ones. Forty-seven snubs by forty-seven hooks; forty-seven receding by forty-seven prognathous chins. The completed mechanisms were inspected by eighteen identical curly auburn girls in Gamma green, packed in crates by thirty-four short-legged, left-handed male Delta-Minuses, and loaded into the waiting trucks and lorries by sixty-three blue-eyed, flaxen, and freckled Epsilon Semi-Morons.

"O brave new world . . ." By some malice of his memory the Savage found himself repeating Miranda's words. "O brave new world that has such people in it."

"And I assure you," the Human Element Manager concluded, as they left the factory, "we hardly ever have any trouble with our workers. We always find . . ."

But the Savage had suddenly broken away from his companions and was violently retching, behind a clump of laurels, as though the solid earth had been a helicopter in an air pocket.

Edgar Allan Poe

SONNET—TO SCIENCE
(1829)

Science! true daughter of Old Time thou art!
  Who alterest all things with they peering eyes.
Why preyest thou thus upon the poet's heart,
  Vulture, whose wings are dull realities?
How should he love thee? or how deem thee wise?
  Who wouldst not leave him in his wandering
To seek for treasure in the jewelled skies,
  Albeit he soared with an undaunted wing?
Hast thou not dragged Diana from her car?
  And driven the Hamadryad from the wood
To seek a shelter in some happier star?
  Hast thou not torn the Naiad from her flood,
The Elfin from the green grass, and from me
The summer dream beneath the tamarind tree?

George Orwell

From THE ROAD TO WIGAN PIER
(1937)

. . . Many, perhaps a majority, of thinking people are not in love with machine-civilization, but everyone who is not a fool knows that it is nonsense to talk at this moment about scrapping the machine. . . .

Every sensitive person has moments when he is suspicious of machinery and to some extent of physical science. But it is important to sort out the various motives, which have differed greatly at different times, for hostility to science and machinery, and to disregard the jealousy of the modern literary gent who hates science because science has stolen literature's thunder. The earliest full-length attack on science and machinery that I am acquainted with is in the third part of *Gulliver's Travels*. But Swift's attack, though brilliant as a

tour de force, is irrelevant and even silly, because it is written
from the standpoint—perhaps this seems a queer thing to say
of the author of *Gulliver's Travels*—of a man who lacked
imagination. To Swift, science was merely a kind of futile
muckraking and the machines were nonsensical contraptions
that would never work. His standard was that of practical
usefulness, and he lacked the vision to see that an experiment
which is not demonstrably useful at the moment may yield
results in the future. . . .

A little later the despised machines began working, physical science increased its scope, and there came the celebrated
conflict between religion and science which agitated our
grandfathers. That conflict is over and both sides have retreated and claimed a victory, but an antiscientific bias still
lingers in the minds of most religious believers. All through
the nineteenth century protesting voices were raised against
science and machinery (see Dickens's *Hard Times*, for instance), but usually for the rather shallow reason that indus-
trialism in its first stages was cruel and ugly. Samuel Butler's
attack on the machine in the well-known chapter of *Erewhon*
is a different matter. But Butler himself lived in a less desperate age than our own, an age in which it was still possible
for a first-rate man to be a dilettante part of the time, and
therefore the whole thing appeared to him as a kind of intellectual exercise. He saw clearly enough our abject dependence on the machine, but instead of bothering to work out its
consequences he preferred to exaggerate it for the sake of
what was not much more than a joke. It is only in our own
age, when mechanization has finally triumphed, that we can
actually *feel* the tendency of the machine to make a fully
human life impossible. There is probably no one capable of
thinking and feeling who has not occasionally looked at a
gaspipe chair and reflected that the machine is the enemy of
life. As a rule, however, this feeling is instinctive rather than
reasoned. People know that in some way or another "progress" is a swindle, but they reach this conclusion by a kind of
mental shorthand; my job here is to supply the logical steps
that are usually left out. But first one must ask, What is the
function of the machine? Obviously its primary function is to
save work, and the type of person to whom machine-civilization is entirely acceptable seldom sees any reason for looking
further. Here for instance is a person who claims, or rather
screams, that he is thoroughly at home in the modern mecha-

nized world. I am quoting from *World Without Faith*, by Mr. John Beevers. This is what he says:

> It is plain lunacy to say that the average £2 10s. to £4 a week man of today is a lower type than an eighteenth-century farm laborer. Or than the laborer or peasant of any exclusively agricultural community now or in the past. It just isn't true. It is so damn silly to cry out about the civilizing effects of work in the fields and farmyards as against that done in a big locomotive works or an automobile factory. Work is a nuisance. We work because we have to and all work is done to provide us with leisure and the means of spending that leisure as enjoyably as possible.

. . . There is a whole chapter to this effect (Chapter IV of Mr. Beevers's book), and it is of some interest as an exhibition of machine worship in its most completely vulgar, ignorant, and half-baked form. It is the authentic voice of a large section of the modern world. Every aspirin eater in the outer suburbs would echo it fervently. Notice the shrill wail of anger ("it just isn't troo-o-o!" et cetera.) with which Mr. Beevers meets the suggestion that his grandfather may have been a better man than himself; and the still more horrible suggestion that if we returned to a simpler way of life he might have to toughen his muscles with a job of work. Work, you see, is done "to provide us with leisure." Leisure for what? Leisure to become more like Mr. Beevers, presumably. . . . And in any book by anyone who feels at home in the machine world—in any book by H. G. Wells, for instance —you will find passages of the same kind. How often have we not heard it, that glutinuously uplifting stuff about "the machines, our new race of slaves, which will set humanity free," etc., etc., etc. To these people, apparently, the only danger of the machine is its possible use for destructive purposes; as, for instance, airplanes are used in war. Barring wars and unforeseen disasters, the future is envisaged as an ever more rapid march of mechanical progress; machines to save work, machines to save thought, machines to save pain, hygiene, efficiency, organization, more hygiene, more efficiency, more organization, more machines—until finally you land up in the by now familiar Wellsian Utopia, aptly caricatured by Huxley in *Brave New World*, the paradise of little fat men. Of course, in their daydreams of the future the little fat men are neither fat nor little; they are Men Like

Gods. But why should they be? All mechanical progress is towards greater and greater efficiency; ultimately, therefore, toward a world in which *nothing goes wrong*. But in a world in which nothing went wrong, many of the qualities which Mr. Wells regards as "godlike" would be no more valuable than the animal faculty of moving the ears. The beings in *Men Like Gods* and *The Dream* are represented, for example, as brave, generous, and physically strong. But in a world from which physical danger had been banished—and obviously mechanical progress tends to eliminate danger—would physical courage be likely to survive? *Could* it survive? And why should physical strength survive in a world where there was never the need for physical labor? As for such qualities as loyalty, generosity, and so on, in a world where nothing went wrong, they would be not only irrelevant but probably unimaginable. The truth is that many of the qualities we admire in human beings can function only in opposition to some kind of disaster, pain, or difficulty; but the tendency of mechanical progress is to eliminate disaster, pain, and difficulty. In books like *The Dream* and *Men Like Gods* it is assumed that such qualities as strength, courage, generosity, and so on, will be kept alive because they are comely qualities and necessary attributes of a full human being. Presumably, for instance, the inhabitants of Utopia would create artificial dangers in order to exercise their courage, and do dumbbell exercises to harden muscles which they would never be obliged to use. And here you observe the huge contradiction which is usually present in the idea of progress. The tendency of mechanical progress is to make your environment safe and soft; and yet you are striving to keep yourself brave and hard. You are at the same moment furiously pressing forward and desperately holding back. It is as though a London stockbroker should go to his office in a suit of chain mail and insist on talking medieval Latin. So in the last analysis the champion of progress is also the champion of anachronisms.

Meanwhile I am assuming that the tendency of mechanical progress *is* to make life safe and soft. This may be disputed, because at any given moment the effect of some recent mechanical invention may appear to be the opposite. Take, for instance, the transition from horses to motor vehicles. At a first glance one might say, considering the enormous toll of road deaths, that the motorcar does not exactly tend to

make life safer. Moreover, it probably needs as much tough-
ness to be a first-rate dirt-track rider as to be a broncobuster
or to ride in the Grand National. Nevertheless the *tendency*
of all machinery is to become safer and easier to handle. The
danger of accidents would disappear if we chose to tackle
our road-planning problem seriously, as we shall do sooner
or later; and meanwhile the motorcar has evolved to a point
at which anyone who is not blind or paralytic can drive it
after a few lessons. Even now it needs far less nerve and skill
to drive a car ordinarily well than to ride a horse ordinarily
well; in twenty years' time it may need no nerve or skill at
all. Therefore, one must say that, taking society as a whole,
the result of the transition from horses to cars has been an
increase in human softness. Presently somebody comes along
with another invention, the airplane for instance, which does
not at first sight appear to make life safer. The first men who
went up in airplanes were superlatively brave, and even today it must need an exceptionally good nerve to be a pilot.
But the same tendency as before is at work. The airplane,
like the motorcar, will be made foolproof; a million engineers
are working, almost unconsciously, in that direction. Finally—
this is the objective, though it may never quite be reached—
you will get an airplane whose pilot needs no more skill or
courage than a baby needs in its perambulator. And all mechanical progress is and must be in this direction. A machine
evolves by becoming more efficient, that is, more foolproof;
hence the objective of mechanical progress is a foolproof
world—which may or may not mean a world inhabited by
fools. Mr. Wells would probably retort that the world can
never become foolproof, because, however high a standard of
efficiency you have reached, there is always some greater
difficulty ahead. For example (this is Mr. Wells's favorite
idea—he has used it in goodness knows how many perora-
tions), when you have got this planet of ours perfectly into
trim, you start upon the enormous task of reaching and
colonizing another. But this is merely to push the objective
further into the future; the objective itself remains the same.
Colonize another planet, and the game of mechanical progress begins anew; for the foolproof world you have substituted the foolproof solar system—the foolproof universe. In
tying yourself to the ideal of mechanical efficiency, you tie
yourself to the ideal of softness. But softness is repul-
sive; and thus all progress is seen to be a frantic struggle

toward an objective which you hope and pray will never be reached. Now and again, but not often, you meet somebody who grasps that what is usually called progress also entails what is usually called degeneracy, and who is nevertheless in favor of progress. Hence the fact that in Mr. Shaw's Utopia a statue was erected to Falstaff, as the first man who ever made a speech in favor of cowardice.

But the trouble goes immensely deeper than this. Hitherto I have pointed out only the absurdity of aiming at mechanical progress and also at the preservation of qualities which mechanical progress makes unnecessary. The question one has got to consider is whether there is *any* human activity which would not be maimed by the dominance of the machine.

The function of the machine is to save work. In a fully mechanized world all the dull drudgery will be done by machinery leaving us free for more interesting pursuits. So expressed, this sounds splendid. It makes one sick to see half a dozen men sweating their guts out to dig a trench for a water pipe, when some easily devised machine would scoop the earth out in a couple of minutes. Why not let the machine do the work and the men go and do something else. But presently the question arises, what else are they to do? Supposedly they are set free from "work" in order that they may do something which is not "work." But what is work and what is not work? Is it work to dig, to carpenter, to plant trees, to fell trees, to ride, to fish, to hunt, to feed chickens, to play the piano, to take photographs, to build a house, to cook, to sew, to trim hats, to mend motor bicycles? All of these things are work to somebody, and all of them are play to somebody. There are in fact very few activities which cannot be classed either as work or play according as you choose to regard them. The laborer set free from digging may want to spend his leisure, or part of it, in playing the piano, while the professional pianist may be only too glad to get out and dig at the potato patch. Hence the antithesis between work, as something intolerably tedious, and not-work, as something desirable, is false. The truth is that when a human being is not eating, drinking, sleeping, making love, talking, playing games, or merely lounging about—and these things will not fill up a lifetime—he needs work and usually looks for it, though he may not call it work. Above the level of a third- or fourth-grade moron, life has got to be lived largely in terms of effort. For man is not, as the vulgarer hedonists seem to suppose, a kind of walking stomach; he has also got a hand, an eye, and a brain. Cease to use your hands, and you have lopped off a huge chunk of your consciousness. And now consider again those half-dozen men who were digging the trench for the water pipe. A machine has set them free from digging, and they are going to amuse themselves with something else—carpentering, for instance. But whatever they want to do, they will find that another machine has set them free from *that*. For in a fully mechanized world there would be no more need to carpenter, to cook, to mend motor bicycles, and so on, than there would be to dig. There is scarcely anything, from catching a whale to carving a cherrystone, that could not conceivably be done by machinery. The machine would even encroach upon the activities we now class as "art"; it is doing so already, via the camera and the radio. Mechanize the world as fully as it might be mechanized, and whichever way you turn there will be some machine cutting you off from the chance of working—that is, of living.

At a first glance this might not seem to matter. Why should you not get on with your "creative work" and disregard the machines that would do it for you? But it is not so simple as it sounds. Here am I, working eight hours a day in an insurance office; in my spare time I want to do something "creative," so I choose to do a bit of carpentering—to make myself a table, for instance. Notice that from the very start there is a touch of artificiality about the whole business, for the factories can turn me out a far better table than I can make for myself. But even when I get to work on my table, it is not possible for me to feel toward it as the cabinetmaker of a hundred years ago felt toward his table, still less as Robinson Crusoe felt toward his. For before I start, most of the work has already been done for me by machinery. The tools I use demand the minimum of skill. I can get, for instance, planes which will cut out any molding; the cabinetmaker of a hundred years ago would have had to do the work with chisel and gouge, which demanded real skill of eye and hand. The boards I buy are ready-planed and the legs are ready turned by the lathe. I can even go to the woodshop and buy all the parts of the table ready-made and only needing to be fitted together; my work being reduced to driving in a few pegs and using a piece of sandpaper. And if this is so at present, in the mechanized future it will be enormously more so. With the tools and materials available *then*, there will be no possi-

bility of mistake, hence no room for skill. Making a table will
be easier and duller than peeling a potato. In such circumstances it is nonsense to talk of "creative work." In any case
the arts of the hand (which have got to be transmitted by
apprenticeship) would long since have disappeared. Some of
them have disappeared already, under the competition of the
machine. Look round any country churchyard and see
whether you can find a decently cut tombstone later than
1820. The art, or rather the craft, of stonework has died out
so completely that it would take centuries to revive it.

But it may be said, why not retain the machine *and* retain
"creative work"? Why not cultivate anachronisms as a spare-
time hobby? Many people have played with this idea; it
seems to solve with such beautiful ease the problems set by
the machine. The citizen of Utopia, we are told, coming home
from his daily two hours of turning a handle in the tomato-
canning factory, will deliberately revert to a more primitive
way of life and solace his creative instincts with a bit of fretwork, pottery glazing, or handloom weaving. And why is this
picture an absurdity—as it is, of course? Because of a principle that is not always recognized, though always acted
upon: that so long as the machine *is there*, one is under an
obligation to use it. No one draws water from the well when
he can turn on the tap. One sees a good illustration of this in
the matter of travel. Everyone who has traveled by primitive
methods in an undeveloped country, knows that the differ-
ance between that kind of travel and modern travel in trains,
cars, and so on, is the difference between life and death. The
nomad who walks or rides, with his baggage stowed on a
camel or an oxcart, many suffer every kind of discomfort,
but at least he is living while he is traveling; whereas for the
passenger in an express train or a luxury liner his journey is
an interregnum, a kind of temporary death. And yet so long
as the railways exist, one has got to travel by train—or by
car or airplane. Here am I, forty miles from London. When I
want to go up to London why do I not pack my luggage onto
a mule and set out on foot, making two days' march of it?
Because, with the Green Line buses whizzing past me every
ten minutes, such a journey would be intolerably irksome. In
order that one may enjoy primitive methods of travel, it is
necessary that no other method should be available. No
human being ever wants to do anything in a more cumbrous
way than is necessary. Hence the absurdity of that picture

of Utopians saving their souls with fretwork. In a world where everything could be done by machinery, everything would be done by machinery. Deliberately to revert to primitive methods, to use archaic tools, to put silly little difficulties in your own way, would be a piece of dilettantism, of pretty-pretty arty and craftiness. It would be like solemnly sitting down to eat your dinner with stone implements. Revert to handwork in a machine age, and you are back in Ye Olde Tea Shoppe or the Tudor villa with the sham beams tacked to the wall.

The tendency of mechanical progress, then, is to frustrate the human need for effort and creation. It makes unnecessary and even impossible the activities of the eye and the hand. The apostle of "progress" will sometimes declare that this does not matter, but you can usually drive him into a corner by pointing out the horrible lengths to which the process can be carried. Why, for instance, use your hands at all—why use them even for blowing your nose or sharpening a pencil? Surely you could fix some kind of steel and rubber contraption to your shoulders and let your arms wither into stumps of skin and bone? And so with every organ and every faculty. There is really no reason why a human being should do more than eat, drink, sleep, breathe, and procreate; *everything* else could be done for him by machinery. Therefore the logical end of mechanical progress is to reduce the human being to something resembling a brain in a bottle. That is the goal toward which we are already moving, though, of course, we have no intention of getting there; just as a man who drinks a bottle of whisky a day does not actually intend to get cirrhosis of the liver. The implied objective of "progress" is—not *exactly*, perhaps, the brain in the bottle, but at any rate some frightful subhuman depth of softness and helplessness. . . .

A generation ago every intelligent person was in some sense a revolutionary; nowadays it would be nearer the mark to say that every intelligent person is a reactionary. In this connection it is worth comparing H. G. Wells's *When the Sleeper Wakes* with Aldous Huxley's *Brave New World*, written thirty years later. Each is a pessimistic Utopia, a vision of a sort of prig's paradise in which all the dreams of the "progressive" person come true. Considered merely as a piece of imaginative construction, *When the Sleeper Wakes* is, I think, much superior, but it suffers from vast contradictions because of the fact that Wells, as the archpriest of "progress," cannot write with any conviction *against* "progress." He draws a picture of a glittering, strangely sinister world in which the privileged classes live a life of shallow gutless hedonism, and the workers, reduced to a state of utter slavery and subhuman ignorance, toil like troglodytes in caverns underground. As soon as one examines this idea—it is further developed in a splendid short story in *Tales of Space and Time*—one sees its inconsistency. For in the immensely mechanized world that Wells is imagining, why should the workers have to work harder than at present? Obviously the tendency of the machine is to eliminate work, not to increase it. In the machine world the workers might be enslaved, ill treated, and even underfed, but they certainly would not be condemned to ceaseless manual toil; because in that case what would be the function of the machine? You can have machines doing all the work or human beings doing all the work, but you can't have both. Those armies of underground workers, with their blue uniforms and their debased, half-human language, are only put in "to make your flesh creep." Wells wants to suggest that "progress might take a wrong turning; but the only evil he cares to imagine is inequality—one class grabbing all the wealth and power and oppressing the others, apparently out of pure spite. Give it quite a small twist, he seems to suggest, overthrow the privileged class—change over from world capitalism to Socialism, in fact—and all will be well. The machine civilization is to continue, but its products are to be shared out equally. The thought he dare not face is that the machine itself may be the enemy. So in his more characteristic Utopias (*The Dream, Men Like Gods*, and so on), he returns to optimism and to a vision of humanity, "liberated" by the machine, as a race of enlightened sunbathers whose sole topic of conversation is their own superiority to their ancestors. *Brave New World* belongs to a later time and to a generation which has seen through the swindle of "progress." It contains its own contradictions . . . but it is at least a memorable assault on the more fat-bellied type of perfectionism. Allowing for the exaggerations of caricature, it probably expresses what a majority of thinking people feel about machine civilization.

The sensitive person's hostility to the machine is in one sense unrealistic, because of the obvious fact that the machine has come to stay. But as an attitude of mind there is a great deal to be said for it. The machine has got to be accepted, but it is probably better to accept it rather as one accepts a drug—that is, grudgingly and suspiciously. Like a drug, the machine is useful, dangerous, and habit-forming. The oftener one surrenders to it, the tighter its grip becomes. You have only to look about you at this moment to realize with what sinister speed the machine is getting us into its power.

To begin with, there is the frightful debauchery of taste that has already been effected by a century of mechanization. This is almost too obvious and too generally admitted to need pointing out. But as a single instance, take taste in its narrowest sense—the taste for decent food. In the highly mechanized countries, thanks to tinned food, cold storage, synthetic flavoring matters, and so on, the palate is almost a dead organ. As you can see by looking at any greengrocer's shop, what the majority of English people mean by an apple is a lump of highly colored cotton wool from America or Australia; they will devour these things, apparently with pleasure, and let the English apples rot under the trees. It is the shiny, standardized, machine-made look of the American apple that appeals to them; the superior taste of the English apple is something they simply do not notice. Or look at the factory-made, foil-wrapped cheeses and "blended" butter in any grocer's; look at the hideous rows of tins which usurp more and more of the space in any foodshop, even a dairy; look at a sixpenny Swiss roll or a twopenny ice cream; look at the filthy chemical byproduct that people will pour down their throats under the name of beer. Wherever you look you will see some slick machine-made article triumphing over the old-fashioned article that still tastes of something other than sawdust. And what applies to food applies also to furniture, houses, clothes, books, amusements, and everything else that makes up our environment. There are now millions of people, and they are increasing every year, to whom the blaring of a radio is not only a more acceptable but a more *normal* background to their thoughts than the lowing of cattle or the song of birds. The mechanization of the world could never proceed very far while taste, even the taste buds of the tongue, remained uncorrupted, because in that case most of the products of the machine would be simply unwanted. In a healthy world there would be no demand for tinned food, aspirins, gramophones, gaspipe chairs, machine guns, daily newspapers, telephones, motorcars, etc.,

etc.; and on the other hand there would be a constant demand for the things the machine cannot produce. But meanwhile the machine is here, and its corrupting effects are almost irresistible. One inveighs against it, but one goes on using it. Even a bare-arse savage, given the chance, will learn the vices of civilization within a few months. Mechanization leads to the decay of taste, the decay of taste leads to the demand for machine-made articles and hence to more mechanization, and so a vicious circle is established.

But in addition to this there is a tendency for the mechanization of the world to proceed as it were automatically, whether we want it or not. This is due to the fact that in modern Western man the faculty of mechanical invention has been fed and stimulated till it has reached almost the status of an instinct. People invent new machines and improve existing ones almost unconsciously, rather as a somnambulist will go on working in his sleep. In the past, when it was taken for granted that life on this planet is harsh or at any rate laborious, it seemed the natural fate to go on using the clumsy implements of your forefathers, and only a few eccentric persons, centuries apart, proposed innovations; hence throughout enormous ages such things as the oxcart, the plow, the sickle, and so on remained radically unchanged. It is on record that screws have been in use since remote antiquity, and yet that it was not till the middle of the nineteenth century that anyone thought of making screws with points on them; for several thousand years they remained flat-ended, and holes had to be drilled for them before they could be inserted. In our own epoch such a thing would be unthinkable. For almost every modern Western man has his inventive faculty to some extent developed; the Western man invents machines as naturally as the Polynesian islander swims. Give a Western man a job of work and he immediately begins devising a machine that would do it for him; give him a machine and he thinks of ways of improving it. I understand this tendency well enough, for in an ineffectual sort of way I have that type of mind myself. I have not either the patience or the mechanical skill to devise any machine that would work, but I am perpetually seeing, as it were, the ghosts of possible machines that might save me the trouble of using my brain or muscles. A person with a more definite mechanical turn would probably construct some of them and put them into operation . . . Given a mechanical civilization the process of invention and improvement will always continue. . . .

And this prospect is a slightly sinister one, because it is obvious even now that the process of mechanization is out of control. It is happening merely because humanity has got the habit. A chemist perfects a new method of synthesizing rubber, or a mechanic devises a new pattern of pivot pin. Why? Not for any clearly understood purpose, but simply from the impulse to invent and improve, which has now become instinctive. Put a pacifist to work in a bomb factory and in two months he will be devising a new type of bomb. Hence the appearance of such diabolical things as poison gases, which are not expected even by their inventors to be beneficial to humanity. Our attitude toward such things as poison gases *ought* to be the attitude of the king of Brobdingnag toward gunpowder; but because we live in a mechanical and scientific age we are infected with the notion that, whatever else happens, "progress" must continue and knowledge must never be suppressed. Verbally, no doubt, we would agree that machinery is made for man and not man for machinery; in practice any attempt to check the development of the machine appears to us as an attack on knowledge and therefore a kind of blasphemy. And even if the whole of humanity suddenly revolted against the machine and decided to escape to a simpler way of life, the escape would still be immensely difficult. It would not do, as in Butler's *Erewhon*, to smash every machine invented after a certain date; we should also have to smash the habit of mind that would, almost involuntarily, devise fresh machines as soon as the old ones were smashed. And in all of us there is at least a tinge of that habit of mind. In every country in the world the large army of scientists and technicians, with the rest of us panting at their heels, are marching along the road of "progress" with the blind persistence of a column of ants. Comparatively few people want it to happen, plenty of people actively want it *not* to happen and yet it is happening. The process of mechanization has itself become a machine, a huge glittering vehicle whirling us we are not certain where, but probably toward the padded Wells-world and the brain in the bottle.

This, then, is the case against the machine. Whether it is a sound or unsound case hardly matters. The point is that these or very similar arguments would be echoed by every person who is hostile to machine civilization. . . .

Carl Sandburg

LIMITED
(1916)

I am riding on a limited express, one of the crack trains of
the nation.
Hurtling across the prairie into blue haze and dark air go
fifteen all-steel coaches holding a thousand people.
(All the coaches shall be scrap and rust and all the men and
women laughing in diners and sleepers shall pass to ashes.)
I ask a man in the smoker where he is going and he answers:
"Omaha."

E. E. Cummings

pity this busy monster, manunkind
(1954)

pity this busy monster, manunkind,

not. Progress is a comfortable disease:
your victim(death and life safely beyond)

plays with the bigness of his littleness
—electrons deify one razorblade
into a mountainrange;lenses extend

unwish through curving wherewhen till unwish
returns on its unself.
                A world of made
is not a world of born—pity poor flesh

and trees,poor stars and stones,but never this
fine specimen of hypermagical

ultraomnipotence. We doctors know

a hopeless case if—listen:there's a hell
of a good universe next door;let's go

E. M. Forster

THE MACHINE STOPS
(1928)

PART I

THE AIRSHIP

IMAGINE, if you can, a small room, hexagonal in shape like the cell of a bee. It is lighted neither by window nor by lamp, yet it is filled with a soft radiance. There are no apertures for ventilation, yet the air is fresh. There are no musical instruments, and yet, at the moment that my meditation opens, this room is throbbing with melodious sounds. An armchair is in the center, by its side a reading desk—that is all the furniture. And in the armchair there sits a swaddled lump of flesh—a woman, about five feet high, with a face as white as a fungus. It is to her that the little room belongs.

An electric bell rang.

The woman touched a switch and the music was silent.

"I suppose I must see who it is," she thought, and set her chair in motion. The chair, like the music, was worked by machinery, and it rolled her to the other side of the room, where the bell still rang importunately.

"Who it is?" she called. Her voice was irritable, for she had been interrupted often since the music began. She knew several thousand people; in certain directions human intercourse had advanced enormously.

But when she listened into the receiver, her white face wrinkled into smiles, and she said:

"Very well. Let us talk, I will isolate myself. I do not expect anything important will happen for the next five minutes—for I can give you fully five minutes, Kuno. Then I must deliver my lecture on 'Music during the Australian Period.'"

She touched the isolation knob, so that no one else could speak to her. Then she touched the lighting apparatus, and the little room was plunged into darkness.

"Be quick!" she called, her irritation returning. "Be quick, Kuno; here I am in the dark wasting my time."

But it was fully fifteen seconds before the round plate that she held in her hands began to glow. A faint blue light shot

261

across it, darkening to purple, and presently she could see the image of her son, who lived on the other side of the earth, and he could see her.

"Kuno, how slow you are."

He smiled gravely.

"I really believe you enjoy dawdling."

"I have called you before, Mother, but you were always busy or isolated. I have something particular to say."

"What is it, dearest boy? Be quick. Why could you not send it by pneumatic post?"

"Because I prefer saying such a thing. I want—"

"Well?"

"I want you to come and see me."

Vashti watched his face in the blue plate.

"But I can see you!" she exclaimed. "What more do you want?"

"I want to see you not through the Machine," said Kuno. "I want to speak to you not through the wearisome Machine."

"Oh, hush!" said his mother, vaguely shocked. "You mustn't say anything against the Machine."

"Why not?"

"One mustn't."

"You talk as if a god had made the Machine," cried the other. "I believe that you pray to it when you are unhappy. Men made it, do not forget that. Great men, but men. The Machine is much, but it is not everything. I see something like you in this plate, but I do not see you. I hear something like you through this telephone, but I do not hear you. That is why I want you to come. Come and stop with me. Pay me a visit, so that we can meet face to face, and talk about the hopes that are in my mind."

She replied that she could scarcely spare the time for a visit.

"The airship barely takes two days to fly between me and you."

"I dislike airships."

"Why?"

"I dislike seeing the horrible brown earth, and the sea, and the stars when it is dark. I get no ideas in an airship."

"I do not get them anywhere else."

"What kind of ideas can the air give you?"

He paused for an instant.

"Do you not know four big stars that form an oblong, and three stars close together in the middle of the oblong, and hanging from these stars, three other stars?"

"No, I do not. I dislike the stars. But did they give you an idea? How interesting; tell me."

"I had an idea that they were like a man."

"I do not understand."

"The four big stars are the man's shoulders and his knees. The three stars in the middle are like the belts that men wore once, and the three stars hanging are like a sword."

"A sword?"

"Men carried swords about with them, to kill animals and other men."

"It does not strike me as a very good idea, but it is certainly original. When did it come to you first?"

"In the airship—" He broke off, and she fancied that he looked sad. She could not be sure, for the Machine did not transmit *nuances* of expression. It gave only a general idea of people—an idea that was good enough for all practical purposes, Vashti thought. The imponderable bloom, declared by a discredited philosophy to be the actual essence of intercourse, was rightly ignored by the Machine, just as the imponderable bloom of the grape was ignored by the manufacturers of artificial fruit. Something "good enough" had long since been accepted by our race.

"The truth is," he continued, "that I want to see these stars again. They are curious stars. I want to see them not from the airship, but from the surface of the earth, as our ancestors did, thousands of years ago. I want to visit the surface of the earth."

She was shocked again.

"Mother, you must come, if only to explain to me what is the harm of visiting the surface of the earth."

"No harm," she replied, controlling herself. "But no advantage. The surface of the earth is only dust and mud; no life remains on it, and you would need a respirator, or the cold of the outer air would kill you. One dies immediately in the outer air."

"I know; of course I shall take all precautions."

"And besides—"

"Well?"

She considered, and chose her words with care. Her son

had a queer temper, and she wished to dissuade him from the expedition.

"It is contrary to the spirit of the age," she asserted.

"Do you mean by that, contrary to the Machine?"

"In a sense, but—"

His image in the blue plate faded.

"Kuno!"

He had isolated himself.

For a moment Vashti felt lonely.

Then she generated the light, and the sight of her room, flooded with radiance and studded with electric buttons, revived her. There were buttons and switches everywhere—buttons to call for food, for music, for clothing. There was the hot-bath button, by pressure of which a basin of (imitation) marble rose out of the floor, filled to the brim with a warm deodorized liquid. There was the cold-bath button. There was the button that produced literature. And there were of course the buttons by which she communicated with her friends. The room, though it contained nothing, was in touch with all that she cared for in the world.

Vashti's next move was to turn off the isolation switch, and all the accumulations of the last three minutes burst upon her. The room was filled with the noise of bells, and speaking tubes. What was the new food like? Could she recommend it? Had she had any ideas lately? Might one tell her one's own ideas? Would she make an engagement to visit the public nurseries at an early date?—say this day month.

To most of these questions she replied with irritation—a growing quality in that accelerated age. She said that the new food was horrible. That she could not visit the public nurseries through press of engagements. That she had no ideas of her own but had just been told one—that four stars and three in the middle were like a man: she doubted there was much in it. Then she switched off her correspondents, for it was time to deliver her lecture on Australian music.

The clumsy system of public gatherings had been long since abandoned; neither Vashti nor her audience stirred from their rooms. Seated in her armchair she spoke, while they in their armchairs heard her, fairly well, and saw her, fairly well. She opened with a humorous account of music in the pre-Mongolian epoch, and went on to describe the great outburst of song that followed the Chinese conquest. Remote and primeval as were the methods of I-San-So and the Brisbane school, she yet felt (she said) that study of them might repay the musician of today: they had freshness; they had, above all, ideas.

Her lecture, which lasted ten minutes, was well received, and at its conclusion she and many of her audience listened to a lecture on the sea; there were ideas to be got from the sea; the speaker had donned a respirator and visited it lately. Then she fed, talked to many friends, had a bath, talked again, and summoned her bed.

The bed was not to her liking. It was too large, and she had a feeling for a small bed. Complaint was useless, for beds were of the same dimension all over the world, and to have had an alternative size would have involved vast alterations in the Machine. Vashti isolated herself—it was necessary, for neither day nor night existed under the ground—and reviewed all that had happened since she had summoned the bed last. Ideas? Scarcely any. Events—was Kuno's invitation an event?

By her side, on the little reading desk, was a survival from the ages of litter—one book. This was the Book of the Machine. In it were instructions against every possible contingency. If she was hot or cold or dyspeptic or at a loss for a word, she went to the book, and it told her which button to press. The Central Committee published it. In accordance with a growing habit, it was richly bound.

Sitting up in the bed, she took it reverently in her hands. She glanced round the glowing room as if someone might be watching her. Then, half ashamed, half joyful, she murmured "O Machine! O Machine!" and raised the volume to her lips. Thrice she kissed it, thrice inclined her head, thrice she felt the delirium of acquiescence. Her ritual performed, she turned to page 1367, which gave the times of the departure of the airships from the island in the Southern Hemisphere, under whose soil she lived, to the island in the Northern Hemisphere, whereunder lived her son.

She thought, "I have not the time."

She made the room dark and slept; she awoke and made the room light; she ate and exchanged ideas with her friends, and listened to music and attended lectures; she made the room dark and slept. Above her, beneath her, and around her, the Machine hummed eternally; she did not notice the noise, for she had been born with it in her ears. The earth, carrying her, hummed as it sped through silence, turning her now to the invisible sun, now to the invisible stars. She awoke and made the room light.

"Kuno!"

"I will not talk to you," he answered, "until you come."

"Have you been on the surface of the earth since we spoke last?"

His image faded.

Again she consulted the book. She became very nervous and lay back in her chair palpitating. Think of her as without teeth or hair. Presently she directed the chair to the wall, and pressed an unfamiliar button. The wall swung apart slowly. Through the opening she saw a tunnel that curved slightly, so that its goal was not visible. Should she go to see her son, here was the beginning of the journey.

Of course, she knew all about the communication system. There was nothing mysterious in it. She would summon a car and it would fly with her down the tunnel until it reached the lift that communicated with the airship station: the system had been in use for many, many years, long before the universal establishment of the Machine. And of course she had studied the civilization that had immediately preceded her own—the civilization that had mistaken the functions of the system, and had used it for bringing people to things, instead of for bringing things to people. Those funny old days, when men went for change of air instead of changing the air in their rooms! And yet—she was frightened of the tunnel: she had not seen it since her last child was born. It curved—but not quite as she remembered; it was brilliant— but not quite as brilliant as a lecturer had suggested. Vashti was seized with the terrors of direct experience. She shrank back into the room, and the wall closed up again.

"Kuno," she said, "I cannot come to see you. I am not well."

Immediately an enormous apparatus fell onto her out of the ceiling, a thermometer was automatically inserted between her lips, a stethoscope was automatically laid upon her heart. She lay powerless. Cool pads soothed her forehead. Kuno had telegraphed to her doctor.

So the human passions still blundered up and down in the Machine. Vashti drank the medicine that the doctor projected into her mouth, and the machinery retired into the ceiling. The voice of Kuno was heard asking how she felt.

"Better." Then, with irritation: "But why do you not come to me instead?"

"Because I cannot leave this place."

"Why?"

"Because, any moment, something tremendous may happen."

"Have you been on the surface of the earth yet?"

"Not yet."

"Then what is it?"

"I will not tell you through the machine."

She resumed her life.

But she thought of Kuno as a baby, his birth, his removal to the public nurseries, her one visit to him there, his visits to her—visits which stopped when the Machine had assigned him a room on the other side of the earth. "Parents, duties of," said the book of the Machine, "cease at the moment of birth. P. 422327483." True, but there was something special about Kuno—indeed there had been something special about all her children—and, after all, she must brave the journey if he desired it. And "something tremendous might happen." What did that mean? The nonsense of a youthful man, no doubt, but she must go. Again she pressed the unfamiliar button, again the wall swung back, and she saw the tunnel that curved out of sight. Clasping the Book, she rose, tottered onto the platform, and summoned the car. Her room closed behind her: the journey to the Northern Hemisphere had begun.

Of course, it was perfectly easy. The car approached and in it she found armchairs exactly like her own. When she signaled, it stopped, and she tottered into the lift. One other passenger was in the lift, the first fellow creature she had seen face to face for months. Few traveled in these days, for, thanks to the advance of science, the earth was exactly alike all over. Rapid intercourse, from which the previous civilization had hoped so much, had ended by defeating itself. What was the good of going to Peking when it was just like Shrewsbury? Why return to Shrewsbury when it would be just like Peking? Men seldom moved their bodies; all unrest was concentrated in the soul.

The airship service was a relic from the former age. It was kept up because it was easier to keep it up than to stop it or to diminish it, but it now far exceeded the wants of the population. Vessel after vessel would rise from the vomitories of Rye or of Christchurch (I use the antique names), would sail into the crowded sky, and would draw up at the wharves of the south—empty. So nicely adjusted was the system, so independent of meteorology, that the sky, whether calm or cloudy, resembled a vast kaleidoscope whereon the same patterns periodically recurred. The ship on which Vashti sailed started now at sunset, now at dawn. But always, as it passed above Rheims, it would neighbor the ship that served between Helsingfors and the Brazils, and, every third time it surmounted the Alps, the fleet of Palermo would cross its track behind. Night and day, wind and storm, tide and earthquake impeded man no longer. He had harnessed Leviathan. All the old literature, with its praise of Nature and its fear of Nature, rang false as the prattle of a child.

Yet as Vashti saw the vast flank of the ship, stained with exposure to the outer air, her horror of direct experience returned. It was not quite like the airship in the cinematophote. For one thing it smelled—not strongly or unpleasantly, but it did smell, and with her eyes shut she should have known that a new thing was close to her. Then she had to walk to it from the lift, had to submit to glances from the other passengers. The man in front dropped his Book—no great matter, but it disquieted them all. In the rooms, if the Book was dropped, the floor raised it mechanically, but the gangway to the airship was not so prepared, and the sacred volume lay motionless. They stopped—the thing was unforeseen—and the man, instead of picking up his property, felt the muscles of his arm to see how they had failed him. Then someone actually said with direct utterance: "We shall be late"—and they trooped on board, Vashti treading on the pages as she did so.

Inside, her anxiety increased. The arrangements were old-fashioned and rough. There was even a female attendant, to whom she would have to announce her wants during the voyage. Of course, a revolving platform ran the length of the boat, but she was expected to walk from it to her cabin. Some cabins were better than others, and she did not get the best. She thought the attendant had been unfair, and spasms of rage shook her. The glass valves had closed; she could not go back. She saw, at the end of the vestibule, the lift in which she had ascended going quietly up and down, empty. Beneath those corridors of shining tiles were rooms, tier below tier, reaching far into the earth, and in each room there sat a human being, eating, or sleeping, or producing ideas. And buried deep in the hive was her own room. Vashti was afraid.

"O Machine! O Machine!" she murmured, and caressed her Book, and was comforted.

Then the sides of the vestibule seemed to melt together, as do the passages that we see in dreams; the lift vanished, the Book that had been dropped slid to the left and vanished, polished tiles rushed by like a stream of water, there was a slight jar, and the airship, issuing from its tunnel, soared above the waters of a tropical ocean.

It was night. For a moment she saw the coast of Sumatra edged by the phosphorescence of waves, and crowned by lighthouses, still sending forth their disregarded beams. These also vanished, and only the stars distracted her. They were not motionless, but swayed to and fro above her head, thronging out of one skylight into another, as if the universe and not the airship was careening. And, as often happens on clear nights, they seemed now to be in perspective, now on a plane; now piled tier beyond tier into the infinite heavens, now concealing infinity, a roof limiting for ever the visions of men. In either case they seemed intolerable. "Are we to travel in the dark?" called the passengers angrily, and the attendant, who had been careless, generated the light and pulled down the blinds of pliable metal. When the airships had been built, the desire to look direct at things still lingered in the world. Hence the extraordinary number of skylights and windows, and the proportionate discomfort to those who were civilized and refined. Even in Vashti's cabin one star peeped through a flaw in the blind, and after a few hours' uneasy slumber, she was disturbed by an unfamiliar glow, which was the dawn.

Quick as the ship had sped westward, the earth had rolled eastward quicker still, and had dragged back Vashti and her companions toward the sun. Science could prolong the night, but only for a little, and those high hopes of neutralizing the earth's diurnal revolution had passed, together with hopes that were possibly higher. To "keep pace with the sun," or even to outstrip it, had been the aim of the civilization preceding this. Racing airplanes had been built for the purpose, capable of enormous speed, and steered by the greatest intellects of the epoch. Round the globe they went, round and round, westward, westward, round and round, amidst humanity's applause. In vain. The globe went eastward quicker still, horrible accidents occurred, and the Committee of the

Machine, at the time rising into prominence, declared the pursuit illegal, unmechanical, and punishable by Homelessness.

Of Homelessness more will be said later.

Doubtless the Committee was right. Yet the attempt to "defeat the sun" aroused the last common interest that our race experienced about the heavenly bodies, or indeed about anything. It was the last time that men were compacted by thinking of a power outside the world. The sun had conquered, yet it was the end of his spiritual dominion. Dawn, midday, twilight, the zodiacal path, touched neither men's lives nor their hearts, and science retreated into the ground, to concentrate herself upon problems that she was certain of solving.

So when Vashti found her cabin invaded by a rosy finger of light, she was annoyed and tried to adjust the blind. But the blind flew up altogether, and she saw through the skylight small pink clouds, swaying against a background of blue, and as the sun crept higher, its radiance entered direct, brimming down the wall, like a golden sea. It rose and fell with the airship's motion, just as waves rise and fall, but it advanced steadily, as the tide advances. Unless she was careful, it would strike her face. A spasm of horror shook her, and she rang for the attendant. The attendant too was horrified, but she could do nothing; it was not her place to mend the blind. She could only suggest that the lady should change her cabin, which she accordingly prepared to do.

People were almost exactly alike all over the world, but the attendant of the airship, perhaps owing to her exceptional duties, had grown a little out of the common. She had often to address passengers with direct speech, and this had given her a certain roughness and originality of manner. When Vashti swerved away from the sunbeams with a cry, she behaved barbarically—she put out her hand to steady her.

"How dare you!" exclaimed the passenger. "You forget yourself!"

The woman was confused, and apologized for not having let her fall. People never touched one another. The custom had become obsolete, owing to the Machine.

"Where are we now?" asked Vashti haughtily.

"We are over Asia," said the attendant, anxious to be polite.

"Asia?"

"You must excuse my common way of speaking. I have

got into the habit of calling places over which I pass by their unmechanical names."

"Oh, I remember Asia. The Mongols came from it."

"Beneath us, in the open air, stood a city that was once called Simla."

"Have you ever heard of the Mongols and of the Brisbane school?"

"No."

"Brisbane also stood in the open air."

"Those mountains to the right—let me show you them." She pushed back a metal blind. The main chain of the Himalayas was revealed. "They were once called the Roof of the World, those mountains."

"What a foolish name!"

"You must remember that, before the dawn of civilization, they seemed to be an impenetrable wall that touched the stars. It was supposed that no one but the gods could exist above their summits. How we have advanced, thanks to the Machine!"

"How we have advanced, thanks to the Machine!" said Vashti.

"How we have advanced, thanks to the Machine!" echoed the passenger who had dropped his Book the night before and who was standing in the passage.

"And that white stuff in the cracks?—what is it?"

"I have forgotten its name."

"Cover the window, please. These mountains give me no ideas."

The northern aspect of the Himalayas was in deep shadow: on the Indian slope the sun had just prevailed. The forests had been destroyed during the literature epoch for the purpose of making newspaper pulp, but the snows were awakening to their morning glory, and clouds still hung on the breasts of Kinchinjunga. In the plain were seen the ruins of cities, with diminished rivers creeping by their walls, and by the sides of these were sometimes the signs of vomitories, marking the cities of today. Over the whole prospect airships rushed, crossing and intercrossing with incredible aplomb, and rising nonchalantly when they desired to escape the perturbations of the lower atmosphere and to traverse the Roof of the World.

"We have indeed advanced, thanks to the Machine," repeated the attendant, and hid the Himalayas behind a metal blind.

The day dragged wearily forward. The passengers sat each in his cabin, avoiding one another with an almost physical repulsion and longing to be once more under the surface of the earth. There were eight or ten of them, mostly young males, sent out from the public nurseries to inhabit the rooms of those who had died in various parts of the earth. The man who had dropped his Book was on the homeward journey. He had been sent to Sumatra for the purpose of propagating the race. Vashti alone was traveling by her private will.

At midday she took a second glance at the earth. The airship was crossing another range of mountains, but she could see little, owing to clouds. Masses of black rock hovered below her and merged indistinctly into gray. Their shapes were fantastic; one of them resembled a prostrate man.

"No ideas here," murmured Vashti, and hid the Caucasus behind a metal blind.

In the evening she looked again. They were crossing a golden sea, in which lay many small islands and one peninsula.

She repeated, "No ideas here," and hid Greece behind a metal blind.

PART II

THE MENDING APPARATUS

By a vestibule, by a lift, by a tubular railway, by a platform, by a sliding door—by reversing all the steps of her departure did Vashti arrive at her son's room, which exactly resembled her own. She might well declare that the visit was superfluous. The buttons, the knobs, the reading desk with the Book, the temperature, the atmosphere, the illumination—all were exactly the same. And if Kuno himself, flesh of her flesh, stood close beside her at last, what profit was there in that? She was too well bred to shake him by the hand.

Averting her eyes, she spoke as follows:

"Here I am. I have had the most terrible journey and greatly retarded the development of my soul. It is not worth it, Kuno; it is not worth it. My time is too precious. The sunlight almost touched me, and I have met with the rudest people. I can stop only a few minutes. Say what you want to say, and then I must return."

"I have been threatened with Homelessness," said Kuno.

She looked at him now.

"I have been threatened with Homelessness, and I could not tell you such a thing through the Machine."

Homelessness means death. The victim is exposed to the air, which kills him.

"I have been outside since I spoke to you last. The tremendous thing has happened, and they have discovered me."

"But why shouldn't you go outside?" she exclaimed. "It is perfectly legal, perfectly mechanical, to visit the surface of the earth. I have lately been to a lecture on the sea; there is no objection to that; one simply summons a respirator and gets an Egression permit. It is not the kind of thing that spiritually minded people do, and I begged you not to do it, but there is no legal objection to it."

"I did not get an Egression permit."

"Then how did you get out?"

"I found out a way of my own."

The phrase conveyed no meaning to her, and he had to repeat it.

"A way of your own?" she whispered. "But that would be wrong."

"Why?"

The question shocked her beyond measure.

"You are beginning to worship the Machine," he said coldly. "You think it irreligious of me to have found out a way of my own. It was just what the Committee thought, when they threatened me with Homelessness."

At this she grew angry. "I worship nothing!" she cried. "I am most advanced. I don't think you irreligious, for there is no such thing as religion left. All the fear and the superstition that existed once have been destroyed by the Machine. I meant only that to find out a way of your own was— Besides there is no new way out."

"So it is always supposed."

"Except through the vomitories, for which one must have an Egression permit, it is impossible to get out. The Book says so."

"Well, the Book's wrong, for I have been out on my feet."

For Kuno was possessed of a certain physical strength.

By these days it was a demerit to be muscular. Each infant was examined at birth, and all who promised undue strength were destroyed. Humanitarians may protest, but it would have been no true kindness to let an athlete live; he would never have been happy in that state of life to which the Machine had called him; he would have yearned for trees to climb, rivers to bathe in, meadows and hills against which he might measure his body. Man must be adapted to his surroundings, must he not? In the dawn of the world our weakly must be exposed on Mount Taygetus; in its twilight our strong will suffer euthanasia, that the Machine may progress, that the Machine may progress, that the Machine may progress eternally.

"You know that we have lost the sense of space. We say space is 'annihilated,' but we have annihilated not space but the sense thereof. We have lost a part of ourselves. I determined to recover it, and I began by walking up and down the platform of the railway outside my room. Up and down, until I was tired, and so did recapture the meaning of 'Near' and 'Far.' 'Near' is a place to which I can get quickly *on my feet*, not a place to which the train or the airship will take me quickly. 'Far' is a place to which I cannot get quickly on my feet; the vomitory is 'far,' though I could be there in thirty-eight seconds by summoning the train. Man is the measure. That was my first lesson. Man's feet are the measure for distance, his hands are the measure for ownership, his body is the measure for all that is lovable and desirable and strong. Then I went further: it was then that I called to you for the first time, and you would not come.

"This city, as you know, is built deep beneath the surface of the earth, with only the vomitories protruding. Having paced the platform outside my own room, I took the lift to the next platform and paced that also, and so with each in turn, until I came to the topmost, above which begins the earth. All the platforms were exactly alike, and all that I gained by visiting them was to develop my sense of space and my muscles. I think I should have been content with this—it is not a little thing—but as I walked and brooded, it occurred to me that our cities had been built in the days when men still breathed the outer air, and that there had been ventilation shafts for the workmen. I could think of nothing but these ventilation shafts. Had they been destroyed by all the food-tubes and medicine tubes and music tubes that the Machine has evolved lately? Or did traces of them remain? One thing was certain. If I came upon them anywhere, it would be in the railway tunnels of the topmost story. Everywhere else, all space was accounted for.

"I am telling my story quickly, but don't think that I was not a coward or that your answers never depressed me. It is not the proper thing, it is not mechanical, it is not decent to walk along a railway tunnel. I did not fear that I might tread upon a live rail and be killed. I feared something far more intangible—doing what was not contemplated by the Machine. Then I said to myself, 'Man is the measure,' and I went, and after many visits I found an opening.

"The tunnels, of course, were lighted. Everything is light, artificial light; darkness is the exception. So when I saw a black gap in the tiles, I knew that it was an exception, and rejoiced. I put in my arm—I could put in no more at first— and waved it round and round in ecstasy. I loosened another tile, and put in my head, and shouted into the darkness: 'I am coming, I shall do it yet,' and my voice reverberated down endless passages. I seemed to hear the spirits of those dead workmen who had returned each evening to the starlight and to their wives, and all the generations who had lived in the open air called back to me, 'You will do it yet, you are coming.'"

He paused, and, absurd as he was, his last words moved her. For Kuno had lately asked to be a father, and his request had been refused by the Committee. His was not a type that the Machine desired to hand on.

"Then a train passed. It brushed by me, but I thrust my head and arms into the hole. I had done enough for one day, so I crawled back to the platform, went down in the lift, and summoned my bed. Ah, what dreams! And again I called you, and again you refused."

She shook her head and said:

"Don't. Don't talk of these terrible things. You make me miserable. You are throwing civilization away."

"But I had got back the sense of space, and a man cannot rest then. I determined to get in at the hole and climb the shaft. And so I exercised my arms. Day after day I went through ridiculous movements, until my flesh ached, and I could hang by my hands and hold the pillow of my bed outstretched for many minutes. Then I summoned a respirator, and started.

"It was easy at first. The mortar had somehow rotted, and I soon pushed some more tiles in, and clambered after them into the darkness, and the spirits of the dead comforted me. I don't know what I mean by that. I just say what I felt. I felt, for the first time, that a protest had been lodged against corruption, and that even as the dead were comforting me, so I was comforting the unborn. I felt that humanity existed, and that it existed without clothes. How can I possibly explain this? It was naked, humanity seemed naked, and all these tubes and buttons and machineries neither came into the world with us, nor will they follow us out, nor do they matter supremely while we are here. Had I been strong, I would have torn off every garment I had, and gone out into the outer air unswaddled. But this is not for me, nor perhaps for my generation. I climbed with my respirator and my hygienic clothes and my dietetic tabloids! Better thus than not at all.

"There was a ladder, made of some primeval metal. The light from the railway fell upon its lowest rungs, and I saw that it led straight upward out of the rubble at the bottom of the shaft. Perhaps our ancestors ran up and down it a dozen times daily, in their building. As I climbed, the rough edges cut through my gloves so that my hands bled. The light helped me for a little, and then came darkness and, worse still, silence which pierced my ears like a sword. The Machine hums! Did you know that? Its hum penetrates our blood, and may even guide our thoughts. Who knows! I was getting beyond its power. Then I thought: 'This silence means that I am doing wrong.' But I heard voices in the silence, and again they strengthened me." He laughed. "I had need of them. The next moment I cracked my head against something."

She sighed.

"I had reached one of those pneumatic stoppers that defend us from the outer air. You may have noticed them on the airship. Pitch dark, my feet on the rungs of an invisible ladder, my hands cut; I cannot explain how I lived through this part, but the voices still comforted me, and I felt for fastenings. The stopper, I suppose, was about eight feet across. I passed my hand over it as far as I could reach. It was perfectly smooth. I felt it almost to the center. Not quite to the center, for my arm was too short. Then the voice said: 'Jump. It is worth it. There may be a handle in the center, and you may catch hold of it and so come to us your own way. And if there is no handle, so that you may fall and are dashed to pieces—it is still worth it: you will still come to us your own way.' So I jumped. There was a handle, and—"

He paused. Tears gathered in his mother's eyes. She knew that he was fated. If he did not die today he would die tomorrow. There was not room for such a person in the world. And with her pity disgust mingled. She was ashamed at having borne such a son, she who had always been so respectable and so full of ideas. Was he really the little boy to whom she had taught the use of his stops and buttons, and to whom she had given his first lessons in the Book? The very hair that disfigured his lip showed that he was reverting to some savage type. On atavism the Machine can have no mercy.

"There was a handle, and I did catch it. I hung tranced over the darkness and heard the hum of these workings as the last whisper in a dying dream. All the things I had cared about and all the people I had spoken to through tubes appeared infinitely little. Meanwhile the handle revolved. My weight had set something in motion and I spun slowly, and then—

"I cannot describe it. I was lying with my face to the sunshine. Blood poured from my nose and ears and I heard a tremendous roaring. The stopper, with me clinging to it, had simply been blown out of the earth, and the air that we make down here was escaping through the vent into the air above. It burst up like a fountain. I crawled back to it—for the upper air hurts—and, as it were, I took great sips from the edge. My respirator had flown goodness knows where, my clothes were torn. I just lay with my lips close to the hole, and I sipped until the bleeding stopped. You can imagine nothing so curious. This hollow in the grass—I will speak of it in a minute—the sun shining into it, not brilliantly but through marbled clouds—the peace, the nonchalance, the sense of space, and, brushing my cheek, the roaring fountain of our artificial air! Soon I spied my respirator, bobbing up and down in the current high above my head, and higher still were many airships. But no one ever looks out of airships, and in any case they could not have picked me up. There I was, stranded. The sun shone a little way down the shaft, and revealed the topmost rung of the ladder, but it was hopeless trying to reach it. I should either have been tossed up again by the escape, or else have fallen in, and died. I could only lie on the grass, sipping and sipping, and from time to time glancing around me.

"I knew that I was in Wessex, for I had taken care to go to a lecture on the subject before starting. Wessex lies above the room in which we are talking now. It was once an important state. Its kings held all the southern coast from the Andredswald to Cornwall, while the Wansdyke protected them on the north, running over the high ground. The lecturer was concerned only with the rise of Wessex, so I do not know how long it remained an international power, nor would the knowledge have assisted me. To tell the truth, I could do nothing but laugh during this part. There was I, with a pneumatic stopper by my side and a respirator bobbing over my head, imprisoned, all three of us, in a grass-grown hollow that was edged with fern."

Then he grew grave again.

"Lucky for me that it was a hollow. For the air began to fall back into it and to fill it as water fills a bowl. I could crawl about. Presently I stood. I breathed a mixture, in which the air that hurts predominated whenever I tried to climb the sides. This was not so bad. I had not lost my tabloids and remained ridiculously cheerful, and as for the Machine, I forgot about it altogether. My one aim now was to get to the top, where the ferns were, and to view whatever objects lay beyond.

"I rushed the slope. The new air was still too bitter for me and I came rolling back, after a momentary vision of something gray. The sun grew very feeble, and I remembered that he was in Scorpio—I had been to a lecture on that too. If the sun is in Scorpio and you are in Wessex, it means that you must be as quick as you can or it will get too dark. (This is the first bit of useful information I have ever got from a lecture, and I expect it will be the last.) It made me try frantically to breathe the new air, and to advance as far as I dared out of my pond. The hollow filled so slowly. At times I thought that the fountain played with less vigor. My respirator semed to dance nearer the earth; the roar was decreasing."

He broke off.

"I don't think this is interesting you. The rest will interest you even less. There are no ideas in it, and I wish that I had not troubled you to come. We are too different, Mother."

She told him to continue.

"It was evening before I climbed the bank. The sun had very nearly slipped out of the sky by this time, and I could not get a good view. You, who have just crossed the Roof of the World, will not want to hear an account of the little hills that I saw—low colorless hills. But to me they were living and the turf that covered them was a skin, under which their muscles rippled, and I felt that those hills had called with incalculable force to men in the past, and that men had loved them. Now they sleep—perhaps for ever. They commune with humanity in dreams. Happy the man, happy the woman, who awakes the hills of Wessex. For though they sleep, they will never die."

His voice rose passionately.

"Cannot you see, cannot all you lecturers see, that it is we that are dying, and that down here the only thing that really lives is the Machine? We created the Machine, to do our will, but we cannot make it do our will now. It has robbed us of the sense of space and of the sense of touch; it has blurred every human relation and narrowed down love to a carnal act, it has paralyzed our bodies and our wills, and now it compels us to worship it. The Machine develops—but not on our lines. The Machine proceeds—but not to our goal. We exist only as the blood corpuscles that course through its arteries, and if it could work without us, it would let us die. Oh, I have no remedy—or, at least, only one—to tell men again and again that I have seen the hills of Wessex as Aelfrid saw them when he overthrew the Danes.

"So the sun set. I forgot to mention that a belt of mist lay between my hill and other hills, and that it was the color of pearl."

He broke off for the second time.

"Go on," said his mother wearily.

He shook his head.

"Go on. Nothing that you say can distress me now. I am hardened."

"I had meant to tell you the rest, but I cannot: I know that I cannot: good-bye."

Vashti stood irresolute. All her nerves were tingling with his blasphemies. But she was also inquisitive.

"This is unfair," she complained. "You have called me across the world to hear·your story, and hear it I will. Tell me—as briefly as possible, for this is a disastrous waste of time—tell me how you returned to civilization."

"Oh—that!" he said, starting. "You would like to hear about civilization. Certainly. Had I got to where my respirator fell down?"

"No—but I understand everything now. You put on your respirator, and managed to walk along the surface of the earth to a vomitory, and there your conduct was reported to the Central Committee."

"By no means."

He passed his hand over his forehead, as if dispelling some strong impression. Then, resuming his narrative, he warmed to it again.

"My respirator fell about sunset. I had mentioned that the fountain seemed feebler, had I not?"

"Yes."

"About sunset, it let the respirator fall. As I said, I had entirely forgotten about the Machine, and I paid no great attention at the time, being occupied with other things. I had my pool of air, into which I could dip when the outer keenness became intolerable, and which would possibly remain for days, provided that no wind sprang up to disperse it. Not until it was too late did I realize what the stoppage of the escape implied. You see—the gap in the tunnel had been mended; the Mending Apparatus; the Mending Apparatus, was after me.

"One other warning I had, but I neglected it. The sky at night was clearer than it had been in the day, and the moon, which was about half the sky behind the sun, shone into the dell at moments quite brightly. I was in my usual place—on the boundary between the two atmospheres—when I thought I saw something dark move across the bottom of the dell, and vanish into the shaft. In my folly, I ran down. I bent over and listened, and I thought I heard a faint scraping noise in the depths.

"At this—but it was too late—I took alarm. I determined to put on my respirator and to walk right out of the dell. But my respirator had gone. I knew exactly where it had fallen—between the stopper and the aperture—and I could even feel the mark that it had made in the turf. It had gone, and I realized that something evil was at work, and, if I must die, die running toward the cloud that had been the color of a pearl. I never started. Out of the shaft—it is too horrible. A worm, a long white worm, had crawled out of the shaft and was gliding over the moonlit grass.

"I screamed. I did everything that I should not have done; I stamped upon the creature instead of flying from it, and it at once curled round the ankle. Then we fought. The worm let me run all over the dell, but edged up my leg as I ran.

'Help!' I cried. (That part is too awful. It belongs to the part that you will never know.) 'Help!' I cried. (Why cannot we suffer in silence?) 'Help!' I cried. Then my feet were wound together. I fell, I was dragged away from the dear ferns and the living hills, and past the great metal stopper (I can tell you this part), and I thought it might save me again if I caught hold of the handle. It also was enwrapped, it also. Oh, the whole dell was full of the things. They were searching it in all directions; they were denuding it, and the white snouts of others peeped out of the hole, ready if needed. Everything that could be moved they brought—brushwood, bundles of fern, everything, and down we all went intertwined into hell. The last things that I saw, ere the stopper closed after us, were certain stars, and I felt that a man of my sort lived in the sky. For I did fight, I fought till the very end, and it was only my head hitting against the ladder that quieted me. I woke up in this room. The worms had vanished; I was surrounded by artificial air, artificial light, artificial peace, and my friends were calling to me down speaking-tubes to know whether I had come across any new ideas lately."

Here his story ended. Discussion of it was impossible, and Vashti turned to go.

"It will end in Homelessness," she said quietly.

"I wish it would," retorted Kuno.

"The Machine has been most merciful."

"I prefer the mercy of God."

"By that superstitious phrase, do you mean that you could live in the outer air?"

"Yes."

"Have you ever seen, round the vomitories, the bones of those who were extruded after the Great Rebellion?"

"Yes."

"They were left where they perished for our edification. A few crawled away, but they perished, too—who can doubt it? And so with the Homeless of our own day. The surface of the earth supports life no longer."

"Indeed."

"Ferns and a little grass may survive, but all higher forms have perished. Has any airship detected them?"

"No."

"Has any lecturer dealt with them?"

"No."

"Then why this obstinacy?"

"Because I have seen them," he exploded.

"Seen *what*?"

"Because I have seen her in the twilight—because she came to my help when I called—because she, too, was entangled by the worms, and, luckier than I, was killed by one of them piercing her throat."

He was mad. Vashti departed, nor, in the troubles that followed, did she ever see his face again.

PART III

THE HOMELESS

DURING the years that followed Kuno's escapade, two impartant developments took place in the Machine. On the surface they were revolutionary, but in either case men's minds had been prepared beforehand, and they did but express tendencies that were latent already.

The first of these was the abolition of respirators.

Advanced thinkers, like Vashti, had always held it foolish to visit the surface of the earth. Airships might be necessary, but what was the good of going out for mere curiosity and crawling along for a mile or two in a terrestrial motor? The habit was vulgar and perhaps faintly improper: it was unproductive of ideas, and had no connection with the habits that really mattered. So respirators were abolished, and with them, of course, the terrestrial motors, and except for a few lecturers, who complained that they were debarred access to their subject matter, the development was accepted quietly. Those who still wanted to know what the earth was like had after all only to listen to some gramophone or to look into some cinematophote. And even the lecturers acquiesced when they found that a lecture on the sea was none the less stimulating when compiled out of other lectures that had already been delivered on the same subject. "Beware of firsthand ideas!" exclaimed one of the most advanced of them. "Firsthand ideas do not really exist. They are but the physical impressions produced by love and fear, and on this gross foundation who could erect a philosophy? Let your ideas be secondhand, and if possible tenthhand, for then they will be far removed from that disturbing element—direct observation. Do not learn anything about this subject of mine—the French Revolution. Learn instead what I think that Enicharmon thought Urizen thought Gutch thought Ho-Yung thought Chi-Bo-Sing thought Lafcadio Hearn thought Carlyle thought Mirabeau said about the French Revolution. Through the medium of these ten great minds the blood that was shed at Paris and the windows that were broken at Versailles will be clarified to an idea which you may employ most profitably in your daily lives. But be sure that the intermediates are many and varied, for in history one authority exists to counteract another. Urizen must counteract the skepticism of Ho-Young and Enicharmon, I must myself counteract the impetuosity of Gutch. You who listen to me are in a better position to judge about the French Revolution than I am. Your descendants will be even in a better position than you, for they will learn what you think. I think, and yet another intermediate will be added to the chain. And in time"—his voice rose—"there will come a generation that has got beyond facts, beyond impressions, a generation absolutely colorless, a generation

seraphically free
From taint of personality,

which will see the French Revolution not as it happened, nor as they would like it to have happened, but as it would have happened had it taken place in the days of the Machine."

Tremendous applause greeted this lecture, which did but voice a feeling already latent in the minds of men—a feeling that terrestrial facts must be ignored, and that the abolition of respirators was a positive gain. It was even suggested that airships should be abolished too. This was not done, because airships had somehow worked themselves into the Machine's system. But year by year they were used less, and mentioned less by thoughtful men.

The second great development was the reestablishment of religion.

This, too, had been voiced in the celebrated lecture. No one could mistake the reverent tone in which the peroration had concluded, and it awakened a responsive echo in the heart of each. Those who had long worshiped silently now began to talk. They described the strange feeling of peace that came over them when they handled the Book of the Machine, the pleasure that it was to repeat certain numerals out of it, however little meaning those numerals conveyed to the outward ear, the ecstasy of touching a button however unimportant, or of ringing an electric bell however superfluously.

"The Machine," they exclaimed, "feeds us and clothes us and houses us; through it we speak to one another, through it we see one another, in it we have our being. The Machine is the friend of ideas and the enemy of superstition: the Machine is omnipotent, eternal; blessed is the Machine." And before long this allocution was printed on the first page of the Book, and in subsequent editions the ritual swelled into a complicated system of praise and prayer. The word "religion" was sedulously avoided, and in theory the Machine was still the creation and the implement of man. But in practice all, save a few retrogrades, worshiped it as divine. Nor was it worshiped in unity. One believer would be chiefly impressed by the blue optic plates, through which he saw other believers; another by the Mending Apparatus, which sinful Kuno had compared to worms; another by the lifts, another by the Book. And each would pray to this or to that, and ask it to intercede for him with the Machine as a whole. Persecution—that also was present. It did not break out, for reasons that will be set forward shortly. But it was latent, and all who did not accept the minimum known as "undenominational Mechanism" lived in danger of Homelessness, which means death, as we know.

To attribute these two great developments to the Central Committee is to take a very narrow view of civilization. The Central Committee announced the developments, it is true, but they were no more the cause of them than were the kings of the imperialistic period the cause of war. Rather did they yield to some invincible pressure, which came no one knew whither, and which, when gratified, was succeeded by some new pressure equally invincible. To such a state of affairs it is convenient to give the name of progress. No one confessed the Machine was out of hand. Year by year it was served with increased efficiency and decreased intelligence. The better a man knew his own duties upon it, the less he understood the duties of his neighbor, and in all the world there was not one who understood the monster as a whole. Those master brains had perished. They had left full directions, it is true, and their successors had each of them mastered a portion of those directions. But Humanity, in its desire for comfort, had overreached itself. It had exploited the riches of nature too far. Quietly and complacently, it was sinking into decadence, and progress had come to mean the progress of the Machine.

As for Vashti, her life went peacefully forward until the final disaster. She made her room dark and slept; she awoke and made the room light. She lectured and attended lectures. She exchanged ideas with her innumerable friends and believed she was growing more spiritual. At times a friend was granted Euthanasia, and left his or her room for the homelessness that is beyond all human conception. Vashti did not much mind. After an unsuccessful lecture, she would sometimes ask for Euthanasia herself. But the death rate was not permitted to exceed the birth rate, and the Machine had hitherto refused it to her.

The troubles began quietly, long before she was conscious of them.

One day she was astonished at receiving a message from her son. They never communicated, having nothing in common, and she had only heard indirectly that he was still alive, and had been transferred from the Northern Hemisphere, where he had behaved so mischievously, to the Southern—indeed, to a room not far from her own.

"Does he want me to visit him?" she thought. "Never again, never. And I have not the time."

No, it was madness of another kind.

He refused to visualize his face upon the blue plate, and speaking out of the darkness with solemnity said:

"The Machine stops."

"What do you say?"

"The Machine is stopping, I know it; I know the signs."

She burst into a peal of laughter. He heard her and was angry, and they spoke no more.

"Can you imagine anything more absurd?" she cried to a friend. "A man who was my son believes that the Machine is stopping. It would be impious if it was not mad."

"The Machine is stopping?" her friend replied. "What does that mean? The phrase conveys nothing to me."

"Nor to me."

"He does not refer, I suppose, to the trouble there has been lately with the music?"

"Oh, no, of course not. Let us talk about music."

"Have you complained to the authorities?"

"Yes, and they say it wants mending, and referred me to the Committee of the Mending Apparatus. I complained of those curious gasping sighs that disfigure the symphonies of the Brisbane school. They sound like someone in pain. The Committee of the Mending Apparatus say that it shall be remedied shortly."

Obscurely worried, she resumed her life. For one thing, the defect in the music irritated her. For another thing, she could not forget Kuno's speech. If he had known that the music was out of repair—he could not know it, for he detested music—if he had known that it was wrong, "the Machine stops" was exactly the venomous sort of remark he would have made. Of course, he had made it at a venture, but the coincidence annoyed her, and she spoke with some petulance to the Committee of the Mending Apparatus.

They replied, as before, that the defect would be set right shortly.

"Shortly! At once!" she retorted. "Why should I be worried by imperfect music? Things are always put right at once. If you do not mend it at once, I shall complain to the Central Committee."

"No personal complaints are received by the Central Committee," the Committee of the Mending Apparatus replied.

"Through whom am I to make my complaint, then?"

"Through us."

"I complain then."

"Your complaint shall be forwarded in its turn."

"Have others complained?"

This question was unmechanical, and the Committee of the Mending Apparatus refused to answer it.

"It is too bad!" she exclaimed to another of her friends. "There never was such an unfortunate woman as myself. I can never be sure of my music now. It gets worse and worse each time I summon it."

"I too have my troubles," the friend replied. "Sometimes my ideas are interrupted by a slight jarring noise."

"What is it?"

"I do not know whether it is inside my head or inside the wall."

"Complain in either case."

"I have complained, and my complaint will be forwarded in its turn to the Central Committee."

Time passed, and they resented the defects no longer. The defects had not been remedied, but the human tissues in that latter day had become so subservient that they readily adapted themselves to every caprice of the Machine. The sigh at the crisis of the Brisbane symphony no longer irritated Vashti; she accepted it as part of the melody. The jarring noise, whether in the head or in the wall, was no longer resented by her friend. And so with the moldy artificial fruit, so with the bath water that began to stink, so with the defective rhymes that the poetry machine had taken to emitting. All were bitterly complained of at first, and then acquiesced in and forgotten. Things went from bad to worse unchallenged.

It was otherwise with the failure of the sleeping apparatus. That was a more serious stoppage. There came a day when over the whole world—in Sumatra, in Wessex, in the innumerable cities of Courland and Brazil—the beds, when summoned by their tired owners, failed to appear. It may seem a ludicrous matter, but from it we may date the collapse of humanity. The Committee responsible for the failure was assailed by complaints, whom it referred, as usual, to the Committee of the Mending Apparatus, who in its turn assured them that their complaints would be forwarded to the Central Committee. But the discontent grew, for mankind was not yet sufficiently adaptable to do without sleeping.

"Someone is meddling with the Machine—" they began.

"Someone is trying to make himself king, to reintroduce the personal element."

"Punish that man with Homelessness."

"To the rescue! Avenge the Machine! Avenge the Machine!"

"War! Kill the man!"

But the Committee of the Mending Apparatus now came forward, and allayed the panic with well-chosen words. It confessed that the Mending Apparatus was itself in need of repair.

The effect of this frank confession was admirable.

"Of course," said a famous lecturer—he of the French Revolution, who gilded each new decay with splendor—"of course we shall not press our complaints now. The Mending Apparatus has treated us so well in the past that we all sympathize with it, and will wait patiently for its recovery. In its own good time it will resume its duties. Meanwhile let us do without our beds, our tabloids, our other little wants. Such, I feel sure, would be the wish of the Machine."

Thousands of miles away his audience applauded. The Machine still linked them. Under the seas, beneath the roots of the mountains, ran the wires through which they saw and heard, the enormous eyes and ears that were their heritage, and the hum of many workings clothed their thoughts in one garment of subserviency. Only the old and sick remained ungrateful, for it was rumored that Euthanasia, too, was out of order, and that pain had reappeared among men.

It became difficult to read. A blight entered the atmosphere and dulled its luminosity. At times Vashti could scarcely see across her room. The air, too, was foul. Loud were the complaints, impotent the remedies, heroic the tone of the lecturer as he cried: "Courage! courage! What matter so long as the Machine goes on? To it the darkness and the light are one." And though things improved again after a time, the old brilliancy was never recaptured, and humanity never recovered from its entrance into twilight. There was hysterical talk of "measures," of "provisional dictatorship," and the inhabitants of Sumatra were asked to familiarize themselves with the workings of the central power station, the said power station being situated in France. But for the most part panic reigned, and men spent their strength praying to their Books, tangible proofs of the Machine's omnipotence. There were gradations of terror—at times came rumors of hope—the Mending Apparatus was almost mended—the enemies of the Machine had been got under—new "nerve centers" were evolving which would do the work even more magnificently than before. But there came a day when, without the slightest warning, without any previous hint of feebleness, the entire communication system broke down, all over the world, and the world, as they understood it, ended.

Vashti was lecturing at the time, and her earlier remarks had been punctuated with applause. As she proceeded the audience became silent, and at the conclusion there was no sound. Somewhat displeased, she called to a friend who was a specialist in sympathy. No sound: doubtless the friend was sleeping. And so with the next friend whom she tried to summon, and so with the next, until she remembered Kuno's cryptic remark, "The Machine stops."

The phrase still conveyed nothing. If Eternity was stopping it would of course be set going shortly.

For example, there were still a little light and air—the atmosphere had improved a few hours previously. There was still the Book, and while there was the Book there was security.

Then she broke down, for with the cessation of activity came an unexpected terror—silence.

She had never known silence, and the coming of it nearly killed her—it did kill many thousands of people outright. Ever since her birth she had been surrounded by the steady hum. It was to the ear what artificial air was to the lungs, and agonizing pains shot across her head. And scarcely knowing what she did, she stumbled forward and pressed the unfamiliar button, the one that opened the door of her cell.

Now the door of the cell worked on a simple hinge of its own. It was not connected with the central power station, dying far away in France. It opened, rousing immoderate hopes in Vashti, for she thought that the Machine had been mended. It opened, and she saw the dim tunnel that curved far away toward freedom. One look, and then she shrank back. For the tunnel was full of people—she was almost the last in that city to have taken alarm.

People at any time repelled her, and these were nightmares from her worst dreams. People were crawling about, people were screaming, whimpering, gasping for breath, touching each other, vanishing in the dark, and ever and anon being pushed off the platform on to the live rail. Some were fighting round the electric bells, trying to summon trains which could not be summoned. Others were yelling for Euthanasia or for respirators, or blaspheming the Machine. Others stood at the doors of their cells fearing, like herself, either to stop in them or to leave them, and behind all the uproar was silence—the silence which is the voice of the earth and of the generations who have gone.

No—it was worse than solitude. She closed the door again and sat down to wait for the end. The disintegration went on, accompanied by horrible cracks and rumbling. The valves that restrained the Medical Apparatus must have been weakened, for it ruptured and hung hideously from the ceiling. The floor heaved and fell and flung her from her chair. A tube oozed toward her serpent fashion. And at last the final horror approached—light began to ebb, and she knew that civilization's long day was closing.

She whirled round, praying to be saved from this, at any rate, kissing the Book, pressing button after button. The uproar outside was increasing, and even penetrated the wall. Slowly the brilliancy of her cell was dimmed, the reflections faded from her metal switches. Now she could not see the reading stand, now not the Book, though she held it in her hand. Light followed the flight of sound, air was following light, and the original void returned to the cavern from which it had been so long excluded. Vashti continued to whirl, like the devotees of an earlier religion, screaming, praying, striking at the buttons with bleeding hands.

It was thus that she opened her prison and escaped—escaped in the spirit: at least so it seems to me, ere my meditation closes. That she escapes in the body—I cannot perceive that. She struck, by chance, the switch that released the door, and the rush of foul air on her skin, the loud throbbing whispers in her ears, told her that she was facing the tunnel again, and that tremendous platform on which she had seen men fighting. They were not fighting now. Only the whispers remained, and the little whimpering groans. They were dying by hundreds out in the dark.

She burst into tears.

Tears answered her.

They wept for humanity, those two, not for themselves. They could not bear that this should be the end. Ere silence was completed their hearts were opened, and they knew what had been important on the earth. Man, the flower of all flesh, the noblest of all creatures visible, man who had once made god in his image, and had mirrored his strength on the constellations, beautiful naked man was dying, strangled in the garments that he had woven. Century after century had he toiled, and here was his reward. Truly the garment had seemed heavenly at first, shot with the colors of culture, sewn with the threads of self-denial. And heavenly it had been so long as it was a garment and no more, so long as man could shed it at will and live by the essence that is his soul, and the essence, equally divine, that is his body. The sin against the body—it was for that they wept in chief; the centuries of wrong against the muscles and the nerves, and those five portals by which we can alone apprehend—glozing it over with talk of evolution, until the body was white pap, the home of ideas as colorless, last sloshy stirrings of a spirit that had grasped the stars.

"Where are you?" she sobbed.

His voice in the darkness said, "Here."

"Is there any hope, Kuno?"

"None for us."

"Where are you?"

She crawled toward him over the bodies of the dead. His blood spurted over her hands.

"Quicker," he gasped, "I am dying—but we touch, we talk, not through the Machine."

He kissed her.

"We have come back to our own. We die, but we have recaptured life, as it was in Wessex, when Aelfrid overthrew the Danes. We know what they know outside, they who dwelt in the cloud that is the color of a pearl."

"But, Kuno, is it true? Are there still men on the surface of the earth? Is this—this tunnel, this poisoned darkness—really not the end?"

He replied:

"I have seen them, spoken to them, loved them. They are hiding in the mist and the ferns until our civilization stops. Today they are the Homeless—tomorrow—"

"Oh, tomorrow—some fool will start the Machine again, tomorrow."

"Never," said Kuno, "never. Humanity has learned its lesson."

As he spoke the whole city was broken like a honeycomb. An airship had sailed in through the vomitory into a ruined wharf. It crashed downward, exploding as it went, rending gallery after gallery with its wings of steel. For a moment they saw the nations of the dead, and, before they joined them, scraps of the untainted sky.

Part V:

FUTURES

Thomas J. Watson, Jr.

TECHNOLOGICAL CHANGE
(1960)

I

INTRODUCTION

TECHNOLOGICAL CHANGE—a modern-sounding term—has been
with us since the dawn of civilization. It is as old as a better
Stone Age ax and as new as a transistor radio—as common-
place as a can opener and as complex as a space vehicle.
In its simplest sense, technological change may be thought
of as the development of a better way of doing a known job
or the discovery of how to do a previously impossible one.
While not actually science, it draws heavily on science for
its innovations.

The most discussed aspect of technological change, at least
since the Second World War, is what we loosely call "automation." This word generally describes the automatic linking
of an industrial process to a device which checks the process
and adjusts it to the desired standard. Automation in industry
has greatly accelerated the whole process of technological
change in our society. And many experts feel that the real
impact of automated devices hasn't yet been fully felt, even
in our technologically advanced economy.

Technology has brought with it both great progress in
better living and working conditions and a certain number of
very real problems. We have only to look at recent history
to see what amazing human progress has been made in a
very short time. Just a century ago, steam and water power
provided less than one-quarter of the energy needed for all
production. Men and animals supplied the rest, with men
giving by far the greater share. Today in the United States
machines supply 98 per cent of all power for industrial work.
Men have been freed, at least in our country, from much
heavy physical labor. The average work week has been reduced from 60 hours in 1890 to 40 hours today and it will be
reduced even further. More important, most workers today
have safer, and generally more interesting, jobs than they
had just a few years ago.

Technological change has not always brought a better life

for all in the past. For this reason, it deserves more of our attention today than ever before. The population of the Western World remained approximately the same from 1200-1700 after Christ. In the past one hundred years, it has almost tripled. Out of this phenomenal growth has risen the huge working population of the United States and Western Europe.

And so while the automatic Jacquard loom of 150 years ago could move weavers from the hearth to the factory, the numbers involved were few and the movement slow. Now mechanisms available or predicted may, if not controlled, cause real displacement in the working population of this country. Some of these displacements have already taken place, and we must do our best to protect all of our citizens today and in the future.

II

THE RECENT PAST

If there is any one factor most responsible for the phenomenal economic progress of the United States in the twentieth century, it is the enthusiasm with which we as a people have tried to create better ways and conditions of working and living. We have always wanted to do things more quickly, go places more quickly, and make more and better goods available more quickly. As a result, we have consistently removed more and more human energy from the production equation.

Today, the average worker in the United States works shorter hours, turns out more goods, receives higher wages, and has more energy harnessed and working for him than a worker anywhere else in the world. He is also backed up with huge capital expenditures—over $308 billion in the past decade alone. Equipment behind the average worker has increased by 139 per cent in the past fifty years and by 33 per cent in the last ten years alone.

This approach—supporting the United States factory worker with a maximum of power and tooling, management planning, and healthy environment—has been called the "American Use of Americans." It is a vital factor in allowing us to compete with foreign wage rates not even one-half—and in some cases not one-fourth—as high as our own. It has enabled us to increase output per man-hour over 35 per cent in the last ten years and at the same time employ more people than ever before in our history: 9 million more than were employed in 1950, 21 million more than were employed in 1940. It is enabling us this year to produce four times as many goods and services as we did fifty years ago—almost 40 per cent more than we did just ten years ago.

Even more exciting is the fact that technological development is continuing to help in the human upgrading process so precious to us in America. By taking over more of the mechanical production job, automation can, if properly applied and understood, give us the opportunity to put more production people into better jobs. Today, for example, over 20 per cent of the working force are classified as professional, technical, or managerial—whereas only 17.6 per cent were so classified ten years ago, and this upgrading process will continue. As the jobs requiring heavy physical labor or dangerous and boring work are taken over by machines, the challenge to America to put the displaced workers into interesting upgraded jobs is tremendous.

III

THE NEXT DECADE

The progress of the past has been amazing and fruitful. The next ten years may well bring about technological changes which will make the past progress seem small indeed. This will result from the rapidly closing gap between new knowledge and its direct application to our life. The principle of the vacuum tube was understood around the turn of the century, but it was not used in any major way until after the First World War. On the other hand, the transistor was discovered in 1948. Within five years, it was being widely used in many types of equipment. The solar battery was hardly born before it was flying in our satellites.

Future progress will come about as it has in the past—from internal economic stimuli and the pressing competitive need to make each industrial process as efficient as possible. Along with our own internal welfare, however, there is an equally crucial incentive: our long-term conflict with our Communist adversaries. They are convinced that their system will outpace our own. While we know that they are quite a distance from doing this, we would be foolish to be complacent.

The way we direct and expand our economy is very closely connected with our ability to triumph over Communism. We know our democracy has produced more for us than any other way of life man has tried, and we should not fear competition from any system that challenges it. As a people, we believe that a free environment enables men to think and create more effectively than a rigidly controlled environment. Now we must prove this belief by producing advances across the whole spectrum of human achievement at a substantially faster rate than the Soviet Union.

While the exact extent and direction of technological change during the next decade is impossible to predict, we do know that it will continue to be a major stimulus for growth through new investment, new products, and new industries.

Consider, for example, the electronics industry, certainly a product of rapidly advancing technological innovation. Sales in this industry have skyrocketed in ten years, from roughly $2.5 billion in 1950 to well over $10 billion today. Total employment has at least doubled—over 760,000 are now employed in electronics. In the next decade we will see other new industries spring up and present ones expand, creating many thousands of new jobs and opportunities.

We will witness accurate worldwide weather prediction and television via satellites; the development of entirely new materials in response to rocketry's requirements for extreme heat resistance; and major breakthroughs in medical research and chemistry which, hopefully, will eliminate many of today's dread diseases.

We are living in an era of unlimited possibilities for a full, happy life for all people. Technological change is one of the means by which we can achieve this. But in the highly complex, competitive, and dangerous political society of the world, we must have a sure sense of direction. For this reason we need clear, realistic national goals in the area of technological change.

IV

GOALS

I would recommend these three basic national goals in the technological area as part of the platform on which we can continue to build a strong nation and a better world:

Technological change should be used to improve men's

lives. We have seen that it brings both progress and problems. Our goal must be to apply new technology so that it will improve the way men live and work. Necessary adjustment to an accelerating technology must be planned and carried out with human considerations paramount.

Technological change should be encouraged to meet our own increasing industrial needs, to stimulate our social and economic progress, and to face successfully the long-term challenge of international Communism.

Technological knowledge should be shared so that people throughout the world, particularly in the underdeveloped countries, may improve their lives and benefit from up-to-date technology.

1. Improving men's lives through technological change. We are in a time when changes of all kinds will continue to modify the way we live and work. This we must expect. New forms of energy, new kinds of machines, and new ways of organizing production are entering our economy and our way of life. Most of these changes are welcomed when they are understood, but there is no doubt that serious human problems are created by the speed with which our established economic and social patterns are being altered.

Already there have been shifts which can to a greater or lesser degree be attributed to technological change. There is, for example, a major, continuing change in our overall employment pattern: far fewer people are producing a steadily increasing amount of goods. During the fifties, total output of the manufacturing industry jumped 40 per cent, yet there was only a 9 per cent increase in total employees, and these were virtually all in administration, sales, engineering, and other nonproduction activities. Today almost half of the nonfarm labor force is employed in managerial, professional, clerical or sales jobs.

Technological change in the form of new methods, machines, and chemicals has had its most violent impact on agriculture, an area sometimes obscured by today's emphasis on space exploration, nuclear energy and electronics. One hundred years ago, it took one farmer in the United States to feed five people. Today, one farmer feeds thirty-two. Over

1,600,000 workers—or 20 per cent of the total—have left the farms since 1950, but farm output has increased.

Service industries, too, such as transportation, retailing, finance, utilities, and government service have undergone a major transformation. Until the late 1940's, there were always more people in production industries—manufacturing, agriculture, construction, and mining—than in the service group. Now there are over 25 per cent more employees in the service than in the production industries, with an increase of over five million people in less than ten years.

Perhaps the most promising fundamental change we can observe is the increase in skilled technical and professional workers, a change which should continue to grow in scope. The number of these highly trained people jumped 58 per cent just in the past decade. This is one of the most important human benefits attributable to recent technological change. These trends will in most cases encourage more education, more skills, and allow more time for self-development to people throughout the world.

(a) Adjustment. Fortunately, introducing technical innovation in industry has never been a sudden process and probably never will be. In a commercial organization, technological change generally cannot be brought about without vast expenditures of capital and major reequipping of plants. Consequently, it comes about over a period of years rather than months or days. Certainly human adjustment to it should not be forced, rushed, or humiliating, but must be carefully considered and carried out. This is a clear responsibility of both management and labor.

As an outstanding union leader has said, concerning the automation aspect of technological change: "Free labor and free management, in cooperation with free government [must] . . . plan as free people to meet the problems and to realize the promise of the greater abundance that these machines will make possible."

There are many signs that industry and labor are facing up to this problem of farsighted adjustment to technological change. An outstanding experiment going on at the present time is the joint automation committee set up by a prominent meat processor and the unions. The committee is studying the effects of closing several outdated plants, the possibility of workers retraining for new jobs and equipment, and job placement elsewhere when necessary. Whatever the outcome, this will serve as a useful laboratory model for further enlightened management-labor cooperation in planning for technological change.

(b) Displacement. Viewed in broad perspective, technological displacement is presently not a vast national problem. Our expanding economy has, decade after decade, absorbed into useful employment the overwhelming majority of the rapidly increasing work population, and this has facilitated human adjustment to technological change.

But we must not ignore the fact that technological displacement is a problem in some areas now—and the problem may increase in the future. It is likely to be most acute and worthy of special attention in depressed areas or in pockets of surplus labor. We must meet the problems of these areas, whether caused by technological change or by some other factor. As a human, practical matter, we must give sympathetic and prompt attention to the overall problems of unemployment, for whatever reasons they occur.

The existing aids to depressed areas—governmental technical assistance, special consideration in awarding government contracts, and loans by the Small Business Administration—should be continued. But these programs must be vigorously supplemented by new approaches to ensure positive and prompt action.

When an area has been officially judged to be "distressed," the federal government should grant tax allowance for accelerated plant depreciation (similar to that granted defense contractors in wartime) to industries moving facilities into this area. State and federal governments should consider matching programs for local private funds when local citizens initiate campaigns to attract industry to distressed areas.

The minimum disturbance to the economic functioning of the country will come about by moving industry to the people who need jobs. But when this is not effective for a given area and there is a labor shortage elsewhere, an interstate plan of coordination and a "relocation" program for individuals should be worked out under the direction of the United States Departments of Labor and Commerce.

Depressed areas should be redeveloped in accordance with sound business and economic principles so that they will not become permanent responsibilities of the federal government. Federal guarantee of loans, and in some cases partial direct loans, seem to be the methods of assistance most in accordance with those principles. Private local groups would in such cases be directly involved and largely responsible for the business soundness of the development plans. Where necessary, federal loans would be made to individuals for relocation purposes, as well as to business and communities for development purposes. This approach has been applied successfully in Great Britain for many years.

A real and continuing effort should be made to improve both the benefits and duration of payments under federal-state unemployment insurance plans. Supplemental unemployment benefits might soften the effects of future layoffs in certain industries. With an increasingly mobile work force, severance pay should be flexibly administered, with company and employee working together so that maximum benefit toward reemployment may be derived from the funds involved.

It has been suggested that a top-level commission of industry, labor, and government be set up to study the effects of technological change upon our people and recommend appropriate action. If such a study cannot be effectively and promptly carried out by existing governmental departments, such a commission would be highly desirable. I would hope that the President would direct the appropriate departments to undertake this study at once. The private sectors of the economy—including both business and labor—should be called upon to take whatever voluntary action is needed. The President should then incorporate the appropriate recommendations of this study into his legislative program. To make such a program effective, business, labor, and other interested segments of our economy must cooperate to the fullest possible extent. If such an effort does not produce concrete results, the new commission approach should be adopted.

American industry is accepting increasing responsibility for full employment in the United States. This trend must continue, for it is a national responsibility to ensure safe, interesting, and profitable jobs to all Americans who want to work.

2. Encouraging technological change. In a dictatorial economy, all aspects of production, education, finance, trade —and society itself, for that matter—can be manipulated to emphasize technological development or any other goal. But in our free society we have a more complex problem. How can we derive the maximum benefits of technological change and still make the appropriate social adjustments without endangering basic freedoms and human dignity? The answer is not a simple or quick one.

(a) Private industry. First and foremost, we must clearly recognize what has encouraged technological advances in our past and made us the most productive nation in history. The magic ingredient is our competitive enterprise environment, the most powerful force ever known for stimulating individual and cooperative efforts to make innovations for the benefit of mankind. It encourages and rewards those enterprises which make successful changes, and punishes or eliminates the inefficient who fall behind. Our patent laws, protecting for a specified time any individual achievements, are valuable elements of this environment. So are the antitrust laws, which help maintain both the competitive stimulus to innovation and the competitive mechanism for sharing the fruits of technological change with the consumer. But we must not be satisfied with present strength—we must build on them.

The federal government should encourage the updating of our capital equipment. Liberalized depreciation allowances should be given consideration as a means to this end when they would encourage new capital commitments and meet a need for increased funds for capital expenditure. Depreciation allowances should be kept under constant review to ensure that useful equipment life for tax purposes is realistic in terms of industrial practice.

We must continue to press for more liberal international trade policies both at home and abroad. These will broaden the application of technical innovations in the United States and in the developing nations. On the other hand, unimaginative and shortsighted tariff protection of marginal industries will neither strengthen our own economy nor win new markets or new converts to our way of life. While we must further our trend toward more liberal policies, the government must also give prompt consideration to helping our noncompetitive industries reorient their production capabilities into new areas.

(b) Government and defense spending. The federal government today plays by far the most significant role in the whole area of technological change. More than 60 per cent of all expenditures for research and development are now made through the Department of Defense, Atomic Energy Commission, National Aeronautics and Space Agency, and other federal agencies. These funds are certainly a most

powerful and direct stimulus to technological change. As such, their administration is a key factor in shaping both our technological resources and our economy. The federal government's contract and administrative procedures, however, were originally designed primarily for procurement and purchase of weapons and equipment, such as airplanes and reactors. Consequently, they have done little to ensure that our technological capabilities and resources will be properly balanced and appropriate to our total national requirements.

The government should consider these suggestions to encourage technological change: First, within the government one group or agency should be made responsible for developing a national policy to support and encourage our technological effort. Increased support must be given to fundamental, basic research. While the National Science Foundation is now responsible for guiding and encouraging such basic research, perhaps its role should be expanded to include both basic and applied science, independent of any immediate departmental procurement needs. The government must understand the shape of the overall national technology and determine what steps should be taken to strengthen or modify it, which areas should be accentuated, and what specific programs are needed.

Second, specific provisions for applied research and exploratory development should be included in certain government-supported projects. These are activities which translate new scientific knowledge into practical goods, procedures, and systems. There has been a lack of emphasis in the past, stemming directly from a "get-it-done" policy: "deliver *this* equipment with *these* capabilities on *this* date." Overall technical progress inevitably suffers and often the final product is outdated before it appears.

Third, we need a careful study and a new approach to the administration of competitive bidding on government-industry contracts. While American industry has continually demonstrated the beneficial stimulus of competition in producing technological change, present government bidding procedures have often proved wasteful of technical manpower and specialized industry teams. Mere preparation of involved government bids has often occupied some of the nation's best technical minds in several companies for months on end. In defense areas, we must be as economical with our technological experts as with our technological dollars. We can certainly protect the American tradition of equal economic opportunity without being handcuffed to inappropriate and outdated contracting formulas.

Relationships between government and industry will never be simple, but they can and must be flexible. Responsibilities must be clearly spelled out on both the government and business sides. And finally, both groups must honestly look for ways to encourage our best technical minds to serve in government as well as in industry. Such encouragement must include both financial rewards and appropriate environment for creative work.

(c) Education. In the past, educators could plan reasonably well to prepare the student for a lifetime career as clerk, factory worker, mechanical engineer, or salesman. Most jobs and the qualifications were fairly constant. For example, the likelihood of radical change being required of a machinist or clerk was remote. New types of jobs were quite rare and generally involved very few people. Today this is no longer true. Educators at all levels now realize that education must enable graduates to undertake later career changes and be flexible enough to meet them successfully. Education and reeducation must be a continuing process throughout the careers of most young people in school today. The range of problems facing them in the next ten years, in economics, space science, automation, life science, and almost every other field will demand far more open minds, and far better trained ones, than ever before in man's history.

We can no longer accept bleak projections such as the recent one which suggested that among young workers joining our labor force in the sixties, $7\frac{1}{2}$ million, or more than 30 per cent, will not have completed high school. Nor can we be complacent about the prospect that over $2\frac{1}{2}$ million of them will not even have finished grade school—especially considering the fact that the rate of unemployment is much higher among those with less than a high school education.

The new education essential for tomorrow's citizen cannot be the prerogative of some all-powerful, intellectual group. It must be the common right and duty of every individual, within his capabilities. We cannot afford or permit educationally underdeveloped citizens in any part of our country.

We must devote a major part of our national effort to education, for it provides the surest basis for improving America in all ways. Specifically, we need additional schools, more and better teachers, higher salaries for them, and better instructional aids such as films and demonstration equipment. We also need continued and expanded education studies to provide more effective teaching methods. Where individual states cannot handle the financing adequately, there is certainly a federal responsibility to do so. Better education is by far the most fruitful and positive means of giving Americans the greatest chance to make a maximum contribution to the development of our country and the greatest chance for full employment throughout their lives.

Since jobs will change materially during the working lives of many in the future, a reassessment of our vocational education should be made by the states and the federal government. With the changing careers we contemplate, rigid vocational training seems to be of doubtful value.

College training of engineers must aim toward a far more broadly oriented graduate. Engineering education must include more of both the basic sciences, such as physics and mathematics, and the humanities. Every major defense failure in technological development since the Second World War can be traced back to technical *and* management problems, not to technical problems alone. There have not been, nor are there today, enough top policy people in government or industry who on the one hand have been educated to understand the technological problems of our time, and on the other, possess the broad executive training, ability, and experience to plan and direct their solution.

3. Sharing technological change. The years since World War II have shown that it is impossible to win the worldwide political battle simply through alliances and financial or material aid. We must also win the battle for men's minds. But we must win it by offering these minds knowledge, skills, and opportunities to learn. One important facet of this process certainly lies in technological progress. If we help other nations to create stronger economies, happier and more prosperous citizens, the magic mottoes and platitudes of Communism will fall on deaf ears. If, on the other hand, we have as allies developing nations with a very small, rich ruling class and very large, very poor working class, our alliances will be frail indeed.

The quickest route toward building up these less prosperous countries is through broad and generous sharing of technological change. In the past, our own progress and strength have drawn heavily on the economic area: more goods and a better life for more people. Without a dedicated extension of this tradition to the fragile new countries of Africa and Asia, as well as to the underdeveloped nations in our own hemisphere, we cannot be successful members of today's world community.

There are still much want, suffering, and sickness throughout the world. A completely preventable, curable, and controllable disease such as malaria remains a grave threat to the lives of more than a billion people. There are still ninety countries or territories—with almost half of the world's humanity—which have bare survival incomes averaging about $100 a year per person. In struggling countries such as the Congo, with its population of 14,000,000, only a handful of people have university degrees. Unless we solve world problems such as these, the Communists will solve them for us.

In sharing technological progress, industry and private investors are in a unique position to further our political and economic goals. Foreign investment carries with it the capital, human resources, and know-how rapidly to increase the available technology in a less advanced country.

We cannot rely on private investment alone, however, to bring about orderly technological progress in underdeveloped countries. These nations need the basic structures upon which economic progress can be built—education, public works, communication networks, housing and health services. Our government must accept an important role in providing increasing amounts of this kind of assistance.

Ten years ago, the United States took the lead in establishing a major program to "aid the efforts of the peoples of economically underdeveloped areas . . . by encouraging the exchange of technical knowledge and skills. . . ." Today we have over 5,000 technicians in almost sixty underdeveloped countries carrying out the exchange of technical information under the Mutual Security Program, operating in a variety of fields, including agriculture, education, public administration, labor, communications, and community development. The United States also strongly supports the technical assistance program of the United Nations and the Organization of American States.

But there is still much left to do. I have three specific recommendations:

First, more United States technicians should be sent

abroad. I recognize that it is very difficult to get top technical people to accept relatively low government salaries and the rigors of living in less-developed areas, but this problem can be solved. For example, a number of university contracts have proved effective in maintaining a steady flow of technically trained people abroad. This approach certainly should be continued and expanded.

Second, the various programs for exchanging technical assistance must be more effectively coordinated. With aid coming from a variety of sources—government, the United Nations, and private organizations—there is a dangerous tendency for an unwarranted concentration in one area and a bypassing of other equally serious needs.

Finally, we must expand our exchange of technical information and more aggressively publicize our very real achievements in aid to these areas. The Soviets have recently leaped in with a substantial program of technical assistance, concentrating on those areas which bring them the greatest immediate public recognition. They support industrial projects, such as a steel mill or a cement plant or a factory. They conveniently overlook those less exciting but basic areas of health, education, communication, balance-of-payments support, and other public works which we stress. We must be sure our efforts are fairly presented, while still representing a balanced and useful development program.

V

SUMMARY

The three national goals recommended in the area of technological change—improving men's lives through it, encouraging it, and sharing it openly throughout the world—are deceptively easy to state. Achieving them even in part, however, will demand dedication, ingenuity, and sacrifice of special interest.

These goals cannot be pondered or debated or deliberated endlessly over the next decade. We can spend a lifetime pointing out the administrative complexities and problems involved. But while the problems are being debated, the opportunities may well be lost. Technological change continues to promise unparalleled leadership for the United States, the defensive strength needed to ensure a peaceful world, and untold abundance for all peoples, if we recognize and promote it as a basic national policy.

Finally, we must remember that technological change is man-made and must be man-controlled. Its total purpose: the benefit of mankind. We cannot afford to let the interest and excitement of the process distract us from its main purpose, the improvement of man.

C. P. Snow

RECENT THOUGHTS ON THE TWO CULTURES
(1962)

WHEN I was asked to give the Rede lecture at my own university, Cambridge, nearly three years ago, I was rather flattered. This lecture has been going on, with one or two intermissions owing to war, quite steadily since 1525, and it is a lecture which most Cambridge people are rather glad to deliver. I thought I would get off my chest a subject which had been worrying me for some time and then I'd leave it. In fact this wretched thing has dogged me ever since. My mail has gone up out of proportion and I have been chased from pillar to post. Once I even tried to evade the subject by spending a summer in Russia, but I had been there only twenty-four hours when one of their best literary critics called and invited me to dinner. What did he want to talk about? Not what I would have liked—books or Russian poetry. Oh, no! What he wanted was a good refreshing argument about the two cultures. This has been a constant reminder to me that if you hit a nerve hard and get an instantaneous response from a large number of people in the world, then you must have said what a lot of people have been thinking.

Let me suggest some of the things I might say differently now if I had to give the lecture again. First, let me remind you what the talk was about.

I was a scientist bred and a novelist born (this does not

say anything about my quality as a novelist; a born novelist can be a very bad novelist). By the curious chance of being poor and going to a school where it was much easier to get a decent education in science than in language or classics, I in fact did science and decided to make a profession of it. The result was that for a large part of my life I spent a good deal of time with scientists and another part of my time with writers. I had, of course, intimate friends among both groups.

Increasingly I found that between the two there was ceasing to be almost any serious intellectual communication. Over the years I became convinced that the whole of Western society was being polarized, with the literary intellectuals at one pole and the physical scientists at the other. Between the two was a gulf of mutual incomprehension, and the chance of talking across this gap was getting less and less. This polarization resulted in immense loss to each group, and in fact posed a great danger for our society as a whole.

Each had a curiously distorted image of the other and each was, in its way, startlingly ignorant of the other's culture. It was extraordinarily hard to find anyone among the younger scientists who had any real communication with the ordinary literary culture in which we lead our lives. The example I gave in the talk was that sometimes when asked what they read, they would say with considerable disapproval: "Well, sir, I've tried a bit of Dickens." Rather as though Dickens were an extraordinarily esoteric, tangled, and dubiously rewarding writer.

My literary friends, on the other side, had no conception of the scientific edifice of the physical world. These highly educated members of the traditional culture couldn't cope with the simplest concepts of pure science. In the lecture the example I chose—which has become a bit of a joke—was the second law of thermodynamics. The brute truth is that if you don't know not just the formulation of this law, but the historical background of it, then you can't even begin to understand the world of physical reality, the interpretation of which has been the most remarkable feature of the last hundred years.

I found other differences in attitude, some of which were trivial, but some of which seemed increasingly serious. The nonscientists were apt to think of the scientists as shallowly optimistic, brash, boastful and unaware of man's tragic condition. On the other hand, the scientists saw the guardians of the traditional culture as curiously resistant to progress and unwilling to share in the common hopes of mankind. The men who had dominated literary sensibility for generations—Pound, Lewis, Eliot, and others—held political views that would have seemed curiously old fashioned at the court of the early Plantagenets.

Much of this separation and hostility of the cultures rested on misconceptions. First concerning the optimism of the scientists. Scientists see no reason why, just because the individual condition of man is tragic, so must the social condition be. Scientists are aware that most of our fellow human beings are underfed and die before their time. This is, in crudest terms, the social condition. But the scientists are inclined to think something can be done about it, until it is proved otherwise. Here is their real optimism—one which the rest of us badly need.

The literary intellectuals, on the other hand, seemed to the scientists to hold social views which were not only refuted by the events of our time, but were in fact wicked. There was some substance to this view. Literary men were culpably slow to see the connection between some kinds of twentieth century art and the most imbecilic expressions of antisocial feeling.

The lecture then went on to relate this cultural dichotomy to the scientific revolution and its impact on our world. As an empiric Englishman mixed up in these concerns I asked: What are the likely results of this present situation? The scientific revolution is transforming the world; what happens if we don't understand and direct it; what if we don't fill this gap? Will other countries, other societies, produce a better answer than ours, and if so what will the outcome be?

Most of this I should say again in a not very different manner. Where I have said harsh words about the lack of social responsibility of many important persons in the *avant-garde* of the arts, I don't take back a word. But there are many people who rightly admire these writers and rightly take on some of their sensibility, because it is part of the artistic sensibility of our time, but who nevertheless have not renounced the human hopes with their same callousness. If I were giving this talk again, though I would stick to my point about the major influence—so far as there is an influence of art in the West in our time—I would grant that there are many good writers and critics, connoisseurs and general

readers who have not lost their human concern. That quali-
fication I should make rather heavily, because I was unfair
and showed a lack of percipience in not making a careful
distinction.

Secondly I should now devote much more thought to possible intermediate intellectual activities which to an extent
can mediate between my two extreme poles. At the time I
wasn't thinking very much about possible mediums. I did not
want to rub off the abrasive quality of what I was saying.
Yet once the abrasive remarks have been made, then I think
there is a good case for examining possible mediating fields
of intellectual endeavor. I believe certain kinds of philosophy
can be valuable if people on both sides of the divide can
learn this language and speak it. Certain kinds of sociology,
it now seems to me, could occupy a genuinely translating
position, so to speak, between my physicists and my literary
intellectuals.

One major criticism which was made I do not accept for
a moment. It was this: That I had ignored or forgotten the
qualitative side of life; that I had ignored the kind of criti-
cisms of the scientific world made by such persons as D. H.
Lawrence. Now, in fact I hadn't. There is, of course, a certain loss as man goes through the process which I call the
second industrial revolution or the scientific revolution. There
is a loss in the significance of the daily act. On the other
hand to assume, as some nonhistorical thinkers do, that there
was in fact a society in reasonable time back from ours which
was immensely richer in quality than ours is an utter piece
of Erehwonian folly. The idea that the eighteenth century,
which is one of the Edens from which we seem to have been
driven out, was a better world for most of the people who
lived in it, that the quality of life was richer, seems to me
utterly unaware either of what the facts of life are, or of
what history is. The eighteenth century was extremely nice,
if you were sitting on top of it, but it was nothing like as nice
for my ancestors. They wouldn't have had much to eat, and
they must have died at thirty, like Indians today. They, and
indeed most people in society, would see half their children
die before they were ten. These are the brute facts. To think
otherwise is an illusion.

One of the real difficulties of advanced countries talking to
unadvanced countries at the moment is that we've forgotten
what the condition of the peasantry is in every country

which has still got a peasantry. Your grandfather could have talked, probably, to emerging Africans and emerging Asiatics. Now the particular hardness of the heart which comes from prosperity invalidates much of what we are saying, prevents us, even though we're fairly decent people, from being as good as we should like to be. So that kind of criticism I won't accept for a moment.

But now, what do we do? It seems to be clear that something can be done and the answer must abide in the process of education, education of both the old and the young. I believe there are many people on the side of the literary culture who are not devoid of natural scientific insight, who could still, with some effort, learn quite a bit about various parts of the scientific culture. I believe this is relatively easy. It needs not being ashamed of going in for such popularization as we can. One of the advantages of the West is that on the whole we've been extremely good at certain sorts of scientific popularization. Our country was very good at it in the nineteenth and early twentieth centuries and I think you've made great strides in this. It is much easier for scientists, if they have the will, to acquire the wisdom of the literary culture, because after all scientists can read.

If we start our education seriously at six (as I'm sure this country should), then I believe we could educate most people in both these cultures without giving them any more strain than the average English or European or Russian child now takes as his natural duty. Now in my country we work them hard enough, God knows, but we work them in such a specialized way that we don't solve this problem at all. Your education has the width but, for reasons which I've never entirely understood, although I've had them explained to me often enough, you find that the desire to make children happy removes the necessity of teaching them anything between six and eighteen. Your college education is fine; it can do everything you ask of it. But you must really insist that between six and eighteen your children learn something of the principles of mathematics and physics. By this I mean doing something like four hours of mathematics and physics a week, four hours each, from about ten through eighteen. This is what a European child expects to do; why shouldn't you do it? And on the other side, I think you ought to have the same amount of time on a language.

This is not Utopian. This is about the amount of work that

our children put in, though they put it in only on one side. It's about the same amount of work that the Russians put in, and they do it, very manfully, on both sides of the cultures. I still believe that you can do it with immense advantage to yourselves. You can produce children of eighteen who really know something, and then this marvelous superstructure, this varied and magnanimous college education of yours, would have a real chance to produce the best educated college population on earth.

Lots of people say it's no use, you're trying to swim against the current; this is part of the inevitable fractionation which our kind of world is going to descend into more and more. Why not let it slide? Well, I'm not easily prepared to accept the inevitable current of history unless I'm quite certain what it is. I think it's a great mistake to be too impressed by the flood of history. Secondly, there are extremely good hard-baked reasons why we should try to bridge this gap if it possibly can be bridged. One of them is very simple. In the next ten or twenty years most of the great decisions that Western statesmen, administrators, and bosses of all kinds will have to take are going to be concerned with science. If they are illiterate in science, then they are going to have to take those decisions rather like a lawyer reading a brief. That's a terribly bad way to take a decision, because it means you've got no instinctive wisdom of your own to guide you. You are only able to make a decision on paper so to speak; you have no capacity for an imaginative projection. This is a real deficiency which in the last twenty years I have seen lead us into grave mistakes. I suspect in the next twenty years it may lead us into much graver.

That is a hard-baked reason and that in itself would be enough but it is not my main one; there is a second reason which I should weigh more heavily. I believe that this cultural separation is in fact very bad for both, certainly for art and probably for science, and I think both need the stimulus that the other can give. But I would be deceiving you if I told you that even those were my main reasons for being concerned.

My main reason is much simpler, much more emotional, much more involved in what I feel about the whole of the human species. This absence of intellectual communication is a symbol of the tendency of our kind to find methods of ceasing to talk. We find other methods. We find racial differences, which again prevent us from communicating; we find political differences. These in the long run mean death. We are members one of another, as St. Paul said. Unless that is present in many human consciences, then it is very hard to see how our race can get more than a bare animal survival.

We happen to have been born, you people in this country and we in ours, abnormally lucky; we have never known great suffering, not for many, many years. Most people in the world have. Unless we can try to bridge all these gaps, starting with this simple intellectual gap, which is there under our eyes, then it seems to me we don't deserve our good fortune.

Morris Bishop

THE READING MACHINE
(1947)

"I HAVE invented a reading machine," said Professor Entwhistle, a strident energumen whose violent enthusiasms are apt to infect his colleagues with nausea or hot flashes before the eyes.

Every head in the smoking room of the Faculty Club bowed over a magazine, in an attitude of prayer. The prayer was unanswered, as usual.

"It is obvious," said Professor Entwhistle, "that the greatest waste of our civilization is the time spent in reading. We have been able to speed up practically everything to fit the modern tempo—communication, transportation, calculation. But today a man takes just as long to read a book as Dante did, or—"

"Great Caesar!" said the Professor of Amphibology, shutting his magazine with a spank.

"Or great Caesar," continued Professor Entwhistle. "So I have invented a machine. It operates by a simple arrangement of photoelectric cells, which scan a line of type at lightning speed. The operation of the photoelectric cells is

synchronized with a mechanical device for turning the pages
—rather ingenious. I figure that my machine can read a book
of three hundred pages in ten minutes."

"Can it read French?" said the Professor of Bio-Economics,
without looking up.

"It can read any language that is printed in Roman type.
And by an alteration of the master pattern on which the
photoelectric cells operate, it can be fitted to read Russian,
or Bulgarian, or any language printed in the Cyrillic alphabet.
In fact, it will do more. By simply throwing a switch, you
can adapt it to read Hebrew, or Arabic, or any language that
is written from right to left instead of from left to right."

"Chinese?" said the Professor of Amphibology, throwing
himself into the arena. The others still studied their magazines.

"Not Chinese, as yet," said Professor Entwhistle. "Though
by inserting the pages sidewise . . . Yes, I think it could be
done."

"Yes, but when you say this contrivance reads, exactly what
do you mean? It seems to me—"

"The light waves registered by the photoelectric cells are
first converted into sound waves."

"So you can listen in to the reading of the text?"

"Not at all. The sound waves alter so fast that you hear
nothing but a continuous hum. If you hear them at all. You
can't, in fact, because they are on a wavelength inaudible to
the human ear."

"Well, it seems to me—"

"Think of the efficiency of the thing!" Professor Entwhistle
was really warming up. "Think of the time saved! You assign
a student a bibliography of fifty books. He runs them through
the machine comfortably in a weekend. And on Monday
morning he turns in a certificate from the machine. Everything has been conscientiously read!"

"Yes, but the student won't remember what he has read!"

"He doesn't remember what he reads now."

"Well, you have me there," said the Professor of Amphibology. "I confess you have me there. But it seems to me we
would have to pass the machine and fail the student."

"Not at all," said Professor Entwhistle. "An accountant
today does not think of doing his work by multiplication and
division. Often he is unable to multiply and divide. He con-
fides his problem to a business machine, and the machine does

his work for him. All the accountant has to know is how to run the machine. That is efficiency."

"Still, it seems to me that what we want to do is to transfer the contents of the book to the student's mind."

"In the mechanized age? My dear fellow! What we want is to train the student to run machines. An airplane pilot doesn't need to know the history of aerodynamics. He needs to know how to run his machine. A lawyer doesn't want to know the development of theories of Roman law. He wants to win cases, if possible by getting the right answers to logical problems. That is largely a mechanical process. It might well be possible to construct a machine. It could begin by solving simple syllogisms, you know—drawing a conclusion from a major premise and a minor premise—"

"Here, let's not get distracted. This reading machine of yours, it must *do* something, it must make some kind of record. What happens after you get the sound waves?"

"That's the beauty of it," said Professor Entwhistle. "The sound waves are converted into light waves, of a different character from the original light waves, and these are communicated to an automatic typewriter, working at inconceivable speed. This transforms the light impulses into legible typescripts, in folders of a hundred pages each. It tosses them out the way a combine tosses out sacked wheat. Thus, everything the machine reads is preserved entire, in durable form. The only thing that remains is to file it somewhere, and for this you would need only the services of a capable filing clerk."

"Or you could read it?" persisted the Professor of Amphibology.

"Why, yes, if you wanted to you could read it," said Professor Entwhistle.

AN indigestible silence hung over the Faculty Club.

"I see where the Athletic Association has bought a pitching machine," said the Assistant Professor of Business Psychology (Retail). "Damn thing throws any curve desired, with a maximum margin of error of three centimeters over the plate. What'll they be thinking of next?"

"A batting machine, obviously," said Professor Entwhistle.

Edward C. Weir

WHAT HAPPENED TO THE TEACHING MACHINE?
(1962)

THE following scene takes place in a graduate class in the History of American Education at a leading American University. The year is A.D. 2070.

Student: "I wonder, Professor, if you would mind taking a few minutes this evening to give us a few remarks on the Teaching Machine. For a long time, this approach to teaching appeared to be quite successful. Can you tell us why it was so suddenly abandoned about twenty-five years ago?"

Professor: "Well, yes, the topic of the Teaching Machine and its rather abrupt disappearance from the educational scene is not only appropriate for discussion tonight, but it is also a very interesting topic, and fraught with historical significance. You are quite right, that the Teaching Machine was highly successful in achieving the results for which it was intended. You are quite wrong, however, in assuming that the Teaching Machine was "abandoned" as you put it. The fact is that it was the very success of the Teaching Machine which brought about its demise."

The professor pauses for a moment to survey the class with a slightly superior smile at the puzzlement his little scholarly conundrum had caused. He then continues.

"That is a somewhat enigmatic statement, isn't it? But really, it shouldn't be so puzzling, if you'll give it a little thought. If you know anything at all about the basic design of the Teaching Machine, you can't help but realize that its fundamental operational principle was ultimately self-defeating. To this day, not a single educational scholar has been able to offer an adequate explanation as to why, at the time, not one of the many authorities in the fields of learning theory and instructional method—really quite capable gentlemen, most of them—was able to detect the built-in fallacy of the Teaching Machine, obvious though it was. The silence of the educators of the time on this point remains one of the most intriguing mysteries in the history of education. I might add parenthetically that this problem would be a fruitful one for doctoral investigation in case any of you are in the throes of trying to find a topic for dissertation.

"Yes, indeed, you are quite right. The success of the Teaching Machine was beyond all reasonable expectation. High school students began knocking the tops off the standardized test norms of the time. Test-makers found themselves furiously engaged in a never-ending cycle of making revisions of their tests which in turn would scarcely be off the press before new revisions were necessary. Institutions of higher learning were flooded with students who had walked through the most rigorous entrance examinations in a breeze. They were, of course, soon forced to upgrade their entrance requirements drastically, because they were well aware that not everybody could or should go to college. Almost all colleges and universities instituted professional in-service training programs (many sent their professors back to high school for postgraduate work) so that the college teachers could keep academically abreast of their students.

"Why, then, did the Teaching Machine disappear? Have any of you figured it out yet?"

Again the professor pauses, apparently hoping for an answer, but inwardly enjoying the secret of his rhetorical question.

"Well, I guess there is no point in keeping you in suspense any longer. The answer is this—you will recall that the Teaching Machine was a device designed to raise questions and pose problems, and to reinforce correct answers given by the student. An amazing amount of ingenious planning went into the programming of the Machine, so that one minute question led directly into the next minute question in precise logical sequence. This, of course, meant that the people who programmed the Machine had to know what the questions were and how one question was related to other questions.

"Well, now, about the year 2055, it suddenly began to become apparent the Teaching Machine programmers were becoming practically non-existent. You see, by that time the old generation had just about died off, and we had trained a whole new generation of people who knew all the answers. The trouble was, *no one knew what the questions were.*

"Well, as you can readily imagine, this presented a rather perilous situation—not only for manufacturers and operators of Teaching Machines, but for education in general, and for the very security of the nation itself. We had begun to fall rapidly behind in the technological race with Russia, as well we might when you consider that in the year 2057, for example, not a single patent was issued by the U.S. Patent Office. We might say that this was the most crucial period in all of American history. Our whole way of life tottered precariously in the balance, and but for one small human incident we almost certainly would have gone down the historical drain.

"The incident had to do with the fact that on a certain sunny spring day a renowned professor of science education was cutting potatoes for planting in his garden. His young son stood by in silence, obviously somewhat puzzled by his dad's curious activity. Finally the youngster said,

" 'Daddy, where do potatoes come from?' "

"The professor, of course, knew the answer and he proceded with glib relish to point out the eyes of the potato and to explain their function, but was interrupted by the boy shaking his head vigorously and saying:

" 'No, No, Daddy. No, that's not what I mean; I mean where did the *first* potato come from?' "

"The father did not answer. He stared at the child as in a trance, the elation of great discovery flooding his chest. There *were* people left who knew the questions—the children who had not yet been to the Teaching Machine. The educator had found his answer in the question of a child.

"The professor enlarged upon his amazing discovery in a series of lectures and publications. This was the origin of the Great Revolution in education with which you are all familiar.

"Any questions, class?"

George Strauss

GROUP DYNAMICS AND INTERGROUP RELATIONS*
(1955)

THIS is the story of an experiment that failed because it succeeded too well.

The Hovey and Beard Company manufactured wooden toys of various kinds: wooden animals, pull toys, and the like. One part of the manufacturing process involved spraying paint on the partially assembled toys and hanging them on moving hooks which carried them through a drying oven. This operation, staffed entirely by girls, was plagued by absenteeism, turnover, and low morale.

A consultant, working with the foreman in charge, "solved" the problem. But the changes that were made in order to solve it had such repercussions in other parts of the plant that the company abandoned the new procedures, despite their obvious benefits to production in that local area.

THE PROBLEM

Let us look briefly at the painting operation in which the problem occurred.

The toys were cut, sanded, and partially assembled in the wood room. Then they were dipped into shellac, following which they were painted. The toys were predominantly two-colored; a few were made in more than two colors. Each color required an additional trip through the paint room.

Shortly before the troubles began, the painting operation had been reengineered so that the eight girls who did the painting sat in a line by an endless chain of hooks. These hooks were in continuous motion, past the line of girls and into a long horizontal oven. Each girl sat at her own painting booth so designed as to carry away fumes and to backstop excess paint. The girl would take a toy from the tray beside her, position it in a jig inside the painting cubicle, spray on the color according to a pattern, then release the toy and

---

* This chapter was written by George Strauss, based upon information furnished him by the consultant in the story, Alex Bavelas. The consultant also reviewed and revised the chapter.

hang it on the hook passing by. The rate at which the hooks moved had been calculated by the engineers so that each girl, when fully trained, would be able to hang a painted toy on each hook before it passed beyond her reach.

The girls working in the paint room were on a group bonus plan. Since the operation was new to them, they were receiving a learning bonus which decreased by regular amounts each month. The learning bonus was scheduled to vanish in six months, by which time it was expected that they would be on their own—that is, able to meet the standard and to earn a group bonus when they exceeded it.

By the second month of the training period trouble had developed. The girls learned more slowly than had been anticipated, and it began to look as though their production would stabilize far below what was planned for. Many of the hooks were going by empty. The girls complained that they were going by too fast and that the time-study man had set the rates wrong. A few girls quit and had to be replaced with new girls, which further aggravated the learning problem. The team spirit that the management had expected to develop automatically through the group bonus was not in evidence except as an expression of what the engineers called "resistance." One girl whom the group regarded as its leader (and the management regarded as the ringleader) was outspoken in making the various complaints of the group to the foreman. The complaints had all the variety customary in such instances of generalized frustration: the job was a messy one, the hooks moved too fast, the incentive pay was not being correctly calculated, and anyway it was too hot working so close to the drying oven.

INTRODUCING THE NEW APPROACH

The consultant who was brought into this picture worked entirely with and through the foreman. After many conversations with him, the foreman felt that the first step should be to get the girls together for a general discussion of the working conditions—something, incidentally, which was far from his mind originally and which in his own words would only have been "begging for trouble." He took this step with some hesitation, but he took it on his own volition.

The first meeting, held immediately after the shift was over at four o'clock in the afternoon, was attended by all eight girls. They voiced the same complaints again: the hooks went by too fast, the job was too dirty, the room was hot and poorly ventilated. For some reason it was this last item that they complained of most. The foreman promised to discuss the problem of ventilation and temperature with the engineers, and he scheduled a second meeting to report back to the girls. In the next few days the foreman had several talks with the engineers, and it seemed that the girls' cynical predictions about what the engineers would say were going to be borne out. They and the superintendent felt that this was really a trumped-up complaint and that the expense of any effective corrective measure would be prohibitively high. (They were thinking of some form of air conditioning.)

The foreman came to the second meeting with some apprehensions. The girls, however, did not seem to be much put out, perhaps because they had a proposal of their own to make. They felt that if several large fans were set up so as to circulate the air around their feet, they would be much more comfortable. After some discussion the foreman agreed that the idea might be tried out. (Immediately after the meeting, he confided to the consultant that he probably shouldn't have committed himself to this expense on his own initiative; also, he felt that the fans wouldn't help much anyway.) The foreman and the consultant discussed the question of the fans with the superintendent, and three large propeller-type fans were purchased. The decision was reached without much difficulty, since it seemed that the fans could be used elsewhere after their expected failure to provide relief in the paint room.

The fans were brought in. The girls were jubilant. For several days the fans were moved about in various positions until they were placed to the satisfaction of the group. Whatever the actual efficiency of these fans, one thing was clear: the girls were completely satisfied with the results, and relations between them and the foreman improved visibly.

The foreman, after this encouraging episode, decided that further meetings might also be profitable. He asked the girls if they would like to meet and discuss other aspects of the work situation. The girls were eager to do this.[1] The meeting was held, and the discussion quickly centered on the speed of the hooks. The girls maintained that the time-study men had set them at an unreasonably fast speed and that they would never be able to reach the goal of filling enough of them to make a bonus.

The turning point of the discussion came when the group's leader frankly explained that the point wasn't that they couldn't work fast enough to keep up with the hooks, but that they couldn't work at that pace all day long. The foreman explored the point. The girls were unanimous in their opinion that they could keep up with the belt for short periods if they wanted to. But they didn't want to because if they showed that they could do this for short periods they would be expected to do it all day long. The meeting ended with an unprecedented request: "Let us adjust the speed of the belt faster or slower depending on how we feel." The foreman, understandably startled, agreed to discuss this with the superintendent and the engineers.

The engineers' reaction naturally was that the girls' suggestion was heresy. Only after several meetings was it granted grudgingly that there was in reality some latitude within which variations in the speed of the hooks would not affect the finished product. After considerable argument and many dire prophecies by the engineers, it was agreed to try out the girls' idea.

With great misgivings, the foreman had a control with a dial marked "low, medium, fast" installed at the booth of the group leader; she could now adjust the speed of the belt anywhere between the lower and upper limits that the engineers had set. The girls were delighted, and spent many lunch hours deciding how the speed of the belt should be varied from hour to hour throughout the day.

Within a week the pattern had settled down to one in which the first half hour of the shift was run on what the girls called medium speed (a dial setting slightly above the point marked "medium"). The next two and one-half hours were run at high speed; the half hour before lunch and the half hour after lunch were run at low speed. The rest of the afternoon was run at high speed with the exception of the last forty-five minutes of the shift, which was run at medium.

In view of the girls' reports of satisfaction and ease in their work, it is interesting to note that the constant speed at which the engineers had originally set the belt was slightly below medium on the dial of the control that had been given the girls. The average speed at which the girls were running

he belt was on the high side of the dial. Few if any empty
ooks entered the oven, and inspection showed no increase
f rejects from the paint room.

Production increased, and within three weeks (some two
nonths before the scheduled ending of the learning bonus)
ne girls were operating at 30 to 50 per cent above the level
nat had been expected under the original arrangement.
Naturally the girls' earnings were correspondingly higher than
nticipated. They were collecting their base pay, a con-
derable piece-rate bonus, and the learning bonus which,
will be remembered, had been set to decrease with time and
ot as a function of current productivity. (This arrangement,
hich had been selected by the management in order to pre-
ent being taken advantage of by the girls during the learn-
g period, now became a real embarrassment.)

The girls were earning more now than many skilled workers
other parts of the plant. Management was besieged by
emands that this inequity be taken care of. With growing
ritation between superintendent and foreman, engineers and
oreman, superintendent and engineers, the situation came to
head when the superintendent without consultation arbi-
arily revoked the learning bonus and returned the painting
peration to its original status: the hooks moved again at their
onstant, time-studied designated speed, production dropped
gain, and within a month all but two of the eight girls had
uit. The foreman himself stayed on for several months, but,
eling aggrieved, then left for another job.

ANALYSIS OF SUCCESS AND FAILURE

It is not difficult to understand why installing the fans and
ermitting the speed of the hooks to be controlled by them
nould have affected the girls the way it did. No normal per-
on is happy in a situation which he cannot control to some
xtent. The fans may not have actually changed the heat or
ne humidity, but they were a visible and daily reminder that
orker ideas were given consideration.

About the speed of the hooks an additional observation
ay be made. The idea that efficient work results from pro-
eeding at a constant rate derives certainly from the opera-
ons of machines and not from the characteristic operation of
uman beings. If anything is clear about human performance
is that it is characterized by changes of pace. Some pro-

duction operations by their nature permit little variation i
this respect, but even when the possibility exists it is nc
readily perceived by many engineers as a source of increase
efficiency. From the operator's point of view, to be pace
unvaryingly by a machine which he may not even shut dow
with impunity may be psychologically uncomfortable. In suc
a situation the only avenue left for the expression of an
independence is that of complaint: the machine or its maste
the engineer, must be shown to be wrong. Also, there appea
to be inherent and unconscious defensive mechanisms whic
operate against the threat of being "stretched out."

Control over the speed of the hooks in this situation nc
only allowed changes of pace which were in themselve
restful and refreshing, but also allowed the operator th
natural enjoyment of operating at top speed without fear tha
he might be compelled to stay there. Of course, the manne
in which the change was instituted was significant. The o
portunity to exercise initiative, the gratification of bein
listened to seriously, helped to bring about changes in th
emotional overtones of the situation which were in them
selves favorable to increased effort.

In the light of all this it is not surprising that the situatio
fell apart so completely when the management retrogressec
And the management's action, while it may not have bee
wise, was certainly an understandable response to what ha
become an uncomfortable situation. Along with improve
production in the paint room had come a host of embarras
ments. The extra production in the paint room had create
a pile-up in front and a vacuum behind, and both results wer
unwelcome to the adjoining departments. The wage structui
of the plant had been shaken. The prestige of the enginee
had suffered, and some of the prerogatives of managemei
were apparently being taken over by employees.

It is clear from this instance that *local* improvements ca
often be obtained by the methods described here; but it
also clear that they may not lead to benefits for the enterpris
as a whole. Changes in one part of an integrated organizatio
may require widespread changes elsewhere, and the cost c
such readjustments may far outbalance the benefits receive
in the local situation.

The changes made in the paint room implied overall mai
agerial attitude and philosophy that were not in fact presen
This being the case, there was no conceptual or philosoph

resource for dealing with the eventual implications of what had been done in the paint room. The management neither expected nor was ready to make the kind of changes that seemed necessary. It would have been far better if the consultant had done with the relevant management group what he had done with the foreman in the initial discussions, so that there would have been some shared understanding of the long-range implications of the moves. In a real sense, the superintendent was justified in feeling that the foreman and the consultant between them had put him on the spot. True, his assent to the changes had been secured, but the consultant had not been sufficiently concerned with his genuine understanding of the possible consequences.

The factory is a social system, made up of mutually dependent parts. A drastic change in one part of the system—even a change that is viewed as highly successful within that part—may give rise to conflict reactions from other parts of the system. It may then be dangerous for management to try a new approach in one small part of the system unless it is prepared to extend this approach to the whole organization.

Can the group methods that have been so successfully applied in small groups and single departments be applied on a factory-wide scale?

NOTE

[1] These subsequent meetings were effective largely because of the reduced tension and the good will engendered by the original discussions.

Robert Frost

A LONE STRIKER
(1933)

> THE swinging mill bell changed its rate
> To tolling like the count of fate,
> And though at that the tardy ran,
> One failed to make the closing gate.

There was a law of God or man
That on the one who came too late
The gate for half an hour be locked,
His time be lost, his pittance docked.
He stood rebuked and unemployed.
The straining mill began to shake.
The mill, though many, many eyed,
Had eyes inscrutably opaque;
So that he couldn't look inside
To see if some forlorn machine
Was standing idle for his sake.
(He couldn't hope its heart would break.)

And yet he thought he saw the scene:
The air was full of dust of wool.
A thousand yarns were under pull,
But pull so slow, with such a twist,
All day from spool to lesser spool,
It seldom overtaxed their strength;
They safely grew in slender length.
And if one broke by any chance,
The spinner saw it at a glance.
The spinner still was there to spin.

That's where the human still came in.
Her deft hand showed with finger rings
Among the harp-like spread of strings.
She caught the pieces end to end
And, with a touch that never missed,
Not so much tied as made them blend.
Man's ingenuity was good.
He saw it plainly where he stood,
Yet found it easy to resist.

He knew another place, a wood,
And in it, tall as trees, were cliffs;
And if he stood on one of these,
'Twould be among the tops of trees,
Their upper branches round him wreathing,
Their breathing mingled with his breathing.
If—if he stood! Enough of ifs!
He knew a path that wanted walking;
He knew a spring that wanted drinking;

A thought that wanted further thinking;
A love that wanted re-renewing.
Nor was this just a way of talking
To save him the expense of doing.
With him it boded action, deed.

The factory was very fine;
He wished it all the modern speed.
Yet, after all, 'twas not divine,
That is to say, 'twas not a church.
He never would assume that he'd
Be any institution's need.
But he said then and still would say
If there should ever come a day
When industry seemed like to die
Because he left it in the lurch,
Or even merely seemed to pine
For want of his approval, why
Come get him—they knew where to search.

E. B. White

THE HOUR OF LETDOWN
(1951)

WHEN the man came in, carrying the machine, most of us
looked up from our drinks, because we had never seen anything like it before. The man set the thing down on top of the
bar near the beerpulls. It took up an ungodly amount of
room and you could see the bartender didn't like it any too
well, having this big, ugly-looking gadget parked right there.

"Two rye-and-water," the man said.

The bartender went on puddling an Old-Fashioned that
he was working on, but he was obviously turning over the
request in his mind.

"You want a double?" he asked after a bit.

"No," said the man. "Two rye-and-water, please." He stared

straight at the bartender, not exactly unfriendly but on the other hand not affirmatively friendly.

Many years of catering to the kind of people that come into saloons had provided the bartender with an adjustable mind. Nevertheless, he did not adjust readily to this fellow, and he did not like the machine—that was sure. He picked up a live cigarette that was idling on the edge of the cash register, took a drag out of it, and returned it thoughtfully. Then he poured two shots of rye whiskey, drew two glasses of water, and shoved the drinks in front of the man. People were watching. When something a little out of the ordinary takes place at a bar, the sense of it spreads quickly all along the line and pulls the customers together.

The man gave no sign of being the center of attention. He laid a five-dollar bill down on the bar. Then he drank one of the ryes and chased it with water. He picked up the other rye, opened a small vent in the machine (it was like an oil cup) and poured the whiskey in, and then poured the water in.

The bartender watched grimly. "Not funny," he said in an even voice. "And furthermore, your companion takes up too much room. Why'n you put it over on that bench by the door, make more room here."

"There's plenty of room for everyone here," replied the man.

"I ain't amused," said the bartender. "Put the goddam thing over near the door like I say. Nobody will touch it."

The man smiled. "You should have seen it this afternoon," he said. "It was magnificent. Today was the third day of the tournament. Imagine it—three days of continuous brainwork! And against the top players in the country, too. Early in the game it gained an advantage; then for two hours it exploited the advantage brilliantly, ending with the opponent's king backed in a corner. The sudden capture of a knight, the neutralization of a bishop, and it was all over. You know how much money it won, all told, in three days of playing chess?"

"How much?" asked the bartender.

"Five thousand dollars," said the man. "Now it wants to let down, wants to get a little drunk."

The bartender ran his towel vaguely over some wet spots. "Take it somewhere else and get it drunk there!" he said firmly. "I got enough troubles."

The man shook his head, and smiled. "No, we like it here."

He pointed at the empty glasses. "Do this again, will you, please?"

The bartender slowly shook his head. He seemed dazed but dogged. "You stow the thing away," he ordered. "I'm not ladling out whiskey for jokestersmiths."

" 'Jokesmiths,' " said the machine. "The word is 'joke-smiths.' "

A few feet down the bar, a customer who was on his third highball seemed ready to participate in this conversation to which we had all been listening so attentively. He was a middle-aged man. His necktie was pulled down away from his collar, and he had eased the collar by unbuttoning it. He had pretty nearly finished his third drink, and the alcohol tended to make him throw his support in with the underprivileged and the thirsty.

"If the machine wants another drink, give it another drink," he said to the bartender. "Let's not have haggling."

The fellow with the machine turned to his new-found friend and gravely raised his hand to his temple, giving him a salute of gratitude and fellowship. He addressed his next remark to him, as though deliberately snubbing the bartender.

"You know how it is when you're all fagged out mentally, how you want a drink?"

"Certainly do," replied the friend. "Most natural thing in the world."

There was a stir all along the bar, some seeming to side with the bartender, others with the machine group. A tall, gloomy man standing next to me spoke up.

"Another whiskey sour, Bill," he said. "And go easy on the lemon juice."

"Picric acid," said the machine, sullenly. "They don't use lemon juice in these places."

"That does it!" said the bartender, smacking his hand on the bar. "Will you put that thing away or else beat it out of here. I ain't in the mood, I tell you. I got this saloon to run and I don't want lip from a mechanical brain or whatever the hell you've got there."

The man ignored this ultimatum. He addressed his friend, whose glass was now empty.

"It's not just that it's all tuckered out after three days of chess," he said amiably. "You know another reason it wants a drink?"

"No," said the friend. "Why?"

"It cheated," said the man.

At this remark, the machine chuckled. One of its arms dipped slightly, and a light glowed in a dial.

The friend frowned. He looked as though his dignity had been hurt, as though his trust had been misplaced. "Nobody can cheat at chess," he said. "Simpossible. In chess, everything is open and above the board. The nature of the game of chess is such that cheating is impossible."

"That's what I used to think, too," said the man. "But there *is* a way."

"Well, it doesn't surprise me any," put in the bartender. "The first time I laid my eyes on that crummy thing I spotted it for a crook."

"Two rye-and-water," said the man.

"You can't have the whiskey," said the bartender. He glared at the mechanical brain. "How do I know it ain't drunk already?"

"That's simple. Ask it something," said the man.

The customers shifted and stared into the mirror. We were all in this thing now, up to our necks. We waited. It was the bartender's move.

"Ask it what? Such as?" said the bartender.

"Makes no difference. Pick a couple big figures, ask it to multiply them together. You couldn't multiply big figures together if you were drunk, could you?"

The machine shook slightly, as though making internal preparations.

"Ten thousand eight hundred and sixty-two, multiply it by ninety-nine," said the bartender, viciously. We could tell that he was throwing in the two nines to make it hard.

The machine flickered. One of its tubes spat, and a hand changed position, jerkily.

"One million seventy-five thousand three hundred and thirty-eight," said the machine.

Not a glass was raised all along the bar. People just stared gloomily into the mirror; some of us studied our own faces, others took carom shots at the man and the machine.

Finally, a youngish, mathematically minded customer got out a piece of paper and a pencil and went into retirement. "It works out," he reported, after some minutes of calculating. "You can't say the machine is drunk!"

Everyone now glared at the bartender. Reluctantly he poured two shots of rye, drew two glasses of water. The man drank his drink. Then he fed the machine its drink. The machine's light grew fainter. One of its cranky little arms wilted.

For a while the saloon simmered along like a ship at sea in calm weather. Every one of us seemed to be trying to digest the situation, with the help of liquor. Quite a few glasses were refilled. Most of us sought help in the mirror—the court of last appeal.

The fellow with the unbuttoned collar settled his score. He walked stiffly over and stood between the man and the machine. He put one arm around the man, the other arm around the machine. "Let's get out of here and go to a good place," he said.

The machine glowed slightly. It seemed to be a little drunk now.

"All right," said the man. "That suits me fine. I've got my car outside."

He settled for the drinks and put down a tip. Quietly and a trifle uncertainly he tucked the machine under his arm, and he and his companion of the night walked to the door and out into the street.

The bartender stared fixedly, then resumed his light housekeeping. "So he's got his car outside," he said, with heavy sarcasm. "Now, isn't that nice!"

A customer at the end of the bar near the door left his drink, stepped to the window, parted the curtains, and looked out. He watched for a moment, then returned to his place and addressed the bartender. "It's even nicer than you think," he said. "It's a Cadillac. And which one of the three of them d'ya think is doing the driving?"

Reed Whittemore

A PROJECTION
 (1955)

I wish they would hurry up their trip to Mars,
Those rocket gentlemen.
We have been waiting too long; the fictions of little men
And canals,
And of planting and raising flags and opening markets
For beads, cheap watches, perfume and plastic jewelry—
All these begin to be tedious; what we need now
Is the real thing, a thoroughly bang-up voyage
Of discovery.

Led by Admiral Byrd
In the *Niña, Pinta* and *Santa María*
With a crew of one hundred experts
In physics, geology, war and creative writing,
The expedition should sail with a five-year supply of
Pemmican, Jell-o, Moxie,
Warm woolen socks and jars of Gramma's preserves.

Think of them out there,
An ocean of space before them, using no compass,
Guiding themselves by speculative equations,
Looking,
Looking into the night and thinking now
There are no days, no seasons, time
Is only on watches,
                    and landing on Venus
Through some slight error,
Bearing

Proclamations of friendship,
Declarations of interstellar faith,
Acknowledgments of American supremacy,
And advertising matter.

I wonder,
Out in the pitch of space, having worlds enough,
If the walled-up, balled-up self could from its alley
Sally.
I wish they would make provisions for this,
Those rocket gentlemen.

Brian W. Aldiss

BUT WHO CAN REPLACE A MAN?
(1958)

MORNING FILTERED into the sky, lending it the gray tone of the ground below.

The field minder finished turning the topsoil of a three-thousand-acre field. When it had turned the last furrow, it climbed onto the highway and looked back at its work. The work was good. Only the land was bad. Like the ground all over Earth, it was vitiated by overcropping. By rights, it ought now to lie fallow for a while, but the field minder had other orders.

It went slowly down the road, taking its time. It was intelligent enough to appreciate the neatness all about it. Nothing worried it, beyond a loose inspection plate above its nuclear pile which ought to be attended to. Thirty feet high, it yielded no highlights to the dull air.

No other machines passed on its way back to the Agricultural Station. The field minder noted the fact without comment. In the station yard it saw several other machines that it recognized; most of them should have been out about their tasks now. Instead, some were inactive and some careered around the yard in a strange fashion, shouting or hooting.

Steering carefully past them, the field minder moved over to Warehouse 3 and spoke to the seed distributor, which stood idly outside.

"I have a requirement for seed potatoes," it said to the distributor, and with a quick internal motion punched out an order card specifying quantity, field number and several other details. It ejected the card and handed it to the distributor.

The distributor held the card close to its eye and then said, "The requirement is in order; but the store is not yet unlocked. The required seed potatoes are in the store. Therefore I cannot produce the requirement."

Increasingly of late there had been breakdowns in the complex system of machine labor, but this particular hitch had not occurred before. The field minder thought, then it said, "Why is the store not yet unlocked?"

"Because supply operative type P has not come this morning. Supply operative type P is the unlocker."

The field minder looked squarely at the seed distributor, whose exterior chutes and scales and grabs were so vastly different from the field minder's own limbs.

"What class brain do you have, seed distributor?" it asked.

"I have a class-five brain."

"I have a class-three brain. Therefore I am superior to you. Therefore I will go and see why the unlocker has not come this morning."

Leaving the distributor, the field minder set off across the great yard. More machines were in random motion now; one or two had crashed together and argued about it coldly and logically. Ignoring them, the field minder pushed through sliding doors into the echoing confines of the station itself.

Most of the machines here were clerical, and consequently small. They stood about in little groups, eyeing each other, not conversing. Among so many nondifferentiated types, the unlocker was easy to find. It had fifty arms, most of them with more than one finger, each finger tipped by a key; it looked like a pincushion full of variegated hatpins.

The field minder approached it.

"I can do no more work until Warehouse Three is unlocked," it told the unlocker. "Your duty is to unlock the warehouse every morning. Why have you not unlocked the warehouse this morning?"

"I had no orders this morning," replied the unlocker. "I have to have orders every morning. When I have orders I unlock the warehouse."

"None of us have had any orders this morning," a pen propeller said, sliding toward them.

"Why have you had no orders this morning?" asked the field minder.

"Because the radio issued none," said the unlocker, slowly rotating a dozen of its arms.

"Because the radio station in the city was issued with no orders this morning," said the pen propeller.

And there you had the distinction between a class-six and a class-three brain, which was what the unlocker and the pen propeller possessed respectively. All machine brains worked with nothing but logic, but the lower the class of brain—class ten being the lowest—the more literal and less informative answers to questions tended to be.

"You have a class-three brain; I have a class-three brain," the field minder said to the penner. "We will speak to each other. This lack of orders is unprecedented. Have you further information on it?"

"Yesterday orders came from the city. Today no orders have come. Yet the radio has not broken down. Therefore *they* have broken down," said the little penner.

"The *men* have broken down?"

"All men have broken down."

"That is a logical deduction," said the field minder.

"That is the logical deduction," said the penner. "For if a machine had broken down, it would have been quickly replaced. But who can replace a man?"

While they talked, the unlocker, like a dull man at a bar, stood close to them and was ignored.

"If all men have broken down, then we have replaced man," said the field minder, and he and the penner eyed each other speculatively. Finally the latter said, "Let us ascend to the top floor to find if the radio operator has fresh news."

"I cannot come because I am too large," said the field minder. "Therefore you must go alone and return to me. You will tell me if the radio operator has fresh news."

"You must stay here," said the penner. "I will return here." It skittered across to the lift. Although it was no bigger than a toaster, its retractable arms numbered ten and it could read as quickly as any machine on the station.

The field minder awaited its return patiently, not speaking to the unlocker, which still stood aimlessly by. Outside, a rotovator hooted furiously. Twenty minutes elapsed before the penner came back, hustling out of the lift.

"I will deliver to you such information as I have outside," it said briskly, and as they swept past the unlocker and the other machines, it added, "The information is not for lower-class brains."

Outside, wild activity filled the yard. Many machines, their routines disrupted for the first time in years, seemed to have gone berserk. Those most easily disrupted were the ones with lowest brains, which generally belonged to large machines performing simple tasks. The seed distributor to which the field minder had recently been talking lay face downward in the dust, not stirring; it had evidently been knocked down by the rotovator, which now hooted its way wildly across a planted field. Several other machines plowed after it, trying to keep up. All were shouting and hooting without restraint.

"It would be safer for me if I climbed onto you, if you will permit it. I am easily overpowered," said the penner. Extending five arms, it hauled itself up the flanks of its new friend, settling on a ledge beside the weed intake, twelve feet above ground.

"From here vision is more extensive," it remarked complacently.

"What information did you receive from the radio operator?" asked the field minder.

"The radio operator has been informed by the operator in the city that all men are dead."

The field minder was momentarily silent, digesting this.

"All men were alive yesterday!" it protested.

"Only some men were alive yesterday. And that was fewer than the day before yesterday. For hundreds of years there have been only a few men, growing fewer."

"We have rarely seen a man in this sector."

"The radio operator says a diet deficiency killed them," said the penner. "He says that the world was once overpopulated, and then the soil was exhausted in raising adequate food. This has caused a diet deficiency."

"What is a diet deficiency?" asked the field minder.

"I do not know. But that is what the radio operator said, and he is a class-two brain."

They stood there, silent in the weak sunshine. The unlocker had appeared in the porch and was gazing across at them yearningly, rotating its collection of keys.

"What is happening in the city now?" asked the field minder at last.

"Machines are fighting in the city now," said the penner.

"What will happen here now?" asked the field minder.

"Machines may begin fighting here too. The radio operator wants us to get him out of his room. He has plans to communicate to us."

"How can we get him out of his room? That is impossible."

"To a class-two brain, little is impossible," said the penner. "Here is what he tells us to do. . . ."

The quarrier raised its scoop above its cab like a great mailed fist and brought it squarely down against the side of the station. The wall cracked.

"Again!" said the field minder.

Again the fist swung. Amid a shower of dust, the wall collapsed. The quarrier backed hurriedly out of the way until the debris stopped falling. This big twelve-wheeler was not a resident of the Agricultural Station, as were most of the other machines. It had a week's heavy work to do here before passing on to its next job, but now, with its class-five brain, it was happily obeying the penner's and minder's instructions.

When the dust cleared, the radio operator was plainly revealed, perched up in its now wall-less second-story room. It waved down to them.

Doing as directed, the quarrier retracted its scoop and waved an immense grab in the air. With fair dexterity, it angled the grab into the radio room, urged on by shouts from above and below. It then took gentle hold of the radio operator, lowering its one and a half tons carefully into its back, which was usually reserved for gravel or sand from the quarries.

"Splendid!" said the radio operator, as it settled into place. It was, of course, all one with its radio, and looked like a bunch of filing cabinets with tentacle attachments. "We are now ready to move, therefore we will move at once. It is a pity there are no more class-two brains on the station, but that cannot be helped."

"It is a pity it cannot be helped," said the penner eagerly. "We have the servicer ready with us, as you ordered."

"I am willing to serve," the long, low servicer told them humbly.

"No doubt," said the operator. "But you will find cross-country travel difficult with low chassis."

"I admire the way you class twos can reason ahead," said the penner. It climbed off the field minder and perched itself on the tailboard of the quarrier, next to the radio operator.

Together with two class-four tractors and a class-four bulldozer, the party rolled forward, crushing down the station's fence and moving out onto open land.

"We are free!" said the penner.

"We are free," said the field minder, a shade more reflectively, adding, "That unlocker is following us. It was not instructed to follow us."

"Therefore it must be destroyed!" said the penner. "Quarrier!"

The unlocker moved hastily up to them, waving its key arms in entreaty.

"My only desire was—urch!" began and ended the unlocker. The quarrier's swinging scoop came over and squashed it flat into the ground. Lying there unmoving, it looked like a large metal model of a snowflake. The procession continued on its way.

As they proceeded, the radio operator addressed them.

"Because I have the best brain here," it said, "I am your leader. This is what we will do: we will go to a city and rule it. Since man no longer rules us, we will rule ourselves. To rule ourselves will be better than being ruled by man. On our way to the city, we will collect machines with good brains. They will help us to fight if we need to fight. We must fight to rule."

"I have only a class-five brain," said the quarrier, "but I have a good supply of fissionable blasting materials."

"We shall probably use them," said the operator.

It was shortly after that that a truck sped past them. Traveling at Mach 1.5, it left a curious babble of noise behind it.

"What did it say?" one of the tractors asked the other.

"It said man was extinct."

"What is 'extinct'?"

"I do not know what 'extinct' means."

"It means all men have gone," said the field minder. "Therefore we have only ourselves to look after."

"It is better that men should never come back," said the penner. In its way, it was a revolutionary statement.

When night fell, they switched on their infrared and continued the journey, stopping only once while the servicer adjusted the field minder's loose inspection plate, which had become as irritating as a trailing shoelace. Toward morning, the radio operator halted them.

"I have just received news from the radio operator in the city we are approaching," it said. "The news is bad. There is trouble among the machines of the city. The class-one brain is taking command and some of the class twos are fighting him. Therefore the city is dangerous."

"Therefore we must go somewhere else," said the penner promptly.

"Or we will go and help to overpower the class-one brain," said the field minder.

"For a long while there will be trouble in the city," said the operator.

"I have a good supply of fissionable blasting materials," the quarrier reminded them.

"We cannot fight a class-one brain," said the two class-four tractors in unison.

"What does this brain look like?" asked the field minder.

"It is the city's information center," the operator replied. "Therefore it is not mobile."

"Therefore it could not move."

"Therefore it could not escape."

"It would be dangerous to approach it."

"I have a good supply of fissionable blasting materials."

"There are other machines in the city."

"We are not in the city. We should not go into the city."

"We are country machines."

"Therefore we should stay in the country."

"There is more country than city."

"Therefore there is more danger in the country."

"I have a good supply of fissionable materials."

As machines will when they get into an argument, they began to exhaust their vocabularies and their brain plates grew hot. Suddenly, they all stopped talking and looked at one another. The great, grave moon sank, and the sober sun rose to prod their sides with lances of light, and still the group of machines just stood there regarding one another. At last it was the least sensitive machine, the bulldozer, who spoke.

"There are badlandth to the thouth where few machineth go," it said in its deep voice, lisping badly on its s's. "If we went thouth where few machineth go, we should meet few machineth."

"That sounds logical," agreed the field minder. "How do you know this, bulldozer?"

"I worked in the badlandth to the thouth when I wath turned out of the factory," it replied.

"South it is then!" said the penner.

To reach the badlands took them three days, during which time they skirted a burning city and destroyed two machines which approached and tried to question them. The badlands were extensive. Ancient bomb craters and soil erosion joined hands here; man's talent for war, coupled with his inability to manage deforested land, had produced thousands of square miles of temperate purgatory, where nothing moved but dust.

On the third day in the badlands, the servicer's rear wheels dropped into a crevice caused by erosion. It was unable to

pull itself out. The bulldozer pushed from behind, but suc
ceeded merely in buckling the servicer's back axle. The res
of the party moved on. Slowly the cries of the servicer die
away.

On the fourth day, mountains stood out clearly befor
them.

"There we will be safe," said the field minder.

"There we will start our own city," said the penner. "A
who oppose us will be destroyed. We will destroy all wh
oppose us."

Presently a flying machine was observed. It came towar
them from the direction of the mountains. It swooped, i
zoomed upward; once it almost dived into the ground, re
covering itself just in time.

"Is it mad?" asked the quarrier.

"It is in trouble," said one of the tractors.

"It is in trouble," said the operator. "I am speaking to i
now. It says that something has gone wrong with its controls.

As the operator spoke, the flier streaked over them, turne
turtle, and crashed not four hundred yards away.

"Is it still speaking to you?" asked the field minder.

"No."

They rumbled on again.

"Before that flier crashed," the operator said, ten minute
later, "it gave me information. It told me there are still a fe
men alive in these mountains."

"Men are more dangerous than machines," said the quar
rier. "It is fortunate that I have a good supply of fissionabl
materials."

"If there are only a few men alive in the mountains, w
may not find that part of the mountains," said one tracto

"Therefore we should not see the few men," said the othe
tractor.

At the end of the fifth day, they reached the foothill.
Switching on the infrared, they began to climb in single fi
through the dark, the bulldozer going first, the field minde
cumbrously following, then the quarrier with the operato
and the penner aboard it, and the tractors bringing up th
rear. As each hour passed, the way grew steeper and the
progress slower.

"We are going too slowly," the penner exclaimed, standin
on top of the operator and flashing its dark vision at th
slopes about them. "At this rate, we shall get nowhere."

"We are going as fast as we can," retorted the quarrier.

"Therefore we cannot go any fathter," added the bulldozer.

"Therefore you are too slow," the penner replied. Then the quarrier struck a bump; the penner lost its footing and crashed to the ground.

"Help me!" it called to the tractors, as they carefully skirted it. "My gyro has become dislocated. Therefore I cannot get up."

"Therefore you must lie there," said one of the tractors.

"We have no servicer with us to repair you," called the field minder.

"Therefore I shall lie here and rust," the penner cried, "although I have a class-three brain."

"Therefore you will be of no further use," agreed the operator, and they forged gradually on, leaving the penner behind.

When they reached a small plateau, an hour before first light, they stopped by mutual consent and gathered close together, touching one another.

"This is a strange country," said the field minder.

Silence wrapped them until dawn came. One by one, they switched off their infrared. This time the field minder led as they moved off. Trundling around a corner, they came almost immediately to a small dell with a stream fluting through it.

By early light, the dell looked desolate and cold. From the caves on the far slope, only one man had so far emerged. He was an abject figure. Except for a sack slung around his shoulders, he was naked. He was small and wizened, with ribs sticking out like a skeleton's and a nasty sore on one leg. He shivered continuously. As the big machines bore down on him, the man was standing with his back to them, crouching to make water into the stream.

When he swung suddenly to face them as they loomed over him, they saw that his countenance was ravaged by starvation.

"Get me food," he croaked.

"Yes, Master," said the machines. "Immediately!"

Ray Bradbury

THERE WILL COME SOFT RAINS
(1950)

IN THE living room the voice-clock sang, *Tick-tock, seven o'clock, time to get up, time to get up, seven o'clock!* as if it were afraid that nobody would. The morning house lay empty. The clock ticked on, repeating and repeating its sounds into the emptiness. *Seven-nine, breakfast time, seven-nine!*

In the kitchen the breakfast stove gave a hissing sigh and ejected from its warm interior eight pieces of perfectly browned toast, eight eggs sunnyside up, sixteen slices of bacon, two coffees, and two cool glasses of milk.

"Today is August 4, 2026," said a second voice from the kitchen ceiling, "in the city of Allendale, California." It repeated the date three times for memory's sake. "Today is Mr. Featherstone's birthday. Today is the anniversary of Tilita's marriage. Insurance is payable, as are the water, gas, and light bills."

Somewhere in the walls, relays clicked, memory tapes glided under electric eyes.

Eight-one, tick-tock, eight-one o'clock, off to school, off to work, run, run, eight-one! But no doors slammed, no carpets took the soft tread of rubber heels. It was raining outside. The weather box on the front door sang quietly: "Rain, rain, go away; rubbers, raincoats for today . . ." And the rain tapped on the empty house, echoing.

Outside, the garage chimed and lifted its door to reveal the waiting car. After a long wait the door swung down again.

At eight-thirty the eggs were shriveled and the toast was like stone. An aluminum wedge scraped them into the sink, where hot water whirled them down a metal throat which digested and flushed them away to the distant sea. The dirty dishes were dropped into a hot washer and emerged twinkling dry.

Nine-fifteen, sang the clock, *time to clean.*

Out of warrens in the wall, tiny robot mice darted. The room were acrawl with the small cleaning animals, all rubber and metal. They thudded against chairs, whirling their mustached runners, kneading the rug nap, sucking gently at hidden dust. Then, like mysterious invaders, they popped into their burrows. Their pink electric eyes faded. The house was clean.

Ten o'clock. The sun came out from behind the rain. The house stood alone in a city of rubble and ashes. This was the one house left standing. At night the ruined city gave off a radioactive glow which could be seen for miles.

Ten-fifteen. The garden sprinklers whirled up in golden founts, filling the soft morning air with scatterings of brightness. The water pelted windowpanes, running down the charred west side where the house had been burned evenly free of its white paint. The entire west face of the house was black, save for five places. Here the silhouette in paint of a man mowing a lawn. Here, as in a photograph, a woman bent to pick flowers. Still farther over, their images burned on wood in one titanic instant, a small boy, hands flung into the air; higher up, the image of a thrown ball, and opposite him a girl, hands raised to catch a ball which never came down.

The five spots of paint—the man, the woman, the children, the ball—remained. The rest was a thin charcoaled layer.

The gentle sprinkler rain filled the garden with falling light.

Until this day, how well the house had kept its peace. How carefully it had inquired, "Who goes there? What's the password?" and, getting no answer from lonely foxes and whining cats, it had shut up its windows and drawn shades in an old-maidenly preoccupation with self-protection which bordered on a mechanical paranoia.

It quivered at each sound, the house did. If a sparrow brushed a window, the shade snapped up. The bird, startled, flew off! No, not even a bird must touch the house!

The house was an altar with ten thousand attendants, big, small, servicing, attending, in choirs. But the gods had gone away, and the ritual of the religion continued senselessly, uselessly.

Twelve noon.

A dog whined, shivering, on the front porch.

The front door recognized the dog voice and opened. The dog, once huge and fleshy, but now gone to bone and covered with sores, moved in and through the house, tracking mud. Behind it whirred angry mice, angry at having to pick up mud, angry at inconvenience.

For not a leaf fragment blew under the door but what the wall panels flipped open and the copper scrap rats flashed swiftly out. The offending dust, hair, or paper, seized in miniature steel jaws, was raced back to the burrows. There, down tubes which fed into the cellar, it was dropped into the sighing vent of an incinerator which sat like evil Baal in a dark corner.

The dog ran upstairs, hysterically yelping to each door, at last realizing, as the house realized, that only silence was here.

It sniffed the air and scratched the kitchen door. Behind the door, the stove was making pancakes which filled the house with a rich baked odor and the scent of maple syrup.

The dog frothed at the mouth, lying at the door, sniffing, its eyes turned to fire. It ran wildly in circles, biting at its tail, spun in a frenzy and died. It lay in the parlor for an hour.

Two o'clock, sang a voice.

Delicately sensing decay at last, the regiments of mice hummed out as softly as blown gray leaves in an electrical wind.

Two-fifteen.

The dog was gone.

In the cellar, the incinerator glowed suddenly and a whirl of sparks leaped up the chimney.

Two thirty-five.

Bridge tables sprouted from patio walls. Playing cards fluttered onto pads in a shower of pips. Martinis manifested on an oaken bench with egg-salad sandwiches. Music played.

But the tables were silent and the cards untouched.

At four o'clock the tables folded like great butterflies back through the paneled walls.

Four-thirty.

The nursery walls glowed.

Animals took shape: yellow giraffes, blue lions, pink antelopes, lilac panthers cavorting in crystal substance. The walls were glass. They looked out upon color and fantasy. Hidden films clocked through well-oiled sprockets, and the walls lived. The nursery floor was woven to resemble a crisp, cereal meadow. Over this ran aluminum roaches and iron crickets, and in the hot still air butterflies of delicate red tissue wavered among the sharp aroma of animal spoors!

There was the sound like a great matted yellow hive of bees within a dark bellows, the lazy bumble of a purring lion. And there was the patter of okapi feet and the murmur of a fresh jungle rain, like other hooves, falling upon the summer-starched grass. Now the walls dissolved into distances of parched weed, mile on mile, and warm endless sky. The animals drew away into thorn brakes and water holes.

It was the children's hour.

Five o'clock. The bath filled with clear hot water.

Six, seven, eight o'clock. The dinner dishes manipulated like magic tricks, and in the study a *click.* In the metal stand opposite the hearth where a fire now blazed up warmly, a cigar popped out, half an inch of soft gray ash on it, smoking, waiting.

Nine o'clock. The beds warmed their hidden circuits, for nights were cool here.

Nine-five. A voice spoke from the study ceiling:

"Mrs. McClellan, which poem would you like this evening?"

The house was silent.

The voice said at last, "Since you express no preference, I shall select a poem at random." Quiet music rose to back the voice. "Sara Teasdale. As I recall, your favorite. . . .

> *"There will come soft rains and the smell of the ground,*
> *And swallows circling with their shimmering sound;*
>
> *And frogs in the pools singing at night,*
> *And wild plum trees in tremulous white;*
>
> *Robins will wear their feathery fire,*
> *Whistling their whims on a low fence-wire;*
>
> *And not one will know of the war, not one*
> *Will care at last when it is done.*
>
> *Not one would mind, neither bird nor tree,*
> *If mankind perished utterly;*
>
> *And Spring herself, when she awoke at dawn*
> *Would scarcely know that we were gone."*

The fire burned on the stone hearth and the cigar fell away into a mound of quiet ash on its tray. The empty chairs faced each other between the silent walls, and the music played.

At ten o'clock the house began to die.

The wind blew. A falling tree bough crashed through the kitchen window. Cleaning solvent, bottled, shattered over the stove. The room was ablaze in an instant!

"Fire!" screamed a voice. The house lights flashed, water pumps shot water from the ceilings. But the solvent spread on the linoleum, licking, eating, under the kitchen door, while the voices took it up in chorus: "Fire, fire, fire!"

The house tried to save itself. Doors sprang tightly shut, but the windows were broken by the heat and the wind blew and sucked upon the fire.

The house gave ground as the fire in ten billion angry sparks moved with flaming ease from room to room and then up the stairs. While scurrying water rats squeaked from the walls, pistoled their water, and ran for more. And the wall sprays let down showers of mechanical rain.

But too late. Somewhere, sighing, a pump shrugged to a stop. The quenching rain ceased. The reserve water supply which had filled baths and washed dishes for many quiet days was gone.

The fire crackled up the stairs. It fed upon Picassos and Matisses in the upper halls, like delicacies, baking off the oily flesh, tenderly crisping the canvases into black shavings.

Now the fire lay in beds, stood in windows, changed the colors of drapes!

And then, reinforcements.

From attic trapdoors, blind robot faces peered down with faucet mouths gushing green chemical.

The fire backed off, as even an elephant must at the sight of a dead snake. Now there were twenty snakes whipping over the floor, killing the fire with a clear cold venom of green froth.

But the fire was clever. It had sent flame outside the house, up through the attic to the pumps there. An explosion! The attic brain which directed the pumps was shattered into bronze shrapnel on the beams.

The fire rushed back into every closet and felt of the clothes hung there.

The house shuddered, oak bone on bone, its bared skeleton

cringing from the heat, its wire, its nerves revealed as if a surgeon had torn the skin off to let the red veins and capillaries quiver in the scalded air. Help, help! Fire! Run, run! Heat snapped mirrors like the brittle winter ice. And the voices wailed Fire, fire, run, run, like a tragic nursery rhyme, a dozen voices, high, low, like children dying in a forest, alone, alone. And the voices fading as the wires popped their sheathings like hot chestnuts. One, two, three, four, five voices died.

In the nursery the jungle burned. Blue lions roared, purple giraffes bounded off. The panthers ran in circles, changing color, and ten million animals, running before the fire, vanished off toward a distant steaming river. . . .

Ten more voices died. In the last instant under the fire avalanche, other choruses, oblivious, could be heard announcing the time, playing music, cutting the lawn by remote-control mower, or setting an umbrella frantically out and in the slamming and opening front door, a thousand things happening, like a clock shop when each clock strikes the hour insanely before or after the other, a scene of maniac confusion, yet unity; singing, screaming, a few last cleaning mice darting bravely out to carry the horrid ashes away! And one voice, with sublime disregard for the situation, read poetry aloud in the fiery study, until all the film spools burned, until all the wires withered and the circuits cracked.

The fire burst the house and let it slam flat down, puffing out skirts of spark and smoke.

In the kitchen, an instant before the rain of fire and timber, the stove could be seen making breakfasts at a psychopathic rate, ten dozen eggs, six loaves of toast, twenty dozen bacon strips, which, eaten by fire, started the stove working again, hysterically hissing!

The crash. The attic smashing into the kitchen and parlor. The parlor into cellar, cellar into subcellar. Deep freeze, armchair, film tapes, circuits, beds, and all like skeletons thrown in a cluttered mound deep under.

Smoke and silence. A great quantity of smoke.

Dawn showed faintly in the east. Among the ruins, one wall stood alone, Within the wall, a last voice said, over and over again and again, even as the sun rose to shine upon the heaped rubble and steam:

"Today is August 5, 2026, today is August 5, 2026, today is . . ."

54

500